CHEMISTRY

OCR
RECOGNISING ACHIEVEMENT

D0522394

for OCR A

FOR SEPARATE AWARD

David Lees and John Payne
Series editor: Bob McDuell

Heinemann Educational Publishers
Halley Court, Jordan Hill, Oxford, OX2 8EJ
Part of Harcourt Education
Heinemann is the registered trademark of
Harcourt Education Limited

© David Lees, John Payne, 2001

First published 2001

ISBN 0 435 582925

04
10 9 8 7 6 5

Edited by Helen Roberts

Designed and typeset by Oxford Designers &
Illustrators

Printed and bound in the UK by Bath Colourbooks

Photo research by Helen Reilly

Acknowledgements

The authors and publishers would like to thank the
following for permission to use photographs:
Cover photo by Science Photo Library/Martin Bond
TB1: Fig 3, e.t. archive. Fig 15, Peter Gould. Fig 16,
John Payne. Figs 17, 18, Peter Gould. Fig 19, Holt
Studios. Fig 20, Still Pictures. Fig 21, Peter Gould.
Fig 22, Daimler-Crysler. Fig 25, Still Pictures. Fig 12,
Holt Studios. Fig 28, Science Photo Library. Figs 29,
32, Collections. Fig 33, Holt Studios. TB2: Fig 1,
Ancient Art and Architecture. Figs 4, 5, Geoscience
Features. Fig 6, Environmental Images. TB3: Figs 1,
12, Science Photo Library. Fig 13, Peter Gould. Fig
14, ACE. Fig 15, Science Photo Library. Figs 19, 20,
23, 28, Peter Gould. Figs 29, 31, Environmental
Picture Library. Fig 32 Tony Waltham / Geophotos.
Figs 34, 37, Science Photo Library. Fig 38, Quadrant.
Figs 40, 41, Science Photo Library. TB4: Fig 4. Taken
from Chemistry by Richard harwood. Figs 9, 11,
Peter Gould. Fig 12, Peter Gould. Fig 15, Peter
Gould. Fig 18 Wadworth and Co. / New Engand
Associates Ltd. TB5: Figs 1, 2, Science Photo Library.
Fig 10, Geoscience Features. Fig 22, Q.A. Photos.
Figs 23, 26, Peter Gould. TB6: Fig 2, Science Photo
Library. Fig 3, Environmental Picture Library. Figs 4,
6, Science Photo Library. Fig 6, Peter Gould. Fig 7,
Environmental Picture Library. Fig 12, Still Pictures.
Fig 19 Peter Gould. Fig 22, Science Photo Library.
Fig 33, Peter Gould. Fig 34, Science and Society.
TB7: Fig 9, Science Photo Library. Fig 10,
Geoscience Features. Fig 11, Still Pictures. Fig 12,
Geoscience Features. Fig 16, Environmental Picture
Library. Fig 17, Geoscience Photo Library. Fig 18,
(top) Geoscience Features, (bottom) Science Photo
Library. Fig 19, Science Photo Library. Fig 20,
Geoscience Features. Fig 21, Tony Waltham /
Geophotos. Fig 22, Collections. TB8: Fig 1, Science
Photo Library. Figs 2, 3, Peter Gould. Fig 9,
Collections. Fig 10, Holt Studios. Fogs 11, 12,
Science Photo Library.

The publishers have made every effort to trace the
copyright holders, but if they have inadvertently
overlooked any, they will be pleased to make the
necessary arrangements at the first opportunity.
p120, fig14, Nelson Thornes. p120, fig 15,
Cambridge University Press.

Tel: 01865 888058 www.heinemann.co.uk

Introduction

This book provides coverage of OCR Chemistry (1981). The first examination of these specifications is in June 2003. It concentrates on Extension Block A only. Further information about the alternative Extension Block B is available from OCR.

The book has been written by examiners who have been involved in the writing of the new specifications. It is supported by other materials published by Heinemann including a Homework book, a Teacher's Resource pack and a CD-ROM.

The book is divided into two parts.

Material common to the Chemistry of Double Award is covered by the first eight Teaching blocks. Each Teaching block has an introductory spread. This reminds you of what you should already know from Key Stage 3. It also gives a quick Check-up test. If you feel there are things you do not remember, your teacher should have a Summary sheet to help you.

Extension A material is covered by four additional Teaching blocks, A1–A6. These also have an introductory spread so that you can check what you already know from Double award. Remember that this material can only be tested on Paper 3 or 4.

Throughout the book there are:

Key Points
Each Teaching block is split into double-page spreads. Each double-page spread starts by listing the key points it covers.

Higher tier material
If you are taking the Higher tier papers (1981/2 and 1981/4) you will be expected to know and understand all the material in this book. If, however, you are taking Foundation tier (1981/1 and 1981/3), you can miss out the parts that are shown in pink boxes or by a pink bar at the side of the page. This is Higher or H material.

Thinking further
At the end of each double-page spread there are questions to test your understanding. They are at two levels. The easier questions are shown by a ■ and the harder questions by a ◆.

Ideas and evidence
In the new specifications there will be questions about how scientists worked in the past and how they work today. Throughout the book there are Ideas and evidence boxes and questions.

Taking it further
Taking if further boxes include interesting facts which are not on the specification. You will not be examined on the material in these boxes.

Key words
Key words are important scientific terms that you need to know. They are emboldened in the text, listed at the end of the double-page spread and explained in the Glossary. Key words for Higher only are shown in pink.

Key facts and formulae
These are shown in blue tinted boxes throughout. It is important that you remember these.

Questions
At the end of each Teaching block there are examination-type questions. Questions with symbols ● and ■ are similar to those found on Foundation papers; those with ■ and ◆ are similar to questions found on Higher papers.

Skills sections
At the back of the book are sections to help you improve your skills in particular areas.

We hope that this book will help you throughout your course.

Contents

Chemical reactions

Introduction

People have found out about how substances react with one another for many thousands of years. They have used many ways to represent these substances.

The Ancient Egyptians represented the seven metals that they knew about by 'planets'. They believed that since there were seven known 'planets' (they thought that the Sun was a planet too) and seven known metals there must be a link between the two. The Sun was associated with gold, Venus with copper, Jupiter with tin and so on.

fig 1 | The Ancient Egyptians, Dalton and chemists today used different symbols to represent gold

We now use a system of symbols to represent chemical elements. As all matter is made up from these elements or combinations of these elements, we can represent all chemicals and their reactions using our system of symbols.

- Each element is represented by a symbol. This is a single letter or a pair of letters. Each element contains just one type of atom.
- The symbols for all the elements are shown in the Periodic Table (on the back page).
- An element, such as gold, is made up from just gold atoms.
- Compounds contain two or more elements chemically combined.
- The elements in a compound are represented by a formula.
- Chemical reactions can be represented by word equations that show all of the reactants and products.
- When a chemical reaction takes place the mass of all the products is the same as the mass of all the reactants.
- Acids and alkalis are examples of types of compounds.
- Indicators can be used to show whether a substance is an acid, is neutral or is an alkali.
- Acids neutralise alkalis.

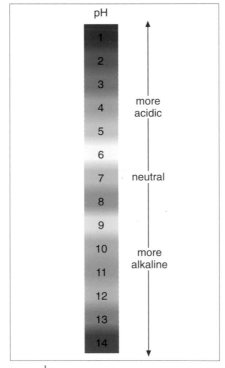

fig 2 | The pH scale

Check-up

a What are the symbols for carbon and oxygen? (Use the Periodic Table on the back page to find out.)

b How many different types of atoms are present in the compound carbon dioxide, CO_2?

c Write a word equation to show the formation of carbon dioxide from carbon and oxygen.

d 1.2 g of carbon completely burns in 3.2 g of oxygen. What mass of carbon dioxide forms?

e Describe a test you could do to show that a gas is carbon dioxide.

If you have difficulty, ask your teacher for a Summary sheet.

Contents of the Teaching block

1.1 Hazards and safety

It is essential that before chemists do any practical work they are aware of possible dangers. It is also important that chemicals are stored and transported safely. This section shows how safety information is displayed and used.

1.2 Compounds

Chemists all over the world use the same system to write the names of chemicals in shorthand. This section will show you how to do this.

1.3 Equations

Word equations are useful to show the names of reactants and products but symbol equations are better because they show the numbers of each type of atom involved. This section will show you how to write balanced symbol equations.

1.4 Limestone

Limestone is an extremely useful compound. We rely on it to make cement, glass and quicklime. Quicklime can be changed easily into slaked lime which has an important use in neutralising unwanted acidity.

1.5 Acids

You should already know that indicators can detect acids. You may also know that acids react with some metals, carbonates and alkalis. This section will remind you of these reactions and give you a chance to practise writing symbol equations.

1.6 Hydrogen

When a lighted splint is put into a test-tube containing hydrogen, a squeaky pop is heard. This reaction produces water and has some practical benefits.

1.7 Energy transfer

The reaction between quicklime and water gives out a lot of heat. This heat comes from the reaction between the water and the quicklime and warms up the container they are in. Other reactions give out heat as they take place but some absorb heat and so cool their container down as they take place.

1.8 Extracting minerals

We rely very much on the minerals we extract from the ground. This section looks at the balance that must be struck between extracting the minerals and looking after the environment.

Links with other Teaching blocks

1.1 Hazards and safety

Safety in chemistry

Four hundred years ago the science we call chemistry was not known. The 'science' that most resembled **chemistry** was called alchemy. This name came from Ancient Egypt where some people had knowledge of how to embalm the dead. Those who practised **khemeia** were thought to be magicians. The practices of khemeia soon included knowledge of glass making, metallurgy and dyeing.

Alchemists tried to find out about materials and how they were useful. Their main aim, however, was to try to change metals such as lead into gold.

a Suggest where the word alchemist comes from.

b Why do you think alchemists wanted to turn lead into gold?

One of the tests that alchemists used on new substances was taste. They would classify materials by a description of their taste so that others would then be able to recognise them. One of the consequences of this was that there was often illness amongst the alchemists' assistants.

c Suggest how substances were first found to be poisonous.

fig 3 | Alchemists were trying to turn metals, such as lead, into gold

Knowledge about the danger of chemical elements and their compounds gradually increased but even in 1900 Marie Curie suffered from radiation poisoning when investigating the elements radium and polonium.

Our knowledge of the toxicity of substances is still advancing. Forty years ago a substance called benzene was commonly used in school laboratories to clean apparatus. In 1971 all benzene had to be removed from school laboratories immediately when it was proved that there was a link between it and some types of cancers.

All chemists now have to follow strict rules when handling chemicals. This applies just as much to industrial locations and research laboratories as it does to school laboratories.

Before your teacher does any experiment with you, they will have checked for possible hazards and will warn you of these. It is vital that you follow all instructions that you are given.

Hazard symbols

Any substance that is hazardous will carry a warning on its container. This container could be a tiny jar or even a lorry.

There are many hazard signs but the four that you need to be aware of are shown below. These signs are known as the **Hazchem code**.

| corrosive | highly flammable | toxic | harmful |

fig 4 | The Hazchem code

Thinking further

■ **1** You have made some copper(II) sulphate crystals in the laboratory. Why is it important to wash your hands before lunch?

■ **2** Fig 5 shows three more Hazchem symbols. They each warn about one of these hazards: irritant, explosive, biological hazard. Match them to the hazard they warn about.

■ **3** Why are Hazchem labels on the side of a road tanker important for the emergency services (fire service, police)?

◆ **4** Is it safe to assume that scientists have now found all the hazards that exist when handling substances? Explain your answer.

fig 5 | Three Hazchem symbols

KEY WORDS

alchemists • chemistry • corrosive • harmful • Hazchem code • highly flammable • khemeia • toxic

1.2 Compounds

> ## Key points
>
> - Compounds contain two or more types of atom chemically combined.
> - The particles in compounds are held together by strong bonds.
> - Chemical formulae are used to represent compounds.
> - Compounds have properties which are different from those of the elements from which they are made.

Symbols

There are over 100 different elements. **Elements** are substances that contain only one type of atom. Each element is given a different **symbol** to represent it. Some symbols are just a single capital letter, such as H. Others have two letters, the first of which is always a capital, such as Mg. All of the elements are listed in the **Periodic Table** of the elements (see the back page).

a Use the Periodic Table (back page) to find the symbols for calcium, aluminium, magnesium and chlorine.

b What is unusual about the symbols for iron, silver and gold?

Symbols are particularly useful when more than one atom is present in a substance. For example, hydrogen gas consists of pairs of hydrogen atoms joined together, so hydrogen gas is shown as H_2. When more than one atom is joined together like this we call the substance formed a **molecule**.

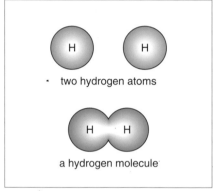

two hydrogen atoms

a hydrogen molecule

fig 6 Two hydrogen atoms and a hydrogen molecule

Compounds

Compounds are molecules that contain more than one different sort of atom chemically joined together. This is a very important difference from mixtures. Mixtures can contain more than one element but the elements are not chemically combined.

The forces holding the atoms together in compounds are very strong and are called **chemical bonds**. Chemical bonds are sometimes shown in diagrams as lines holding the atoms together.

c Explain why a jar containing hydrogen gas, H_2, and oxygen gas, O_2, contains a mixture but a jar containing steam, H_2O, contains a compound.

Compounds have very different properties from the elements that they are made up from. For example, water, H_2O, is a colourless liquid at room temperature but the elements that have formed water, hydrogen and oxygen, are both gases.

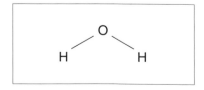

fig 7 H_2O molecule shown with 'lines' for bonds

Formulae

A chemical **formula** shows how many atoms of each element are present in a compound. When there is more then one formula we say formulae and not 'formulas'. Water has the formula, H_2O. This tells us that each water molecule contains two hydrogen atoms and one oxygen atom chemically joined together.

d Why is the formula of steam the same as the formula of water?

The formula of sulphuric acid is H_2SO_4. This tells us that sulphuric acid is made up from three elements, hydrogen, sulphur and oxygen chemically combined. It also tells us that one molecule of sulphuric acid contains two hydrogen atoms, one sulphur atom and four oxygen atoms.

Brackets

Sometimes formulae put groups of atoms together in brackets. An example of this is the hydroxide group (OH). For example, calcium hydroxide has the formula $Ca(OH)_2$. When a group of atoms is put in brackets like this, the number that follows the brackets applies to all of the atoms inside the brackets. In the case of calcium hydroxide the formula tells us that there are two oxygen atoms and two hydrogen atoms, as well as the one calcium atom.

e What is the total number of atoms present in $Ca(OH)_2$?

Combining power

Why is the formula for calcium hydroxide $Ca(OH)_2$ and not $Ca(OH)$ or $Ca(OH)_3$? Different atoms, or groups of atoms, have different **combining powers**. The combining power is a measure of how many bonds each atom, or group of atoms, can form with others. In the case of calcium hydroxide a calcium atom has a combining power of 2 and a hydroxide group has a combining power of 1. Two hydroxide groups will join up with one calcium and so the formula is $Ca(OH)_2$.

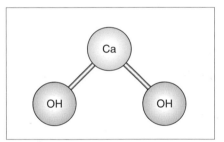

fig 8 One calcium atom joins with two hydroxide groups

Thinking further

■ **1** Copy and complete this table.

name	formula	total number of atoms	number of different atoms
nitric acid	HNO_3		
	NaCl		
hydrochloric acid		2	2
iron(III) oxide	Fe_2O_3		
ammonium sulphate	$(NH_4)_2SO_4$		

fig 9

--- KEY WORDS ---
chemical bonds • combining power • formula • molecule • Periodic Table • symbol

1.3 Equations

Word equations

Chemical reactions can be summarized by **word equations** that show all the reactants and products. For example, the combustion of methane gas in oxygen is represented by the following word equation.

methane + oxygen → carbon dioxide + water

a Write a word equation for the combustion of camping gas, butane. The products are the same as for the combustion of methane.

Symbol equations

Symbol equations are much more useful than word equations. They give us information about the numbers of particles reacting. The equation for the reaction between iron and sulphur to make iron sulphide is written as:

$Fe + S \rightarrow FeS$

We can see from this that one atom of iron combines with one atom of sulphur in this reaction.

Reactions may also involve molecules such as oxygen, O_2. These must also be represented accurately in symbol equations. Oxygen gas is always O_2. So the reaction between sulphur and oxygen to make sulphur dioxide is written as:

$S + O_2 \rightarrow SO_2$

b Write a symbol equation for the combustion of carbon in oxygen.

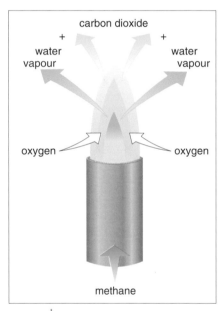

fig 10 | Combustion of methane

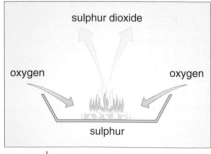

fig 11 | Sulphur burning

Balancing symbol equations

Sometimes the number of atoms in the **reactants** is not the same as the number of atoms in the **products**. An example of this is the combustion of methane in oxygen.

$$CH_4 + O_2 \rightarrow CO_2 + H_2O$$

If we left the equation like this it would mean that oxygen atoms have been created and hydrogen atoms destroyed as the reaction took place. This is not possible. The equation must be balanced so that the number of atoms of each element is the same on both sides of the equation. This is then called a **balanced equation**.

When an equation is balanced it is important to put numbers in front of the atoms or molecules. The formulae of the chemicals themselves can never be changed and so the small numbers that follow elements or compounds are always fixed.

The balanced equation for the combustion of methane is:

$$CH_4 + 2O_2 \rightarrow CO_2 + 2H_2O$$

c   Balance this equation for the combustion of propane, C_3H_8.

$$C_3H_8 + O_2 \rightarrow CO_2 + H_2O$$

Thinking further

■ 1 Write out the following equations correctly. Some may need to be balanced, but not all.
  a $NaOH + HCl \rightarrow NaCl + H_2O$
  b $Mg + HCl \rightarrow MgCl_2 + H_2$
  c $Mg + O_2 \rightarrow MgO$
  d $Mg + H_2SO_4 \rightarrow MgSO_4 + H_2$
  e $N_2 + H_2 \rightarrow NH_3$

◆ 2 Write out the following ionic equations correctly. Some may need to be balanced, but not all.
  a $H^+ + OH^- \rightarrow H_2O$
  b $Zn + H^+ \rightarrow Zn^{2+} + H_2$
  c $Mg + Cu^{2+} \rightarrow Cu + Mg^{2+}$
  d $Cl_2 + Br^- \rightarrow Br_2 + Cl^-$
  e $Al^{3+} + e^- \rightarrow Al$ (e^- is an electron)

Ionic equations

Some particles are electrically charged. They have either lost electrons (and are positively charged) or have gained electrons (and are negatively charged). (You will learn more about these particles in Teaching block 5.) The particles formed are called ions. **Ionic equations** have to be balanced for both numbers of particles and charges.

One example is the reaction between magnesium and the hydrogen ions that are present in acids. The magnesium fizzes and dissolves forming magnesium ions. The particles involved are:

$$Mg + H^+ \rightarrow Mg^{2+} + H_2$$

At the moment this ionic equation is not balanced. However, by putting a 2 in front of the H^+, the number of atoms of each element becomes the same on each side of the equation and also the charges (2+) on each side become the same.

$$Mg + 2H^+ \rightarrow Mg^{2+} + H_2$$

d   Balance this ionic equation:

$$H^+ + O^{2-} \rightarrow H_2O$$

── **KEY WORDS** ──────────────────────────
  balanced equation • ionic equation • products • reactants • symbol equation • word equation

1.4 Limestone

> ### Key points
>
> - Limestone is a plentiful and useful mineral.
> - It consists mostly of calcium carbonate.
> - It is used to manufacture glass and cement
> - It decomposes to quicklime (calcium oxide) and carbon dioxide when strongly heated.
> - Quicklime and slaked lime are used to neutralise excess acidity in lakes and on the land.

Calcium carbonate

Pure calcium carbonate is a white solid. Bones, teeth and shells all contain calcium carbonate.

Over millions of years deposits of shells fall to the seabed and form layers of calcium carbonate. This can turn into the sedimentary rock called **limestone**. **Chalk** is just a form of limestone made up from very small particles.

a Suggest why limestone and chalk may not be pure calcium carbonate.

There are many areas of the UK where limestone or chalk is found on the surface. It is often seen in areas that are hilly, such as Derbyshire, or that have white sea cliffs, such as in Dorset.

b Suggest why limestone or chalk, deposited at the bottom of seas millions of years ago, can now be seen above sea level in cliffs.

fig 12 | These contain calcium carbonate

Uses of limestone

Limestone has many uses and is quarried on a large scale. There has to be a fine balance between economic and environmental considerations when possible quarry sites are considered.

Heating limestone very strongly with a mixture of sodium carbonate and sand produces a clear melt. When this is cooled, **glass** forms. The interesting thing about glass is that it is not strictly a solid but a supercooled liquid. The method of making glass has been known for thousands of years.

Limestone is also used to make **cement**. Limestone powder and clay are roasted and the product is ground to a fine powder When water is added to this powder and allowed to evaporate, a rigid solid forms. Strong chemical bonds bind the substances in the cement together when water is added.

fig 13 | These cliffs are made of limestone

Gray chalk historically used to make mortar, render on St Andrew's chapel
Stone itself is Kentish Ragstone

c Concrete is made by adding gravel or small stones to the cement before adding water. Suggest what advantage concrete has over cement.

Is its carbon footprint better than that of grey chalk.

Heating limestone

When limestone is heated strongly it glows orange-red. The dull orange-red light from heated limestone was used to light theatres before electricity. This is the origin of the term 'in the lime-light'.

The limestone decomposes to **quicklime** when it is heated. Carbon dioxide gas is also given off.

d Why is it difficult to tell that carbon dioxide is given off?

$$CaCO_3 \rightarrow CaO + CO_2$$
calcium carbonate → calcium oxide + carbon dioxide
(limestone)   (quicklime)

e Is the mass of quicklime formed the same as the mass of limestone used, or less or more?

This process is carried out on a large scale in **limekilns**. The reaction is an example of **thermal decomposition**.

Quicklime reacts violently with water to produce **slaked lime**.

The quicklime cracks apart, grows in size and gets so hot that some of the water turns to steam.

$$CaO + H_2O \rightarrow Ca(OH)_2$$
calcium oxide + water → calcium hydroxide
(quicklime)   (slaked lime)

f What safety precautions are needed when using quicklime?

Quicklime and slaked lime are used to neutralise excess acidity. This can be in lakes, waterways or on the land.

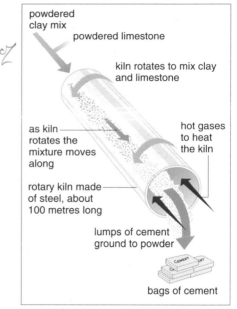

fig 14 | Making cement in a rotary kiln

powdered clay mix
powdered limestone
kiln rotates to mix clay and limestone
as kiln rotates the mixture moves along
hot gases to heat the kiln
rotary kiln made of steel, about 100 metres long
lumps of cement ground to powder
bags of cement

fig 15 | Water reacts violently with quicklime

Thinking further

1 This picture shows a public house called 'The Limekiln'.

fig 16

What sort of rock is quarried in the area?

2 Magnesium carbonate, $MgCO_3$, undergoes thermal decomposition in a similar way to calcium carbonate, $CaCO_3$.

a Write a symbol equation for the decomposition.

b Predict the reaction of the solid product from the decomposition with water.

c Write an equation for the reaction with water.

3 How could you show that sodium carbonate does not undergo thermal decomposition when heated strongly?

KEY WORDS

cement • chalk • glass • limekiln • limestone • quicklime • slaked lime • thermal decomposition

 Effect of heat on limestone and addition of water.

1.5 Acids

Reactions of acids

1 With metals

More reactive metals, such as magnesium and zinc, react with **acids** to produce a salt and hydrogen gas. We can write word and symbol equations for these reactions. For example:

$$Zn + H_2SO_4 \rightarrow ZnSO_4 + H_2$$
zinc + sulphuric acid → zinc sulphate + hydrogen

a Write word and symbol equations for the reaction between magnesium and sulphuric acid.

fig 17 | Zinc reacting with sulphuric acid

2 With carbonates

Carbonate compounds also give off a gas when they react with acids. This gas is carbon dioxide. The reaction also produces a salt and water. For example:

$$CaCO_3 + 2HCl \rightarrow CaCl_2 + H_2O + CO_2$$
calcium carbonate + hydrochloric acid → calcium chloride + water + carbon dioxide

Notice how this equation has been balanced by putting 2 in front of the HCl.

b Write word and symbol equations for the reaction between magnesium carbonate and sulphuric acid.

3 With alkalis and bases

Alkalis and **bases** react with acids to form a salt and water only. For example, sodium hydroxide reacts with hydrochloric acid to form water and sodium chloride (common salt).

$$NaOH + HCl \rightarrow NaCl + H_2O$$
sodium hydroxide + hydrochloric acid → sodium chloride + water

c Explain why this equation does not need further balancing.

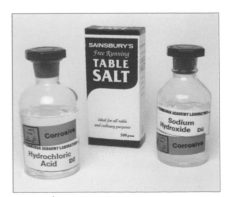

fig 18 | Common salt is made by neutralising two hazardous substances

Neutralisation

The reaction between an acid and a base or alkali produces a salt and water. It is called a **neutralisation** reaction because the properties of the acid and the alkali are cancelled out by the formation of water, which is neutral.

Neutralisation is extremely useful in agriculture because farmers can neutralise soils which are too acidic by the addition of an alkali. The alkali used is often calcium hydroxide, which is a weak alkali, is only slightly soluble in water and will not itself damage the soil.

d Suggest two reasons why sodium hydroxide is not used to neutralise acid soils.

fig 19 | This aeroplane is being used to lime soil

Some lakes are particularly badly affected by acid rain. The change in the pH of the water harms fish and other water life. Large amounts of calcium hydroxide are put into these lakes to neutralise the acidity.

Patterns in neutralisation reactions

Neutralisation reactions are typical of many reaction types in chemistry. They follow a pattern. This pattern allows us to make predictions for reactions between other acids and alkalis that we may be unfamiliar with. For example, nitric acid forms nitrate salts, so sodium hydroxide and nitric acid would form sodium nitrate and water when they react. Ammonia is a base. When it neutralises sulphuric acid, ammonium sulphate forms. This is used as a fertiliser.

e Phosphoric acid forms phosphate salts. Name the products when potassium hydroxide neutralises phosphoric acid.

fig 20 | This lake is too acidic, so lime is being added to it

Thinking further

■ **1** Name the products from the following reactions.
  a zinc and hydrochloric acid
  b sodium carbonate and hydrochloric acid
  c potassium hydroxide and sulphuric acid.

◆ **2** Suggest why old marble statues have worn away more in the past 50 years than in the rest of their existence.

◆ **3** Write balanced equations for the reactions in question 1.

◆ **4** Assume that the acid in the lake shown in fig 20 above is sulphuric acid. Write a balanced equation for the reaction between calcium hydroxide and sulphuric acid.

KEY WORDS

acid • alkali • base • neutralisation

 Reactions of acids.

1.6 Hydrogen

Testing for hydrogen

Hydrogen, H_2, is a colourless gas that is much less dense than air. A mixture of hydrogen and oxygen will not react at room temperature. At higher temperatures, or when a flame is applied, the mixture will explode.

a Explain why a mixture of hydrogen and air will also explode when a flame is applied.

The students shown in fig 21 are testing for hydrogen. They are putting a burning splint near the mouth of the test-tube that contains hydrogen gas.

b What might happen if the top of the tube is opened well before the burning splint is put near it? Explain your answer.

When hydrogen and oxygen explode, the product is water. When a dry mixture of hydrogen and oxygen explodes, condensation can be seen on the sides of the reaction vessel.

$$2H_2 \ + \ O_2 \ \rightarrow \ 2H_2O$$
$$\text{hydrogen} + \text{oxygen} \rightarrow \text{water}$$

Water is just the common name for the substance 'hydrogen oxide'.

c Explain why water is described as a compound.

The reaction between hydrogen and oxygen is an example of a **combustion** reaction.

fig 21 | These students are testing for hydrogen gas

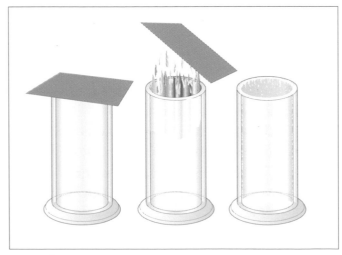

fig 22 | Notice how water has condensed on the sides of the jar after the explosion

Oxidation reactions

Whenever an element combines with oxygen, the reaction is called an **oxidation** reaction. Hydrogen is oxidised to water when it reacts with oxygen.

Many metals undergo oxidation reactions in air. This can be expensive because the metal corrodes. The metal oxide produced does not have the properties of a metal. Measures have to be taken to prevent oxidation reactions.

d What are the chemical name and the common name for the substance produced when iron oxidises?

e Why is this car being treated with zinc before painting?

fig 23 | The steel car frame is being coated in zinc

Reduction reactions

Reduction is the opposite of oxidation. Reduction is the removal of oxygen from a compound. It is important in the extraction of metals (see 2.1 Extraction of metals).

Fuel cells

The reaction between hydrogen and oxygen can be controlled in fuel cells. These allow us to use the energy given out in the reaction to do useful work.

The only product from the reaction in the cell is water.

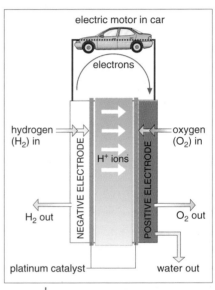

fig 24 | A fuel cell

Thinking further

1 State whether the substance underlined in each of the following reactions is oxidised or reduced.

a  magnesium burning in air

b copper(II) oxide reacting with hydrogen to produce copper metal

c sodium reacts with air to form sodium oxide

d $PbO + H_2 \rightarrow Pb + H_2O$

2 Fuel cells are described as 'environmentally friendly'. Explain why.

3 Look at the equation in question **1d**. Explain why both oxidation and reduction are taking place in this reaction.

KEY WORDS
combustion • oxidation • reduction

1.7 Energy transfer

Energy changes in chemical reactions

When a substance such as TNT detonates a large explosion takes place. This explosion releases energy to the surroundings. We certainly hear the energy that is released as sound; we may even see energy released in the form of light. Energy may also be released as heat.

Many other chemical reactions release heat to the surrounding as they take place. This can be very useful if we can control how quickly the energy is given out.

a Name two examples where energy released to the surroundings, in the form of heat, is useful.

The energy that is released to the surroundings has to come from somewhere. Energy cannot be created nor destroyed, it can only be changed form one form to another. The energy released in a chemical reaction comes from changes in the chemical bonds in the substances involved. You will find out much more about this in Teaching block 5.

fig 25 | Explosions are very fast chemical reactions

Energy changes in solutions

When hydrochloric acid is added to sodium hydroxide solution a neutralisation reaction takes place.

b What are the products of this reaction?

If the reaction is carried out in a glass beaker, the beaker gets warm.

c Where has this heat energy come from?

When a reaction such as this gives out energy to the surroundings we say it is an **exothermic** reaction.

It is possible to measure the energy released more accurately using the apparatus shown in fig 26.

d Suggest why a polystyrene beaker is better than a glass beaker.

The thermometer allows an accurate measurement of the temperature increase. It is possible to compare how exothermic different reactions are but fair testing is essential.

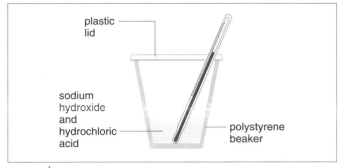

fig 26 | Simple apparatus to measure energy change

Exothermic reactions

Fig 15 on page 11 shows water being added to calcium oxide. So much energy is given out that some of the water turns to steam. This is not a reaction between two liquids but it is clearly a highly exothermic reaction. The energy given out is coming from energy changes within the chemicals that are reacting.

Endothermic reactions

Some chemical reactions are the opposite of exothermic reactions. As they take place they remove energy from the surroundings and take this energy into their chemical bonds.

We notice that this has happened because the container that the reactants are in becomes colder. Energy has been removed from the container. This sort of reaction is called an **endothermic** reaction. These reactions are much less common than exothermic reactions.

e Suggest apparatus that could be used to measure how endothermic a reaction is.

Thinking further

■ **1** You are comparing neutralisation reactions between sodium hydroxide + hydrochloric acid and sodium hydroxide + sulphuric acid. The acids are the same concentration. Suggest what else you would do to carry out a fair test.

■ **2** A fair test is carried out to find out about energy changes between sodium hydroxide and some acids. Look at table of data in fig 27. Comment on the results.

	25 cm³ sodium hydroxide and 25 cm³ sulphuric acid	25 cm³ sodium hydroxide and 25 cm³ hydrochloric acid	25 cm³ sodium hydroxide and 25 cm³ nitric acid	25 cm³ sodium hydroxide and 25 cm³ ethanoic acid
temperature at start in °C	25	25	25	25
temperature at end in °C	46	44	45	37

fig 27

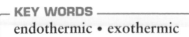

KEY WORDS
endothermic • exothermic

1.8 Extracting minerals

> ### Key points
>
> - Extracting minerals from the Earth's crust is vital if we are to provide raw materials for the construction, road and metal extraction industries.
> - Care must be taken, however, to minimise the impact that this extraction has on the environment.
> - This section considers the extraction of limestone.

Advantages of limestone extraction

Limestone has been quarried over many years for use as a building material. There are many regions in the United Kingdom where limestone is found.

a Where is the nearest limestone to your home?

Limestone is also used for road construction. It is also converted into quicklime and slaked lime.

b What are the chemical names for limestone, quicklime and slaked lime?

In areas where limestone is quarried, many people rely on the industry for employment. Not only are people needed to extract the limestone but also it must be crushed to suitable sizes and then transported away.

c Why are fewer quarry workers needed today compared to 200 years ago?

fig 28 | Modern limestone quarries are heavily mechanised

Disadvantages of limestone extraction

The demand for minerals has increased steadily. Some people become concerned about the expansion of old quarries or the creation of new ones. It may be that the new quarry will destroy an important habitat for wildlife, the noise and dust may be a problem if people live nearby, and there may a problem with transport of the rock because roads are inadequate.

d In addition to the reasons above, why do you think a quarry would not be sited at the location in fig 29?

A balance has to be struck between the advantages and disadvantages of mineral extraction.

fig 29 | This beauty spot is in a limestone area

Thinking further

■ **1** Suggest why there are no limestone mines.

■ **2** Today new buildings made from limestone can be found in parts of the country many miles from any limestone quarries. Why are very few limestone buildings more than 200 years old found in these areas?

IDEAS AND EVIDENCE

3 It is suggested that a new quarry is to be developed. Fig 30 shows the people who are at the initial meeting.

Look at the data shown in fig 31 for two proposed quarry sites X and Y.

a State what each of the people shown in fig 30 would say when selecting the best site.

b Imagine you are chairing the meeting: what is your suggested location, taking into account all of the evidence?

Ann is a geologist – she can advise on the amount and location of limestone

Jerry is an analytical chemist – he can advise on the purity of the limestone

Emily is a conservationist – she has a thorough knowledge of wildlife

David is a geographer – he can advise on how easy it is to transport the limestone away and the proximity of local houses and workforce

Wasim is a quarry engineer – he can advise on the ease of extraction

fig 30

fig 31

	site X	site Y
limestone purity	99% pure	95% pure
amount	5 square km exposed on the surface, thickness of deposit 100 metres.	15 square km exposed on the surface, thickness of deposit 50 metres.
road network	poor local roads but railway runs beside the proposed quarry	good main roads to nearby motorway
houses and people	nearest large town 15 km, two farmhouses on the very edge of the site, little else	nearest large town 2 km away but no houses on or near the edge of the proposed site
extraction	not a problem if the equipment can be put in place at start	no problems anticipated
ecology	wheatears (small birds) breed on the proposed site, they do not breed anywhere else in the locality	there are various rare orchids but these are also found at one other location nearby. However the orchid is listed as an endangered species. Site of Special Scientific Interest (SSSI) applied for
leisure industry	remote, few visitors	visited regularly, there is an alternative proposal that it become a nature reserve

Questions on chemical reactions

● **1** Fig 32 shows the Hope Valley cement works in Derbyshire.

fig 32

a Suggest which mineral is quarried nearby. *(1)*

b Which one of the following is mixed with this mineral to make cement?
clay coal sand *(1)*

c What does the works do to this mixture to make cement? *(1)*

d There is a rail link to the works. Why is this useful? *(1)*

● **2** This farmer is adding quicklime to the field.

fig 33

a Is the soil likely to be acid, neutral or alkali before she adds the quicklime? *(1)*

b What sort of reaction takes place between the quicklime and the soil? *(1)*

c Quicklime is harmful. Which one of the following symbols would be shown on the lime container? *(1)*

fig 34

d Suggest why it may be better to use slaked lime. *(1)*

■ **3** This simplified diagram shows industrial equipment. It is used to manufacture calcium oxide from calcium carbonate. Carbon dioxide is also produced.

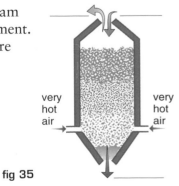

very hot air   very hot air

fig 35

a Copy and label the diagram. There are three spaces. *(3)*

b Write a word equation for the reaction taking place. *(1)*

c What is the common name for this industrial equipment? *(1)*

■ **4** Each of these three tubes contains a different gas.

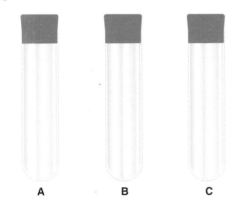

A   B   C

fig 36

One tube contains air, one contains carbon dioxide and the other contains hydrogen.

Describe tests that you could do to show which gas is in which tube. You can assume that you have three tubes of each gas and any other equipment you may require. *(6)*

■ **5** Look at the following word equations. Classify each reaction as neutralisation, thermal decomposition or oxidation. You may use each answer once, more than once or not at all.

a sodium hydroxide + sulphuric acid → sodium sulphate + water

b magnesium carbonate → magnesium oxide + carbon dioxide

c copper + oxygen → copper oxide

d ammonium hydroxide + sulphuric acid → ammonium sulphate + water *(4)*

◆ **6** Copper(II) carbonate, $CuCO_3$, is a pale green powder. It is thermally unstable and decomposes in a similar way to calcium carbonate.

a Write a symbol equation for the thermal decomposition of copper(II) carbonate. *(1)*

b Copper(II) carbonate undergoes typical reactions with acids.

  i Describe what you would see when copper(II) carbonate is added to dilute sulphuric acid *(3)*

  ii Write a symbol equation for the reaction. *(2)*

◆ **7** In each of the following, write down whether the substance underlined is oxidised, reduced or neither. Explain your answer in each case.

  a $\underline{CuO} + H_2 \rightarrow Cu + H_2O$

  b $CuO + \underline{H_2} \rightarrow Cu + H_2O$

  c $\underline{H_2O}$ (liquid) $\rightarrow H_2O$ (gas)

  d $C + \underline{CO_2} \rightarrow 2CO$ *(4)*

◆ **8** Balance the following ionic equations.

  a $H^+ + CO_3^{2-} \rightarrow H_2O + CO_2$

  b $Ca + H^+ \rightarrow Ca^{2+} + H_2$

  c $Cl_2 + I^- \rightarrow Cl^- + I_2$

  d $Cu^+ \rightarrow Cu + Cu^{2+}$ *(4)*

◆ **9** The reaction between an acid and a base produces a salt and water as the only products. Magnesium hydroxide is used to neutralise excess acidity in the stomach. This acidity is caused by hydrochloric acid.
Write:

  a a word equation for this neutralisation reaction *(1)*

  b a balanced symbol equation. [Assume that the formula of magnesium hydroxide is $Mg(OH)_2$.] *(2)*

◆ **10** Your teacher tells you that the reaction between sodium carbonate and ethanoic acid is **endothermic**.

  a What does endothermic mean? *(1)*

  b Describe an experiment that you could do to show that the reaction is endothermic. *(2)*

  c Predict the names of the substances that are formed when ethanoic acid reacts with sodium carbonate. *(3)*

IDEAS AND EVIDENCE

11 John Dalton was a scientist who lived between 1766 and 1844. The symbols that he used to represent substances that he believed to be elements are not the same as those we use today. Fig 37 shows some of the symbols that Dalton used.

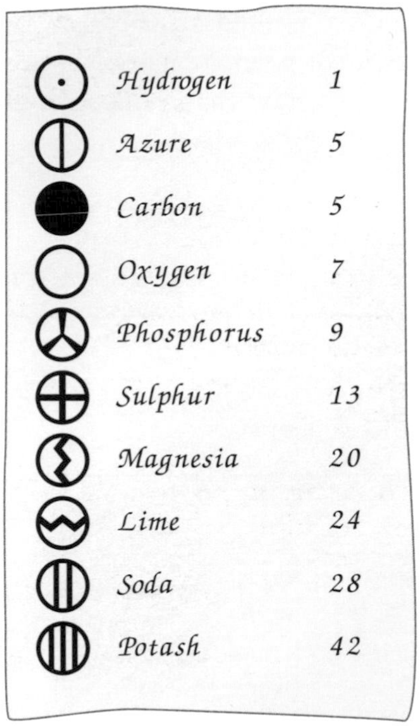

Symbol	Name	Value
⊙	*Hydrogen*	*1*
◐	*Azure*	*5*
●	*Carbon*	*5*
○	*Oxygen*	*7*
⊗	*Phosphorus*	*9*
⊕	*Sulphur*	*13*
Ⓢ	*Magnesia*	*20*
⊗	*Lime*	*24*
⓪	*Soda*	*28*
⑩	*Potash*	*42*

fig 37

a Suggest why we now use different symbols to these. *(2)*

b Some of the symbols that are in Dalton's table we now know are not elements but are compounds.

i Give the symbol of something that we now know is a compound. *(1)*

ii Suggest why scientists may have thought that the symbol you chose was that of an element. *(1)*

iii What is a compound? *(2)*

iv Suggest how Dalton's symbols would be used to write an equation for the reaction between carbon and oxygen atoms to make carbon dioxide. *(2)*

Metals

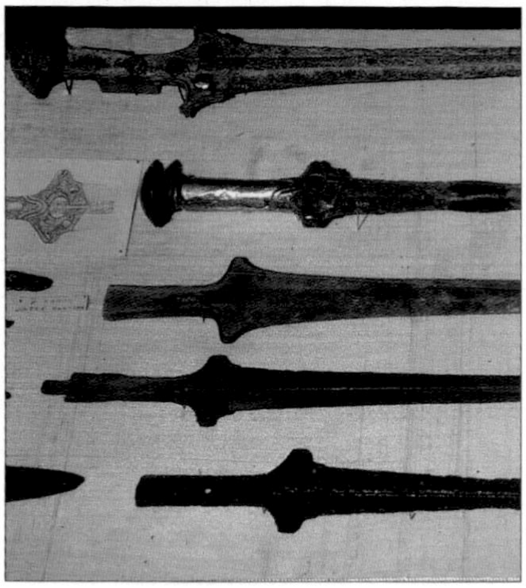

Introduction

Almost two thirds of the naturally occurring elements are metals. Our use of metals has shaped our history. The Bronze Age and the Iron Age were named after metals. For thousands of years gold and silver have been treasured because of their lasting value. More recently, new materials such as steel and aluminium have changed the way we live.

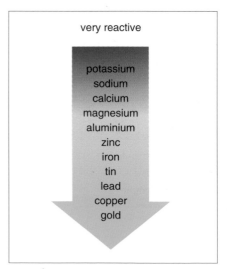

fig 1 | Bronze Age swords and knives

Reactivity of metals

The table in fig 2 gives details of some metal reactions.

metal	reaction with oxygen	reaction with water	reaction with dilute acid
potassium		reacts violently with cold water to form a hydroxide	
sodium		reacts vigorously with cold water to form a hydroxide	
calcium		reacts rapidly with cold water to form a hydroxide	
magnesium	burns vigorously to form an oxide	reacts with steam to form an oxide	reacts vigorously to form a salt and hydrogen
zinc	burns steadily to form an oxide		reacts steadily to form a salt and hydrogen
iron	burns slowly to form an oxide		
copper	does not burn, but slowly forms an oxide		

fig 2 | Some metal reactions

From the information in the table these metals can be placed in order of reactivity. The metals have been written in this order in fig 2. A few more metals have been added to make the reactivity series shown in fig 3.

Metals higher up in the series are more reactive than those lower down. A metal higher up in the series will displace a metal lower down from a solution of one of its salts.

An iron nail dipped into copper(II) sulphate solution turns brown. Iron has taken the place of copper in the solution.

Fe + CuSO$_4$ → Cu + FeSO$_4$
iron + copper(II)sulphate → copper + iron(II) sulphate

Information about displacement reactions can be used to work out the position of a metal in the reactivity series.

very reactive

potassium
sodium
calcium
magnesium
aluminium
zinc
iron
tin
lead
copper
gold

fig 3 | Reactivity series of metals

Check-up

a Potassium is so reactive it is stored in a jar of oil. This prevents it reacting with water and oxygen in the air.

 i What other metal in fig 2 would you expect to be stored in oil?

 ii What compound would be formed by the reaction of potassium with oxygen in the air?

b Aluminium burns rapidly when heated in oxygen. It also reacts rapidly with dilute acids.

 i Where should aluminium fit into the table in fig 2?

 ii Why does aluminium not react with water?

c Copper will displace silver metal from a solution of silver nitrate. Gold will not displace silver from silver nitrate.

 Where should silver be placed in the reactivity series?

d Copper(II) carbonate decomposes when heated gently.
Sodium carbonate does not decompose even when heated strongly.

 i What happens when calcium carbonate is heated?

 ii Explain your answer.

 If you have difficulty, ask your teacher for a Summary sheet.

Contents of the Teaching block

2.1 Extraction of metals

Metals are extracted from ores. Less reactive metals are extracted by reduction using carbon or carbon monoxide and more reactive metals are extracted by electrolysis. Some metals are recycled.

2.2 Extraction of iron

Iron is used in very large quantities. Most of it is turned into steel. Iron is extracted from its ores using the blast furnace. The raw materials for this process are iron ore, coke, limestone and air. Slag is produced as a by-product.

2.3 Extraction of aluminium

Bauxite, the main ore of aluminium, contains aluminium oxide. Aluminium is made by electrolysis of aluminium oxide.

2.4 Purification of copper

Electrical wiring requires copper of high purity. Copper is purified by electrolysis.

2.5 The transition metals

The transition metals have low reactivities, high melting points and high densities. Most compounds of transition metals are coloured.

Links to other Teaching blocks

2.1 Extraction of metals

Ores and minerals

Most metals are found naturally as compounds called **minerals**. Rocks are made up of crystals of minerals.

An **ore** is a rock that contains enough of a metal compound for it to be worth extracting the metal. Sometimes the metal compound needs to be concentrated before extraction.

The most common ores contain metal oxides. An example is the ore haematite, which contains iron(III) oxide.

Some ores contain other metal compounds. Malachite contains copper(II) carbonate.

a Why are most metals found as compounds?

b What is the difference between a mineral and an ore?

fig 4 | Iron ore – haematite

Extracting metals from ores

A few metals are found 'native'. This means that they are uncombined with other elements. Examples are silver and gold. Extraction consists of separating the metal from minerals in the ore.

c Suggest why gold is found uncombined with other elements.

For ores containing minerals, a chemical reaction must be used to separate the metal from other elements.

Most ores contain the metal oxide. To extract the metal the oxygen must be removed from it. This reaction is called **reduction**.

The more reactive the metal is, the more energy is needed to break the bond between the metal and oxygen.

For metals near the middle of the reactivity series the oxygen can be removed by reduction with carbon or carbon monoxide. This method is used for the extraction of zinc, iron and copper.

More reactive metals are extracted from their ores using electricity to reduce the metal compound. This process is called **electrolysis**.

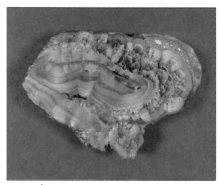

fig 5 | Copper ore – malachite

Electrolysis is a more expensive process than reduction with carbon or carbon monoxide. It is the only economic way to obtain metals such as aluminium.

d Suggest an economic way to extract each of the following metals. Give reasons for your choice.

    lead   magnesium   platinum   sodium   tin

The need for recycling

The ores of some metals are in short supply. This makes these metals very expensive. It also means that we will soon run short of them.

Some metals are expensive to extract from their ores. The high cost is not only in money, but also in energy.

All the Earth's resources are finite, including metal ores. Eventually we may run out of every metal.

fig 6 | Recycling of aluminium cans

For these reasons many metals are **recycled**.

Aluminium cans are collected and melted down. The metal can then be used again.

Recycling aluminium uses only 5% of the energy required to extract aluminium from its ore.

Steel is the most recycled metal in the world. Every year about 300 million tonnes are recycled. This is about 40% of world-wide production.

e Suggest why all metals are not recycled.

Thinking further

■ **1** Iron(III) oxide is reduced by carbon to make iron metal. What gas is also produced in this reaction?

■ **2 a** There is a plentiful supply of aluminium ore. Despite this, aluminium is a particularly good metal to recycle. Explain why.

  b Steel is one of the cheapest metals to buy, but it is the most recycled metal. Suggest why.

◆ **3** Malachite contains copper(II) carbonate, but copper(II) oxide is needed for extraction of copper.

Suggest how copper(II) oxide can be made from copper(II) carbonate.

KEY WORDS

electrolysis • minerals • ore • recycled • reduction

 Extraction of metals using carbon.

2.2 Extraction of iron

> ## Key points
>
> - Iron is extracted from its ores using the blast furnace.
> - The raw materials for this process are iron ore, coke, limestone and air.
> - Slag is produced as a by-product.

Extracting iron

The most common iron ore, haematite, contains iron(III) oxide. Iron is made by reduction of iron(III) oxide using carbon monoxide. This process is carried out in the blast furnace.

Iron ore, coke and limestone are put into the top of the furnace.

At the bottom of the furnace hot air is blasted in.

Coke is an impure form of carbon. It burns in air.

$$C \quad + \quad O_2 \quad \rightarrow \quad CO_2$$
carbon + oxygen → carbon dioxide

The temperature of the furnace rises to about 2000 °C.

a Why does the temperature of the furnace rise?

As the carbon dioxide gas rises up inside the furnace it is reduced by more carbon, making carbon monoxide.

$$C \quad + \quad CO_2 \quad \rightarrow \quad 2CO$$
carbon + carbon dioxide → carbon monoxide

This reaction is **endothermic**. The temperature falls to about 1500 °C.

b What does *endothermic* mean?

Iron(III) oxide is reduced by the carbon monoxide to produce iron metal.

$$Fe_2O_3 \quad + \quad 3CO \quad \rightarrow \quad 2Fe \quad + \quad 3CO_2$$
iron(III) + carbon → iron + carbon
oxide   monoxide   dioxide

This reaction is also endothermic, and the temperature of the furnace falls further.

c Explain why the iron is said to be reduced.

The molten iron trickles down the furnace and gathers at the bottom. Periodically this molten iron is tapped off and run into moulds or containers to be transported to steel-making furnaces. At this stage it is called **pig iron**.

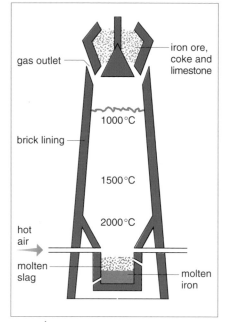

fig 7 | The blast furnace

d Explain why the iron falls to the bottom of the furnace.

The main impurity in iron ore is sand, made of silicon(IV) oxide. Limestone is made of calcium carbonate. This reacts with the silicon(IV) oxide.

$$CaCO_3 + SiO_2 \rightarrow CaSiO_3 + CO_2$$

| calcium carbonate | + | silicon(IV) oxide | → | calcium silicate | + | carbon dioxide |

The calcium silicate is also molten, and falls to the bottom of the furnace. This liquid, called **slag**, settles on top of the molten iron. It is also tapped off periodically.

e Why does the slag settle on top of the molten iron?

Slag is a useful by-product. It is used for road making and in the production of cement.

Each blast furnace works for 24 hours per day. Raw materials are fed into the top, air is blasted in, molten iron and slag are removed. The furnace only goes cold when the lining of insulating brick needs to be replaced.

f Suggest why the furnace is not turned off each night and re-started each morning.

Extending your knowledge

Pig iron from the blast furnace contains about 4% carbon. This makes it hard and brittle. When set in moulds it is called cast iron.

Most iron is converted into mild **steel**. This contains up to 1% carbon. The small amount of carbon makes mild steel much harder than pure iron, but not so brittle as cast iron. It is easily bent into shape, for example to make car bodies.

Special steels are made by adding other metals to mild steel. Tungsten is added to make a very hard steel for the edges of high-speed cutting tools. Chromium and nickel are added to make stainless steel.

g Why are car bodies not made from cast iron?

h Name a use for stainless steel and explain why it is more suited for this use than mild steel.

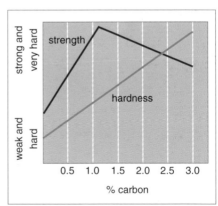

fig 8 Graph showing strength and hardness of steel

Thinking further

■ **1 a** Name the gases leaving the blast furnace.

b These hot gases are used to heat up the air that is blasted in at the bottom of the furnace. What advantage is there in doing this?

■ **2** List three reasons why the furnace contents stay hot.

◆ **3** Suggest what impurities might be present in pig iron.

___ **KEY WORDS** _____

cast iron • endothermic • pig iron • slag • steel

 Video on production of iron and steel.

2.3 Extraction of aluminium

> ### Key points
>
> - Bauxite, the main ore of aluminium, contains aluminium oxide.
> - Aluminium is made by electrolysis of aluminium oxide.

History

Aluminium is the most **abundant** metal in the Earth's crust. Despite this, aluminium used to be an expensive and little used metal.

In the 1860s Napoleon III honoured guests at his court in France by using cutlery made from aluminum instead of gold. Aluminium was more expensive than gold.

At that time aluminium could only be made by displacement using sodium.

$$AlCl_3 \quad + \quad 3Na \quad \rightarrow \quad 3NaCl \quad + \quad Al$$
aluminium + sodium → sodium + aluminium
chloride chloride

a Explain why sodium displaces aluminium from aluminium chloride.

In 1886 Charles Hall and Paul Heroult independently found a way to produce aluminium by **electrolysis**.

Mining of bauxite

In the Hall–Heroult process aluminium is extracted by electrolysis of aluminium oxide. The ore **bauxite** contains about 98% aluminium oxide.

b Much of the Earth's aluminium is present in clay. You probably have lots of this in your garden. Why is aluminium extracted from bauxite rather than clay?

Bauxite is obtained by **open-cast mining**, mainly in countries such as Australia, India, Indonesia and Brazil.

The main impurity in bauxite is iron(III) oxide. This is removed as a red mud, which is pumped into ponds for the solid to settle. The purification process uses large quantities of the strong alkali sodium hydroxide.

The purified aluminium oxide is then exported to other countries where the electrolysis takes place.

fig 9 | Open-cast mining of bauxite

c Why would you not like a bauxite mine near your home?

d Suggest why the purification process is carried out before the ore is exported.

Electrolysis of aluminium oxide

Aluminium oxide has a melting point of 2030 °C. It is too expensive to carry out the electrolysis at this temperature.

Instead the aluminium oxide is dissolved in molten **cryolite**. This is a mineral, sodium aluminium fluoride, Na_3AlF_6. It has a melting point below the temperature of 1000 °C used in the process.

A cell used for the electrolysis is shown in fig 10.

Aluminium is formed at the negative **electrode**. This electrode is made of carbon and lines the cell. The molten metal falls to the bottom of the cell, and is tapped off.

e Why is carbon a good material to use for the electrodes?

At the positive electrodes oxygen is evolved. These carbon electrodes need frequent replacement.

f Suggest what happens to the positive carbon electrodes to make them need to be replaced frequently.

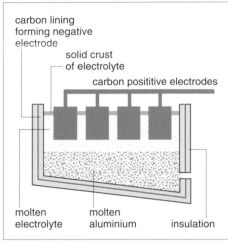

fig 10 | Electrolytic cell used in aluminium manufacture

During the electrolysis to produce aluminium chemical reactions take place at the positive and negative electrodes.

These can be represented by the following half equations:

1 $Al^{3+} + 3e^- \rightarrow Al$
2 $2O^{2-} \rightarrow O_2 + 4e^-$

g Which of these equations represents the reaction at the positive electrode and which at the negative electrode?

Thinking further

1 What is meant by the term electrolysis?

2 The carbon used for the negative electrode is also the lining of the electrolysis cell.

What is the advantage of this?

3 Why does aluminium collect at the bottom of the cell?

◆ 4 To produce 1 tonne of aluminium requires:
4.6 tonnes of bauxite
0.03 tonnes of cryolite
0.06 tonnes carbon electrode
15 000 kWh of electricity

Suggest which of these is most expensive.

◆ 5 Many aluminium-producing factories are in places with hydro-electric power supplies. Suggest why.

KEY WORDS
abundant • bauxite • cryolite • electrode • electrolysis • open-cast mining

 Video on electrolysis of aluminium. *Choosing a site for an aluminium smelter.*

2.4 Purification of copper

> ### Key points
>
> - Electrical wiring requires copper of high purity.
> - Copper is purified by electrolysis.

Why purify copper?

Copper is obtained from its ores by reduction using carbon. This process produces the metal with a purity of about 95%.

This purity is sufficient for some of the uses of copper, for example water pipes in houses.

Copper is also used for electrical wiring. This use demands a purity of 99.99%.

a Why does copper for electrical wiring need to be purer than copper for water pipes?

The impure copper obtained from smelting is further purified by electrolysis.

fig 11 | Impure copper electrodes

Electrolysis of copper(II) sulphate

In this electrolysis the electrolyte is a solution of copper(II) sulphate.

b Which ions are present in a solution of copper(II) sulphate?

A large block of impure copper is the positive electrode. A thin sheet of pure copper is the negative electrode.

At the positive electrode copper atoms in the impure block become ions. They leave the block and go into the solution. The positive electrode gets smaller as the electrolysis proceeds.

At the negative electrode copper ions from the solution become atoms. They stick onto the negative electrode. The negative electrode gets bigger as the electrolysis proceeds.

c Explain why the impure copper is made at the positive electrode and not the negative electrode.

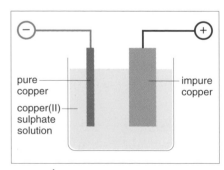

fig 12 | Purification of copper by electrolysis

Only pure copper joins to the negative electrode. Most impurities fall to the bottom of the electrolysis cell. They form a solid material which contains small quantities of precious metals such as silver, gold and platinum. These are purified from the solid.

The electrolysis transfers copper from the positive electrode to the negative electrode. The negative electrode becomes a large block of very pure copper.

d Copper(II) sulphate solution contains hydrogen ions. Explain why these are not discharged at the negative electrode.

Half equations can be written for the reactions taking place at the positive and negative electrodes.

positive electrode $Cu \rightarrow Cu^{2+} + 2e^-$
negative electrode $Cu^{2+} + 2e^- \rightarrow Cu$

e Re-write these half equations to include **state symbols**.

Extending your knowledge

Electrolysis is a **redox reaction**. That is a reaction in which both reduction and oxidation take place.

Oxidation can be described as a reaction in which electrons are lost. Reduction can be described as a reaction in which electrons are gained. You can remember this by using the mnemonic OILRIG. This stands for 'oxidation is loss' and 'reduction is gain'.

During electrolysis both an oxidation reaction and a reduction reaction take place.

f In the purification of copper, at which electrodes do the oxidation and reduction reactions take place?

g Explain your answer to **f**.

Thinking further

■ **1** Copper(II) sulphate solution is blue. The colour of the solution does not change during this electrolysis. Explain why.

■ **2** Electrolysis can be used to cover one metal with a thin layer of another. This is called **electroplating**. For example, copper can be plated with silver.

a Why is copper plated with silver?

b Suggest what you would use as the positive and negative electrodes and the electrolyte.

◆ **3 a** One of the impurities in copper is the precious metal platinum. This metal falls to the bottom of the cell. Why does it not join onto the pure copper at the negative electrode?

b Another impurity is zinc. This stays in the solution as zinc ions. Why does the zinc not join onto the negative electrode?

KEY WORDS
electroplating • redox reaction • state symbols

 Purification of copper.   *Video on copper refining.*

2.5 The transition metals

> ### Key points
>
> - Transition metals have low reactivities.
> - They have high melting points and high densities.
> - Most compounds of transition metals are coloured.

Position in the Periodic Table

Look at the Periodic Table in fig 13 and on the back page.

There is a block of elements in the middle of the Periodic Table, between Group 2 and Group 3. These are the transition metals. They include the three commonly used metals iron, nickel and copper. The precious metals silver, gold and platinum are also transition elements.

a Why are silver, gold and platinum called *precious metals*?

b What property of the precious metals makes them good for use in jewellery?

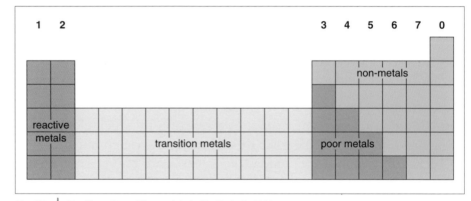

fig 13 | Position of transition metals in the Periodic Table

Properties of transition metals

The transition metals have some common properties.

The table in fig 14 shows some properties of iron and copper, compared with aluminium and magnesium.

element	melting point in C°	density in g/cm³	colour of some compounds
iron	1540	7.9	iron(II) sulphate – green
			iron(III) sulphate – brown
copper	1080	8.9	copper(II) sulphate – blue
			copper(II) chloride – green
aluminium	661	2.7	aluminium chloride – white
magnesium	649	1.7	magnesium sulphate – white

fig 14 | Some properties of copper, aluminium and magnesium

c The table shows three differences between the properties of the transition elements iron and copper and those of the non-transition elements aluminium and magnesium. What are these three differences?

Most transition metals share a number of characteristic properties:
- high melting point
- very hard
- high density
- coloured compounds.

d The element titanium is a transition metal. It is used for the cutting tips of drills. What properties of transition metals makes it useful for this purpose?

Uses of transition metals

Transition metals have many uses. Iron is the most used metal in the world. Copper is the third most widely used, after aluminium.

Catalysts

Many industrial processes use **catalysts** to speed up chemical reactions. These catalysts are usually transition metals or their compounds. Nickel is a catalyst used in the manufacture of margarine.

Another example is the Haber process for the manufacture of ammonia. This uses an iron catalyst. You will learn more about this in Teaching block 4.

Coins

Coins are made from mixtures of several metals. Most of these **alloys** include nickel.

Coins need to last a long time, despite being used every day.

e Why is nickel a good metal to use for making coins?

Wiring and water pipes

Copper is used to make the water pipes in houses. It does not react with the water flowing in the pipes. Copper pipe is easily bent to fit round corners.

Copper is also used to make electrical wiring. It is a good conductor of electricity.

f What other property of copper makes it suitable for electrical wiring?

fig 15 | Coins are made from alloys

Thinking further

■ **1** Spatulas used in chemistry laboratories are usually made of nickel. Suggest why.

■ **2** Iron is the most widely used metal. Use some examples of articles made from iron to show why this is.

■ **3** Copper is a good conductor of heat.

a Why would this be a disadvantage for hot water pipes in a house?

b For what articles in a kitchen would this property of copper be an advantage?

◆ **4** Many transition metals show two or more oxidation states in their compounds. Write formulae for iron(II) sulphate and iron(III) sulphate.

KEY WORDS

alloys • catalyst   *Reactions of transition metal compounds.*

Questions on metals

1 Cassiterite is an ore of the metal tin. It contains tin(IV) oxide, SnO_2.

● **a** Here are five sentences about getting tin metal from the ore. They are written in the wrong order. Place them in the correct order.

    A The mixture is heated strongly.
    B The ore is mixed with coke.
    C The ore is crushed.
    D Molten tin is tapped off.
    E The ore is dug out of the ground. *(4)*

● **b** What name is given to the method used to obtain tin from its ore? *(1)*

● **c** Why is this method used to get tin from its ore? *(1)*

◆ **d** Write an equation for the formation of tin from cassiterite. *(2)*

● **2** Look at the reactivity series in fig 3 on page 22.
    a Suggest how magnesium is extracted from its ore. *(1)*

    b Give a reason for your answer. *(1)*

3 Haematite is a common iron ore.
Another ore from which iron is extracted is magnetite. This contains Fe_3O_4. Iron is extracted from magnetite in the blast furnace.

● **a** What is added to the blast furnace in addition to magnetite? *(3)*

● **b** Describe a use for the waste gases leaving the top of the furnace. *(1)*

■ **c** In the blast furnace magnetite is reduced by carbon monoxide. What is meant by reduction? *(1)*

◆ **d** The furnace produces slag as a by-product. How is this formed? *(2)*

◆ **e** Magnetite is also reduced directly by carbon. Write a symbol equation for this reaction. *(2)*

● **4** Copy and complete the following passage by filling in the gaps. Use words from this list.

    bauxite   carbon   carbon dioxide
    cryolite   electrolysis   electrode
    negative   oxide   oxygen   positive

The most common ore of aluminium is called
_____. This ore contains aluminium
_____. The purified ore is dissolved in
molten _____ at a temperature of about
1000 °C. The process is called _____.
The electrodes are made of _____.
Aluminium is produced at the _____.
electrode. The _____ electrodes burn away
as _____. gas is produced. This forms
the waste gas _____ _____. *(10)*

● **5 a** Which of the metals in the list are transition metals? *(2)*

    aluminium   calcium   iron   lithium
    magnesium   nickel   sodium

    b Copper is also a transition metal. State one use of copper metal. *(1)*

    c What properties of copper make it suitable for this use? *(2)*

    d Why would iron be less suitable? *(1)*

◆ **6** Look at the position of tin in the reactivity series shown in fig 3 on page 22.

Predict how tin reacts with each of the following substances. Write an equation for each reaction.

    a oxygen *(3)*
    b water *(3)*
    c dilute sulphuric acid *(3)*
    d copper(II) sulphate solution *(3)*

■ **7** Four metals, P, Q, R and S, have the following properties.

Metal P does not react with cold water or dilute hydrochloric acid.

Metal Q reacts steadily with cold water and rapidly with dilute hydrochloric acid.

Metal R does not react with cold water, but reacts slowly with dilute hydrochloric acid.

Metal S reacts rapidly with cold water and dilute hydrochloric acid.

Place the metals in order of reactivity. *(3)*

8 The table in fig 16 gives information about some metal ores.

metal	common ore	formula	percentage of metal in ore
aluminium	bauxite	Al_2O_3	28
copper	chalcopyrite	$CuFeS_2$	0.5
gold	native	Au	0.001
zinc	zinc blende	ZnS	20
iron	haematite	Fe_2O_3	40
lead	galena	PbS	5

fig 16

Use the information in the table to help you to answer the following questions.

■ **a** Gold is found native. What does this mean? *(1)*

■ **b** Why is gold so expensive? *(2)*

■ **c** Which ore contains two metals? *(1)*

◆ **d** Which ores need concentration of the metal compound before the metal is extracted? *(2)*

9 The metal titanium occurs in the Earth in an ore called rutile. This contains titanium(IV) oxide.

In the extraction of titanium metal the ore is first heated in a stream of hydrogen chloride to produce titanium(IV) chloride. The titanium(IV) chloride is then heated with sodium to produce titanium.

■ **a** Why is titanium not extracted from titanium(IV) oxide by reduction with carbon? *(1)*

■ **b** What does this extraction process tell you about the position of titanium in the reactivity series compared with that of sodium? *(1)*

◆ **c** Write symbol equations for the reactions involved in the extraction of titanium. *(4)*

◆ **d** Suggest why electrolysis is not used to extract titanium from titanium(IV) oxide. *(1)*

◆ **10** You are working in the research laboratories of a large company making metal cans for food packaging. The company has been asked to supply cans for new range of a supermarket 'own brand' foods. The supermarket plans to sell 'own brand' lager (containing alcohol), fish (in salt water) and fruit juice (which is acidic). You are asked to compare the properties of aluminium cans with those of tin-coated steel cans for this contract. Your results are summarised in the table in fig 17.

	aluminium	tin-coated steel
reaction with water	no reaction even when hot	no reaction even when hot
reaction with acid	bubbles evolved; vigorous when hot	only a few bubbles even when hot
reaction with alkali	gas evolved; vigorous when cold	no reaction even when hot
reaction with salt	no reaction even when hot	no reaction even when hot
reaction with alcohol	no reaction	no reaction
mass of can in g	35.9	59.7
hardness of can	Soft	quite hard
price per tonne in £	1100	800

fig 17

Write a report for your managing director comparing the two types of can and making recommendations about which type should be used. *(8)*

─ **IDEAS AND EVIDENCE** ─

11 Brazil has vast deposits of iron ore.

Before 1950 all of the ore produced was exported. Brazil then bought back iron and steel. Since 1950 some of the ore has been used to make iron in Brazil.

Brazil has no coal deposits from which to make coke, so it has to be imported. Brazil has vast rain forests that can be used to make charcoal. Charcoal can be used instead of coke in the blast furnace. The pig iron produced is cheaper to transport than iron ore. It also contains less sulphur impurity and fetches a higher price than pig iron made using coke.

Imagine you have been asked to produce a report for the Brazilian Government giving the advantages and disadvantage of setting up a major iron producing industry. Your report should conclude with a recommendation. *(8)*

Atomic structure and the Periodic Table

Introduction

All substances are made up of particles. These particles, called atoms, are very small. They cannot be seen with the naked eye or an ordinary microscope. There are very powerful instruments called electron microscopes that can be used to look at large atoms.

There are 92 different sorts of element that occur naturally in the world around us. A few more can only be made in the laboratory. Each different sort of element contains only one kind of atom.

Most of the four million substances that exist are compounds. A compound contains two or more different kinds of atom joined together. In some, but not all, of these compounds the atoms are joined to make molecules.

Many of the materials we see around us are mixtures. Air is a mixture of elements such as oxygen and nitrogen with compounds such as carbon dioxide and water.

The formula of a compound shows how many atoms of each element are joined together. For example, carbon dioxide has the formula CO_2. Each molecule of carbon dioxide has one carbon atom and two oxygen atoms.

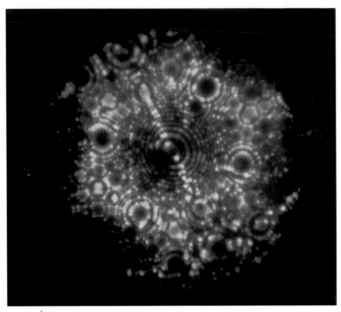

fig 1 | Electron micrograph of tungsten; the coloured dots show the locations of individual atoms within the metal

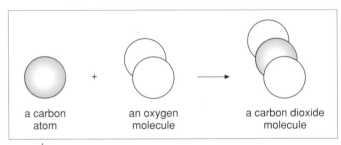

fig 2 | Formation of carbon dioxide from carbon and oxygen

Check-up

a What is the meaning of each of the following terms?

atom   molecule   element   compound

b Place the following materials in three lists: elements, compounds and mixtures.

air carbon carbon dioxide coffee helium iron magnesium milk phosphorus sugar water

c Which elements are joined together in the following compounds.

sodium oxide zinc chloride water methane (CH_4) carbon monoxide ammonia (NH_3) ethanol (C_2H_5OH) sulphuric acid (H_2SO_4) potassium nitrate (KNO_3)

d How many atoms of each element are joined to make each formula of the following compounds?

potassium oxide (K_2O) nitric acid (HNO_3) water

butane (C_4H_{10}) calcium carbonate ($CaCO_3$)

ethanol (C_2H_5OH) glucose ($C_6H_{12}O_6$)

If you have difficulty, ask your teacher for a Summary sheet.

Contents of the Teaching block

3.1 Atomic structure

Atoms are made of protons, neutrons and electrons. In one element each of the atoms has the same number of protons. Nearly all the mass of an atom is from the protons and neutrons.

3.2 Finding a pattern

When elements are listed in order of increasing atomic number, those with similar properties occur at regular intervals. In the Periodic Table these similar elements are in columns called Groups.

3.3 Elements in the Periodic Table

In the Periodic Table elements appear in order of increasing atomic number. The horizontal rows are called Periods and the vertical columns are called Groups.

3.4 Electron arrangement

In atoms the electrons are arranged in shells. Each shell holds a maximum number of electrons. The number of electrons in the outer shell is the same as the Group of the element in the Periodic Table.

3.5 The alkali metals

Group 1 contains the most reactive metal elements. There is a trend in physical properties and the reactivity of the elements increases down the Group.

3.6 The halogens

The halogens (Group 7) are very reactive non-metals. There are patterns in their properties down the Group.

3.7 Uses of chlorine

Chlorine is used to sterilise water and to make bleach and chlorofluorocarbons. There are hazards involved when using chlorine and other halogens.

3.8 Sodium chloride

Sodium and chlorine react to make sodium chloride. Sodium chloride is used to make sodium hydroxide. Impure sodium chloride, rock salt, is used to de-ice winter roads.

3.9 The noble gases

Group 0 contains the noble gases. They show trends in density and boiling point down the Group. The noble gases are unreactive elements, but have many important uses.

3.10 Discovering the secrets of the atom

It took many years to find out what atoms are like. Some important and famous scientists helped make these discoveries.

3.11 Data about elements

Using information about some of the elements, you can discover interesting trends and ideas.

Links with other Teaching blocks

3.1 Atomic structure

> ## Key points
>
> - Atoms are made of protons, neutrons and electrons.
> - Atoms of one element all have the same number of protons.
> - Nearly all the mass of an atom is from protons and neutrons.

The atom

In 1808 John Dalton suggested that all substances are made of atoms; but what are atoms made of?

Atoms contain three kinds of particles – **protons**, **neutrons** and **electrons**. These are called sub-atomic particles.

The centre of an atom is called the **nucleus**. It contains protons and neutrons. The nucleus is very small, occupying only about 1% of the volume of an atom.

The rest of the atom is mostly empty space, with electrons spread out in it.

A comparison of the masses and electrical charges for the three sub-atomic particles is shown in fig 3.
Protons and neutrons have the same mass, but it would take nearly 2000 electrons to have the mass of one proton.

Protons and electrons have opposite charge, but neutrons have no charge.

a Which part of the atom contains nearly all of its mass?

b An atom is neutral, which means it has no overall charge. What does this tell you about the number of protons and electrons in an atom?

Figure 4 gives an idea of what an atom must look like.

sub-atomic particle	relative mass	relative charge
proton	1	+1
neutron	1	0
electron	1/1860	−1

fig 3

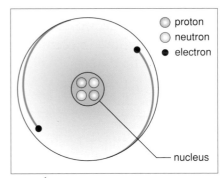

fig 4 | The structure of a helium atom

Atomic number and mass number

All of the atoms of one element have the same number of protons. This is called the **atomic number** of that element.
It is given the symbol Z.

No two elements can have the same atomic number.

A neutral atom contains equal numbers of protons and electrons, so the atomic number also tells us the number of electrons in that atom.

The **mass number** of an atom is found by adding together the number of protons and neutrons. It is given the symbol A.
The mass number is also called the nucleon number.

It is usual to write these two numbers alongside the symbol for the element as shown in fig 5.

c Write the symbol with atomic and mass numbers for an atom of sodium, which has 11 protons and 12 neutrons.

d How many electrons does this atom of sodium have?

e How many protons and neutrons are in an atom of potassium $^{39}_{19}$K?

Ions are formed when an atom loses or gains one or more electrons. In an ion the number of electrons is not equal to the number of protons.

An atom of chlorine has 17 protons and 17 electrons. A chloride ion, Cl⁻ has 17 protons and 18 electrons. One electron does not have its charge cancelled out by a proton, giving the chloride ion a −1 charge.

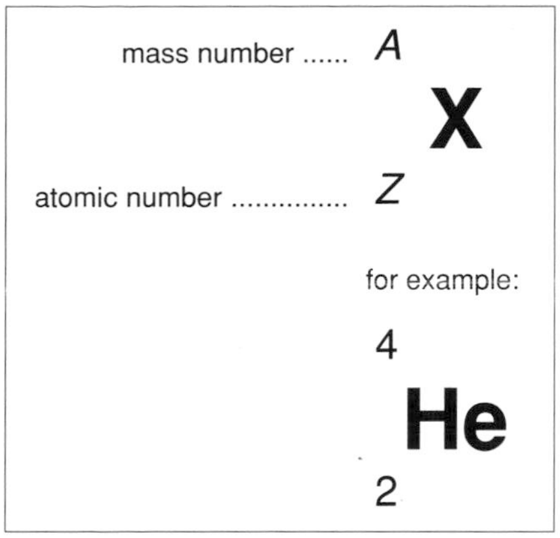

Isotopes

In some elements not all of the atoms have the same number of neutrons. These different versions of the atoms of one element are called **isotopes.**

Chlorine has two isotopes. One has 18 neutrons and the other has 20 neutrons. Both have 17 protons and 17 electrons.

f Write the symbol with atomic and mass numbers for each of the isotopes of chlorine.

The **relative atomic mass** of chlorine is 35.5. This reflects the fact that a sample of chlorine contains 75% of chlorine-35 and 25% of chlorine-37.

g What would be the relative atomic mass of chlorine if the two isotopes existed in equal proportions?

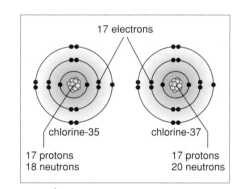

fig 5 | Mass number and atomic number

fig 6 | Isotopes of chlorine

Thinking further

■ **1** When we are thinking about the mass of an atom, we can forget about the mass of the electrons in that atom. Explain why.

■ **2** Atoms are mostly made of nothing. Explain why this statement is correct.

■ **3** John Dalton thought that atoms were solid balls, like miniature marbles. Write a short note to John Dalton telling him what we now believe atoms to be like.

◆ **4** Look at the information given in fig 7.

  a Which particle is a neutral atom of carbon?

particle	number of protons	number of electrons	number of neutrons
A	6	6	8
B	11	10	12
C	9	10	10
D	8	10	8

fig 7

b Write the symbol with atomic and mass numbers for this atom of carbon.

c Particle C is a fluoride ion. What is the charge on this ion?

d An oxygen ion has a charge of −2. Which particle is an oxygen ion?

e What is the charge on particle B?

KEY WORDS

atomic number • electrons • ions • isotopes • mass number • neutrons • nucleus • protons • relative atomic mass

3.2 Finding a pattern

Key points

- Groups of elements have similar properties.
- Elements can be listed in order of increasing atomic number.
- Elements with similar properties occur at regular intervals.
- In the Periodic Table similar elements are in Groups.

Li	Cl
Na	Br
K	I

fig 8 | Döbereiner's triads

Early ideas

Many scientists tried to find a pattern in the way that different chemical elements react.

In 1829 Johann Döbereiner arranged elements into sets of three. Each set has similar **properties**. He called these triads.

a How do the three metals lithium, sodium and potassium react with water?

b Do Döbereiner's triads agree with the properties of these elements?

In 1863 John Newlands made his law of octaves. He placed the elements in order of atomic mass. He then divided them into groups by taking every eighth element.

Although his ideas made some sense, they contained a number of errors. Other scientists ridiculed him.

c Newlands' octaves placed copper in the same group of elements as sodium and potassium. Explain why this is not a good idea.

1	hydrogen	a very reactive gas
2	helium	an unreactive gas
3	lithium	a soft, very reactive metal
4	beryllium	a reactive metal
5	boron	a solid non-metal
6	carbon	a solid non-metal
7	nitrogen	a gaseous non-metal
8	oxygen	a reactive non-metal
9	fluorine	a very reactive gaseous non-metal
10	neon	an unreactive gas
11	sodium	a soft, very reactive metal
12	magnesium	a reactive metal
13	aluminium	a reactive metal
14	silicon	a solid non-metal
15	phosphorus	a solid non-metal
16	sulphur	a reactive non-metal
17	chlorine	a very reactive gaseous non-metal
18	argon	an unreactive gas
19	potassium	a soft, very reactive metal
20	calcium	a reactive metal

fig 9 | Repeated pattern in first 20 elements

In 1869 Dmitri Mendeléev put together a periodic table of the elements. He began by listing all the known elements in order of increasing atomic mass. He spotted that elements with similar properties appear at regular intervals down the list.

d Look at fig 9. Put together a group of elements with similar properties. Begin your group with lithium.

	1	2	3	4	5	6	7	0
1	H							
2	Li	Be	B	C	N	O	F	
3	Na	Mg	Al	Si	P	S	Cl	
4	K Cu	Ca Zn		Ti	V As	Cr Se	Mn Br	Fe Co Ni

fig 10 | Mendeléev's periodic table

Mendeléev placed similar elements into groups. He realised that not all elements had been discovered. Mendeléev left gaps for new ones in the correct places in his table. He also swapped the order of some elements to make them fit better.

e Look at the group of elements you listed in **d**. Now find them on Mendeléev's periodic table. Do they occur together?

The modern Periodic Table is similar to that of Mendeléev, but contains several improvements.

Elements are in order of atomic number instead of atomic mass. This means that elements no longer have to swap places to fit correctly. A number of new elements have been discovered and slotted into the spaces left by Mendeléev.

Also the metals and non-metals are clearly separated.

A simple version of the modern Periodic Table, with just the first 20 elements, is shown in fig 11.

Elements with similar properties are in vertical **Groups**.

f Where are the metals and non-metals found on this simple Periodic Table?

Only 92 elements occur naturally. Elements from 93 to 109 are 'man-made'. Scientists at the University of California, including Glenn Seaborg and Albert Ghiorso, made many of these elements. They include californium (98) and mendelevium (101). In recognition of his work Glenn Seaborg received a Nobel Prize in 1951, and element 106 was named after him: seaborgium.

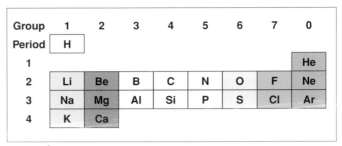

Group	1	2	3	4	5	6	7	0
Period	H							
1								He
2	Li	Be	B	C	N	O	F	Ne
3	Na	Mg	Al	Si	P	S	Cl	Ar
4	K	Ca						

fig 11 | A simple version of the modern Periodic Table

fig 12 | Glenn Seaborg

Thinking further

1 a What similarity is there between Newlands' law of octaves and the modern Periodic Table?

b Scientists like Newlands, who propose new and different scientific ideas, are often ridiculed by other scientists? Why does this happen?

2 Look at the list of elements in fig 9. In 1869 the elements fluorine, neon and argon had not been discovered.

a Mendeléev had no knowledge of these elements. How was he able to construct his periodic table without this information?

b Mendeléev was able to predict the properties of some of the elements yet to be discovered. Suggest how he was able to do this.

3 Tellurium has an atomic mass of 127.6 and atomic number 52. Iodine has an atomic mass of 126.9 and atomic number 53. Tellurium comes before iodine in order of atomic mass. In his table Mendeléev swapped the two elements to place them correctly.

a Explain why tellurium and iodine do not need to be swapped in the modern Periodic Table.

b Iodine has similar properties to fluorine and chlorine. In Mendeléev's periodic table the place of tellurium would have been misleading if he had not swapped it with iodine. Explain why.

KEY WORDS
Groups • properties

3.3 Elements in the Periodic Table

Key points

- Elements in the modern Periodic Table are arranged in order of increasing atomic number.
- Horizontal rows are called Periods.
- Vertical rows are called Groups.
- Elements with similar properties are in the same Group.

Structure of the Periodic Table

Look at the Periodic Table shown on the back page. There are over 100 elements in the Periodic Table. They are arranged in order of increasing atomic number.

All substances are made of one or more of these elements.

Most elements are metals, and are on the left of the table. The 22 non-metals are in the top right corner of the table. The line dividing metals from non-metals is a zig-zag diagonal from boron to astatine.

fig 13 | The alkali metals

a Put these elements in two lists – metals and non-metals.
P Ca Al S K Mn Si Cl Kr Ba Fe Te

The horizontal rows in the Periodic Table are called **Periods**. Period 1 contains only hydrogen and helium. Period 2 has eight elements, and runs from lithium to neon.

The vertical rows are called **Groups**, numbered 1, 2, 3, 4, 5, 6, 7 and 0. Some of these Groups have names.

b In which Group and Period do we find phosphorus?

Alkali metals

The elements in Group 1 are called the alkali metals. These are the most reactive metals in the Periodic Table. The name of this Group comes from the property of these elements to form strong alkalis when they react with water.

c As you can see in the photograph in fig 13, the alkali metals are stored in jars containing oil. This prevents air coming into contact with the metals. What problem is caused by air coming into contact with these metals?

Halogens

Group 7 is the halogens. These are the most reactive non-metals in the Periodic Table. The Group contains chlorine, a poisonous gas used as a weapon in the first World War. Chlorine is now used to kill bacteria in swimming pools.

fig 14 | Chlorine is used to kill bacteria in swimming pools

d If chlorine was used as a poisonous gas, how is it safe to use in swimming pools?

Noble gases

Group 0 contains the noble gases. These gases are very unreactive. They are used in advertising signs, which we usually call 'neon lights'. Argon is also used in light bulbs.

e What would happen to the white hot metal filament if a light bulb was filled with air?

f How does argon prevent this from happening?

Transition metals

In the middle of the Periodic Table is a large block of elements called the transition metals. Most of the metals we see in use around us are in this block. For example, copper is used for electrical wires and water pipes; iron is used to make cars; zinc and manganese are used to make different types of batteries.

g Suggest a property of copper that makes it suitable for use in electrical wires.

Hydrogen has a unique place in the Periodic Table. It is a very reactive non-metal, but its chemical properties are more like those of a metal.

fig 15 | Neon lights

Thinking further

■ **1** Silver, gold and platinum are all found in the transition metal block of the Periodic Table. These metals are used to make jewellery.

  a What property do these metals have in common which makes them suitable for use in jewellery?

  b Why would a bracelet made from the metal lithium be a bad idea?

■ **2** Find the element in the Periodic Table (see the back page) with the symbol Ba.

  a What is the name of this element?

  b Is this element a metal or a non-metal? Give reasons for your answer.

  c Which of the elements in this list would have properties similar to those of Ba?

  aluminium   calcium   chlorine   copper   sodium

◆ **3** Metals conduct electricity but non-metals do not. The non-metal silicon is a semi-conductor of electricity. It will conduct electricity under some conditions.

  a Use the position of silicon in the Periodic Table to suggest a reason for its conducting properties.

  b The semi-conducting properties of silicon make it very good for one purpose. What is this use of silicon?

┌─ **KEY WORDS** ─────
│ Groups • Periods   │   *Internet search for element information.*
└──────────────────

3.4 Electron arrangement

> ### Key points
>
> - Electrons are arranged in shells.
> - Each shell holds a maximum number of electrons.
> - The number of electrons in the outer shell is the same as the Group of the element in the Periodic Table.

Electron shells

Nearly all of the mass of an atom is in the nucleus. This contains protons and neutrons.

The nucleus is in the centre of the atom. It is very tiny.

The rest of the atom is mostly empty space. This space contains the electrons.

Electrons are arranged in **shells**. These shells are at different distances from the nucleus.

Each shell can only contain a certain number of electrons.

The smallest atom is hydrogen. It has one proton in the nucleus and one electron. This electron is in the first shell.

In the Periodic Table the elements are arranged in order of increasing atomic number.

As we move on from hydrogen each element has one more electron than the element before it. The electrons fill up each shell in turn, until it is full. Then the next shell begins.

element	1st shell	2nd shell	3rd shell	4th shell
hydrogen	1			
helium	2			
lithium	2	1		
beryllium	2	2		
boron	2	3		
carbon	2	4		
nitrogen	2	5		
oxygen	2	6		
fluorine	2	7		
neon	2	8		
sodium	2	8	1	
magnesium	2	8	2	
aluminium	2	8	3	
silicon	2	8	4	
phosphorus	2	8	5	
sulphur	2	8	6	
chlorine	2	8	7	
argon	2	8	8	
potassium	2	8	8	1
calcium	2	8	8	2

fig 16 Electron arrangements for the first 20 elements

Fig 16 shows electron arrangements for the first 20 elements. Look at the table in fig 16.

a How many electrons are needed to fill the first shell?

b How many electrons are needed to fill the second shell?

c How many electrons are there in an atom of magnesium?

The electron arrangement of magnesium is written 2,8,2.

d Write down the electron arrangement of silicon, phosphorus and sulphur atoms.

Fig 17 shows neon, magnesium and sulphur atoms.

e Draw similar diagrams of helium, sodium, argon and calcium atoms.

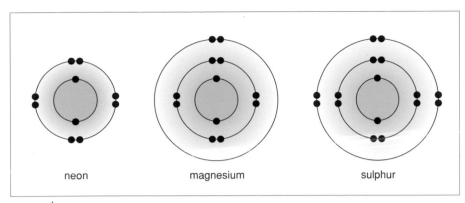

| neon | magnesium | sulphur |

fig 17 | Electron arrangement of some atoms

Electron arrangement and the Periodic Table

Look at the electron arrangement of the first 20 elements and where they are in the Periodic Table.

Lithium, sodium and potassium have one electron in the outer shell. These elements are in Group 1.

Beryllium, magnesium and calcium have two electrons in the outer shell. These elements are in Group 2.

This pattern continues. The Group number in the Periodic Table is the same as the number of electrons in the outer shell.

f The halogens are the elements in Group 7. Bromine is one of the halogens. How many electrons does each bromine atom have in its outer shell?

As we move across each Period the shell of electrons fills. The noble gases are at the end of each Period. They have full outer shells.

As we move down each Group the number of shells in each atom increases. Each element has one more complete shell than the one above it.

g How many complete shells are in atoms of neon, argon and krypton?

Thinking further

■ **1** Describe how the arrangement of elements in the Periodic Table is related to the electron arrangement in their atoms.

■ **2** Oxygen and sulphur are both in Group 6.

  a What is similar about the arrangement of electrons in atoms of oxygen and sulphur?

  b What is different about the arrangement of electrons in atoms of oxygen and sulphur?

◆ **3** Hydrogen is a non-metal but in its reactions it often behaves like a metal. It forms a positive ion like metals. Use information about the arrangement of electrons in a hydrogen atom to explain these facts.

KEY WORDS
shells

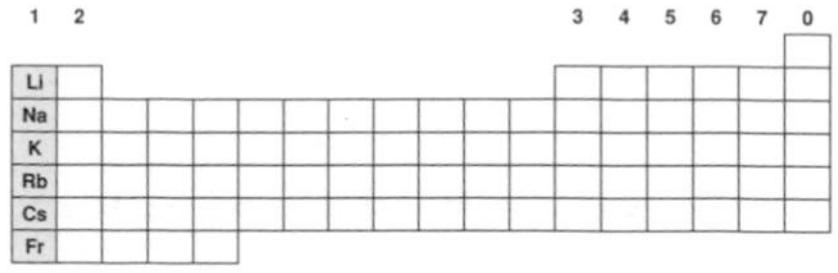

3.5 The alkali metals

Key points

- Group 1 contains the most reactive metal elements.
- There is a trend in physical properties in this Group.
- Reactivity increases down the Group.

Position in the Periodic Table

The alkali metals are the elements in Group 1.

As we move to the left of the Periodic Table the metals increase in **reactivity**. Group 1 therefore contains the most reactive metals.

Physical properties

The table in fig 18 shows some of the physical properties of the first three alkali metals.

alkali metal	density in g/cm^3	melting in point °C	hardness
lithium	0.53	180	fairly soft
sodium	0.97	98	soft
potassium	0.86	64	very soft

fig 18

a Describe how melting point and hardness change down the Group of alkali metals.

b What conclusion can you draw about the **density** of the alkali metals?

Compared with most metals, the elements of Group 1 are much softer and have much lower melting points. They also have lower densities. The first three alkali metals float on water!

Chemical properties

All of the alkali metals are very reactive. They are normally stored under oil to prevent contact with oxygen and water vapour in the air.

Even when stored in oil the metals have a dull layer of oxide on the outside. When freshly cut they are shiny.

c A shiny, freshly cut piece of sodium quickly goes dull. Explain why.

All of the metals in Group 1 react with water. Hydrogen gas is given off.

d Describe how you could test this gas to prove that it is hydrogen.

When Universal Indicator is added to the water it goes blue. An alkali has been formed.

fig 19 | A piece of sodium being cut

The reaction between sodium and water produces the alkali sodium hydroxide.

$$2Na + 2H_2O \rightarrow 2NaOH + H_2$$
sodium + water → sodium hydroxide + hydrogen

e What products are formed when potassium reacts with water?

The vigour of the reaction with water increases down Group 1. Lithium bubbles gently on top of the water. Sodium bubbles

fig 20 | Lithium, sodium and potassium reacting with water

vigorously. It shoots around on the surface. Potassium reacts violently. So much heat is produced that the hydrogen burns. Rubidium reacts explosively with water.

f Suggest how caesium reacts with water.

Care has to be taken when handling the alkali metals.

g What dangers are involved in using alkali metals?

h How can these dangers be minimised?

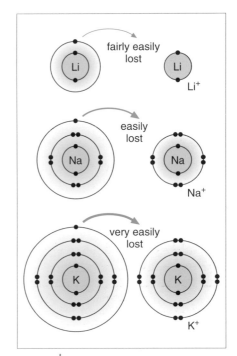

fig 21 | Ion formation in alkali metals

An alkali metal forms a compound by losing the single outer electron. A positive ion is formed. The ion has a full outer shell of electrons. This is a **stable** structure.

As we move down Group 1 of the Periodic Table, each element has one whole shell of electrons more than the one above it. The distance from the nucleus to the outer electron increases. This electron has less attraction from the positive charge in the nucleus. It is more easily lost.

i Why do the alkali metals form ions with a +1 charge?

j Explain why potassium is more reactive than sodium.

Thinking further

1 Why are the elements in Group 1 called the alkali metals?

2 What would you expect the melting points of rubidium and caesium to be?

3 Describe what you would see as a small piece of potassium is dropped into water.

4 Write a symbol equation for the reaction of potassium with water.

KEY WORDS
density • reactivity • stable

 Reactions of alkali metals with water.

3.6 The halogens

Physical properties

Fig 22 shows some physical properties of four halogens.

a What pattern is there in melting points down Group 7?

b What pattern is there in boiling points down Group 7?

halogen	relative atomic mass	colour	melting point in °C	boiling point in °C
fluorine	19	yellow	−220	−188
chlorine	35.5	green	−101	−35
bromine	80	red/brown	−7	58
iodine	127	dark grey	114	183

fig 22 | Some physical properties of four halogens

c Is each halogen solid, liquid or gas at room temperature?

The halogens exist as small molecules each containing two atoms held together by a strong **covalent** bond, e.g. Cl_2.

The forces between the molecules are very weak.

The molecules are easily separated giving the halogens low melting points and boiling points.

As we move from one element to the next down the Group the colour of the element gets darker. This trend is seen clearly when looking at the colour of the vapour of each element.

fig 23 | Colours of halogen vapours

d The halogen below iodine in Group 7 is called astatine. What colour do you think astatine vapour is?

Chemical properties

All of the halogens are reactive **non-metals**. In Group 7 the reactivity decreases down the group.

e Which is the most reactive halogen in Group 7?

Halogens react with most metals to form salts.

For example, iron reacts with chlorine to make iron(III) chloride.

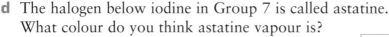

2Fe + 3Cl₂ → 2FeCl₃
iron + chlorine → iron(III) chloride

During the reaction with chlorine the iron glows brightly.

The reaction of iron and bromine is slower. The iron does not glow as much. Iron(III) bromide is formed.

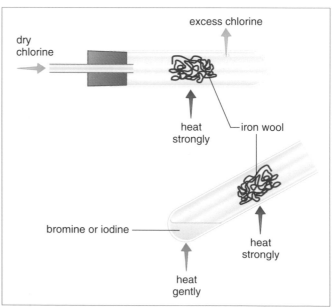

fig 24 | Reactions between iron and the halogens

Iron and iodine react very slowly to produce iron(III) iodide.

The reaction of iron and fluorine is too dangerous to carry out in a school laboratory.

f Put the four halogens in the order of reactivity of their reaction with iron. Put the most reactive one first.

A similar pattern is seen with other halogen reactions.

Displacement reactions

A **displacement reaction** takes place when chlorine gas is bubbled through a solution of potassium bromide. Chlorine takes the place of the less reactive bromine.

g What colour change can you see when this reaction takes place?

h How can you explain the colour change?

A similar reaction takes place if bromine is added to a solution of potassium iodide.

i What are the two products of this reaction?

If bromine is added to a solution of potassium chloride, there is no reaction. Bromine is less reactive than chlorine. It does not displace the chlorine from solution.

These reactions are summarised in fig 25.

These displacement reactions show an increase in reactivity of halogens down the Group.

halogen	solution	result	halogen displaced
chlorine	potassium bromide	red solution	bromine
chlorine	potassium iodide	brown solution	iodine
bromine	potassium chloride	none	none
bromine	potassium iodide	brown solution	iodine
iodine	potassium chloride	none	none
iodine	potassium bromide	none	none

fig 25 | Displacement reactions of halogens

Fig 26 shows the electron arrangement of four halogens.

j How are these electron arrangements similar?

As we move down the Group each halogen has one more complete shell of electrons. The attraction between the positive nucleus and the outer shell of negative electrons decreases down the Group. This makes it more difficult for another electron to be gained in this outer shell. As a result reactivity is reduced.

k Explain why fluorine is the most reactive halogen.

halogen	electron arrangement
fluorine	2,7
chlorine	2,8,7
bromine	2,8,18,7
iodine	2,8,18,18,7

fig 26 | Electron arrangement of four halogens

Thinking further

■ **1** In Russia winter temperatures can fall to −40 °C. How would samples of the halogens look different if they were kept outside at this temperature?

■ **2** Describe one piece of evidence showing that the reactivity of the halogens decreases down the Group.

◆ **3** Predict how astatine reacts with iron.

◆ **4** Write a symbol equation for the displacement reaction between bromine, Br_2, and potassium iodide, KI.

KEY WORDS
covalent • displacement reaction • non-metals

 Displacement reactions of halogens.

3.7 Uses of chlorine

> ### Key points
>
> - Chlorine is used to sterilise water.
> - Bleach is made using chlorine.
> - Chlorine is used to make chlorofluorocarbons.
> - There are hazards involved when using chlorine and other halogens.

Sterilisation of water

Chlorine is used to **sterilise** the water in swimming pools. It is also added to the water supplied to houses.

Chlorine is a very poisonous element. It kills bacteria in the water. If they were not killed these bacteria might cause diseases such as cholera and typhoid.

a Why are only very small quantities of chlorine added to water supplies?

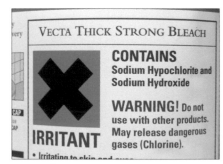

fig 28 | Label from a bleach bottle

Bleach

When chlorine is added to sodium hydroxide solution **bleach** is made.

$$Cl_2 + 2NaOH \rightarrow NaCl + NaClO + H_2O$$
chlorine + sodium → sodium + sodium + water
hydroxide chloride chlorate(I)

The active chemical in bleach is sodium chlorate(I).

Bleach is used to kill bacteria, for example in the toilet. It will also remove colour from dyed materials.

Bleach is one of the most dangerous substances kept in the house. Bottles of bleach carry health warnings.

b The hazard label on a bottle of bleach shows that it is an irritant. What does irritant mean?

c The ingredients of bleach break down after use. Why is this important?

Chlorofluorocarbons

Chlorine is used to make chlorofluorocarbons, or CFCs. These are carbon compounds containing both chlorine and fluorine. An example is trichlorofluoromethane, CCl_3F.

CFCs are very unreactive compounds. They were used in aerosol cans and refrigerators.

CFCs damage the ozone layer. This damage allows more ultraviolet light to reach the surface of the Earth.

Too much ultraviolet light causes sunburn and can cause skin cancer. Sunbathers should use sunblocking creams or lotions to protect their skin.

The production and use of CFCs is now very limited.

d It is more important for sunbathers to use sunblocking creams and lotions now than it was 30 years ago. Explain why.

fig 29 | Sunbathers need to protect their skin

Hazards

Chlorine was used as a poison gas in the first World War. Its use requires special care. When experiments involving chlorine are carried out in schools, a fume cupboard is used.

e Describe how a fume cupboard makes the use of chlorine safer.

Fluorine is an even more dangerous gas to use than chlorine. It is very reactive and is not used in schools.

Bromine is a liquid at room temperature, but quickly turns into a gas. It is said to be volatile.

The liquid causes serious skin damage and the vapour is poisonous. Gloves should be worn when handling bromine. The vapour is poisonous, so bromine is used in a fume cupboard or well-ventilated area.

If bleach is mixed with an acid, chlorine gas is produced. Products used to remove limescale contain acid and should never be mixed with household bleach.

f Why is iodine less hazardous to use than chlorine?

▷▷ Taking it further ▷▷

Chlorine and the other halogens have many more uses.

Silver salts are the basis of photography. When exposed to light silver bromide decomposes to form silver. This gives the black areas on a black and white photograph.

Chlorine is also used in the manufacture of PVC plastic and **disinfectants** such as TCP.

Thinking further

■ **1** The concentration of chlorine in swimming pools is higher than that in drinking water. Suggest why.

■ **2 a** Where else in a house, other than the toilet, might bleach be used to kill bacteria?

b Why is it important to kill bacteria in this place?

◆ **3** Bleach is a component of some washing powders.

a What job does the bleach do?

b What problem might the bleach cause?

KEY WORDS

bleach • disinfectants • sterilise

 Worksheet for simple silver bromide photography.

3.8 Sodium chloride

Reacting sodium with chlorine

When chlorine gas is passed over hot sodium metal a very vigorous reaction takes place. Figure 30 shows apparatus that can be used to carry out this reaction.

a Why is this reaction is carried out in a fume cupboard?

During the reaction a very bright yellow light is seen. The boiling tube often melts.

When the reaction is complete, a white solid can be seen sticking to the sides of the boiling tube. This is sodium chloride, common salt.

b The boiling tube has a glass wool plug. Suggest a purpose for this.

c Why is glass wool used for the plug?

The reaction is typical of a halogen with a metal, producing a **halide**.

$$2Na + Cl_2 \rightarrow 2NaCl$$
$$\text{sodium} + \text{chlorine} \rightarrow \text{sodium chloride}$$

How do we get salt?

Salt is an essential part of the human diet, though too much salt may be bad for the heart.

In some countries sea water is trapped in salt pans. The heat of the sun is used to evaporate off the water, leaving impure sodium chloride. This can be purchased from supermarkets as 'sea salt'. Salt flats are found in some parts of the world.

In other places sodium chloride is found in underground deposits. In Cheshire lorries drive into vast underground caverns to take away **rock salt**. This contains sodium chloride mixed with rock impurities.

d Suggest how impure salt came to be left in salt flats and underground deposits.

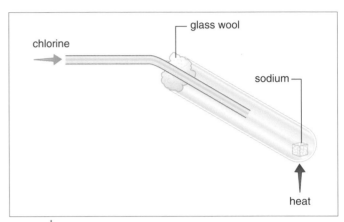

fig 30 | Apparatus for sodium and chlorine reaction

fig 31 | The Great Salt Lake, Utah

fig 32 | Underground mining of salt

Uses of sodium chloride

Large quantities of rock salt are spread on icy roads during the winter. The salt helps to melt the ice.

e In addition to sodium chloride, what else in the rock salt helps to improve the grip of tyres on the road?

Sodium chloride is also extracted as a solution. Water is pumped into the underground salt deposits. Salt solution, called **brine**, is forced to the surface.

The electrolysis of sodium chloride solution is the basis of the chlor-alkali industry. One important product of this industry is sodium hydroxide. This is a strong alkali. Chlorine gas and hydrogen gas are also produced.

Sodium hydroxide is used in the manufacture of bleach, soap, paper and textile fibres.

f Electrolysis uses large quantities of electricity. This is very expensive. Why is the electrolysis of sodium chloride solution worth this cost?

▷▷ Taking it further ▷▷

The electrolysis of brine is carried out in a membrane cell.

fig 33 | A membrane cell

Brine contains the ions Na^+, Cl^-, H^+ and OH^-.

Chlorine is produced at the positive electrode.

$$2Cl^- \rightarrow Cl_2 + 2e^-$$

Hydrogen is given off at the negative electrode.

$$2H^+ + 2e^- \rightarrow H_2$$

Sodium ions, Na^+, and hydroxide ions, OH^-, are left in the solution. This is sodium hydroxide solution.

g What is the job of the porous membrane?

h Why is nickel used for the negative electrode, but titanium for the positive electrode?

Thinking further

■ **1** Describe how you would expect chlorine to react with lithium.

■ **2** Describe how you would expect fluorine to react with sodium.

■ **3** How could you obtain pure sodium chloride from rock salt using normal laboratory apparatus?

■ **4** The electrolysis of brine produces chlorine gas.

  a What hazards does this involve?

  b What safety measures need to be taken?

◆ **5** Write symbol equations for the reactions in 1 and 2.

KEY WORDS

brine • halide • rock salt

 Video on the chlor-alkali industry.   *Video on sodium.*

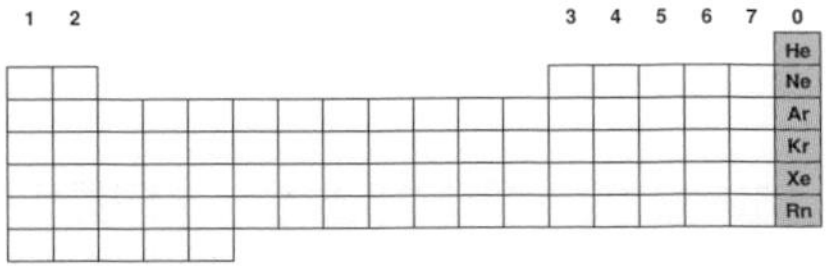

3.9 The noble gases

- Group 0 contains the unreactive noble gases.
- The Group shows trends in density and boiling point.
- The noble gases have many uses.

Discovery

In 1895 William Ramsay removed all of the known gases from a sample of air. He was left with a small volume of an unreactive gas. This was argon.

Argon is in Group 0 of the Periodic Table. Five other unreactive gases are in the same group. These are the noble gases.

a By 1895 most of the chemical elements had already been discovered. Why did it take so long to discover argon?

fig 34 | William Ramsay

Physical properties

All of the elements in Group 0 are **colourless** gases.

The table in fig 35 shows some properties of the first five noble gases.

b Describe how the density of the noble gases changes down the Group.

c How does the boiling point of the noble gases change down the Group?

d Why does the boiling point change down the Group?

e Radon is below xenon in Group 0. Predict the density and boiling point of radon.

noble gas	relative atomic mass	boiling point in °C	density in g/dm³
helium	4	−270	0.17
neon	20	−249	0.83
argon	40	−189	1.7
krypton	84	−157	3.5
xenon	131	−112	5.5

fig 35 | Some properties of the first five noble gases

Chemical properties

There is a surprising fact about the chemical properties of the noble gases. Most do not really have any chemical properties.

Figure 36 shows the arrangement of electrons in neon and argon.

The noble gases have a common feature in the arrangement of their electrons. The outer shell is full.

Atoms react by losing, gaining or sharing electrons in the outer shell. The result of this is a full outer shell. This gives each atom in a compound a stable electron arrangement.

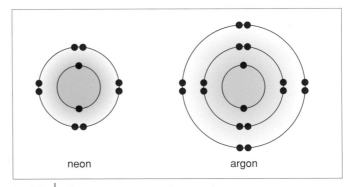

neon   argon

fig 36 | Electron arrangements of neon and argon

The outer shell of each noble gas is already full. Atoms of the noble gases cannot easily lose, gain or share electrons.

Therefore it is difficult for the noble gases to react.

f The electron arrangement of argon is the same as that in the ions of two other elements. Name these elements.

g What are the charges on the ions of these two elements?

Atoms of neon do not even react with each other. Other gaseous elements are made up of molecules, each containing two atoms. Examples are Cl_2 and O_2. These gases are **diatomic**. Atoms of the noble gases do not join in pairs. The noble gases are **monatomic**.

h Give another example of a diatomic element.

fig 37 | Laser light

Uses of the noble gases

The lack of reactivity of the noble gases makes them very useful in some situations. Electric light bulbs are filled with argon to prevent the white hot filaments from burning.

When an electric current is passed through neon, the noble gas gives out a red light. Tubes filled with neon are used in advertising signs.

When excited by electricity krypton gives out an intense light. Krypton is used in **lasers**.

Helium is the lightest of the noble gases. It is used in airships and balloons in place of the more hazardous hydrogen.

i Explain why it is less hazardous to use helium than hydrogen in an airship.

fig 38 | Helium-filled airship

Extending your knowledge

In 1962 Neil Bartlett prepared the first compound of a noble gas. This was a yellow-orange solid with the formula $XePtF_6$.

Since then a number of other xenon compounds have been made, including XeF_2 and XeF_4, and also a compound of argon.

j Compounds of xenon have been made but not of helium. Explain why.

k Most xenon compounds contain fluorine. Suggest why.

Thinking further

■ **1** The noble gases were once called the inert gases. Why was this a suitable name?

■ **2** Air contains about 1% of argon. Commercially argon is obtained from air. Oxygen has a boiling point of −183 °C and nitrogen −196 °C. Suggest how argon is obtained from air.

◆ **3 a** Besides fluorine, what other element might you expect xenon to react with.

b Give a reason for your answer.

KEY WORDS

colourless • diatomic • lasers • monatomic

3.10 Discovering the secrets of the atom

Dalton

In 1807 John Dalton suggested that all materials are made from small particles, which he called atoms. He imagined these atoms to be minute solid balls.

Thomson

In 1897 J.J. Thomson found that cathode ray tubes (similar to the tubes in TV sets) produced beams of small particles.

He discovered that these particles are deflected or bent by an electric field. Thomson concluded that the particles are negatively charged. He called them **electrons**.

a Why are electrons deflected by an electric field?

Later Thomson discovered positive particles. He named these **protons**. Thomson calculated that it would take about 2000 electrons to have the same mass as a proton.

Rutherford, Geiger and Marsden

In 1911 a number of crucial experiments were carried out in the laboratory of Ernest Rutherford.

Most of these experiments were performed by two of his co-workers: Hans Geiger and Ernst Marsden.

They bombarded thin sheets of metal foil with alpha particles. Alpha particles have a positive charge.

Most of the alpha particles went straight through the metal foil. Some were deflected. A few of the alpha particles bounced straight back.

Rutherford concluded that most of the atom is empty space with a very small, positively-charged **nucleus** at its centre.

b How do the results show most of the atom is empty space?

c How do the results show the nucleus is positive?

fig 39 | J.J. Thomson and the apparatus he used

fig 40 | Ernest Rutherford

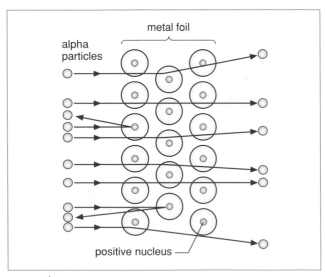

fig 41 | Bombardment of metal foil with alpha particles

Aston

Francis William Aston, a student of J.J.Thomson, built an instrument called a mass spectrometer in 1918.

A mass spectrometer measures the mass of atoms.

Using this instrument Aston found that atoms of the same element have different masses. These are called **isotopes**.

Chadwick

In 1932 James Chadwick bombarded metals with radiation from radioactive material. He discovered neutral particles, which he called **neutrons**.

d Why were neutrons more difficult to discover than electrons and protons?

Isotopes and relative atomic mass

Isotopes are atoms of the same element, with the same number of protons, but with different numbers of neutrons.

They have the same atomic number but different mass numbers.

Chlorine has two isotopes: ^{35}Cl and ^{37}Cl. Both have 17 protons, but one has mass number 35 and the other 37.

e How many neutrons does each isotope have?

In a sample of chlorine 75% of the atoms are ^{35}Cl and 25% are ^{37}Cl.

The average mass of a chlorine atom can be worked out by finding the mass of 100 atoms and dividing by 100.

mass of 100 atoms = (75 × 35) + (25 × 37) = 3550
average mass = 3550/100 = 35.5

This average mass is called the **relative atomic mass**.

Thinking further

1 Dalton thought atoms were solid balls.

a Which piece of evidence disproved Dalton's idea?

b How did this evidence prove that atoms are not solid balls?

◆ **2** A mass spectrometer can be used to find the relative atomic mass of an element. Explain how.

◆ **3** Neon has three isotopes. A sample of neon contains 90.5% ^{20}Ne, 0.3% ^{21}Ne and 9.2% ^{22}Ne.

a How many protons are in each atom of neon?

b How many neutrons are in each isotope of neon?

c Calculate the relative atomic mass of neon.

KEY WORDS

electrons • isotopes • neutrons • nucleus • protons • relative atomic mass

 Biography of Dalton.

3.11 Data about elements

The table in fig 42 gives information about some of the elements.

atomic number	name of element	formula	structure	date of discovery	m.p. in °C	b.p. in °C
13	aluminium	Al	giant atomic	1827	659	2447
95	americium	Am		1944		
51	antimony	Sb		ancient		
18	argon	Ar	single atoms	1894	−189	−186
33	arsenic	As		1250	613	(sublimes)
85	astatine	At		1940		
56	barium	Ba	giant atomic	1808	710	1637
97	berkelium	Bk		1949		
4	beryllium	Be	giant atomic	1798	1283	2487
35	bromine	Br_2	molecules	1826	−7	58
55	caesium	Cs	giant atomic	1860	29	685
20	calcium	Ca	giant atomic	1808	850	1492
98	californium	Cf		1950		
6	carbon	C	giant molecular	ancient	3550	4827
17	chlorine	Cl_2	molecules	1774	−101	−34
24	chromium	Cr	giant atomic	1797	1903	2642
27	cobalt	Co	giant atomic	1735	1495	2877
29	copper	Cu	giant atomic	ancient	1083	2582
96	curium	Cm		1944		
99	einsteinium	Es		1952		
100	fermium	Fm		1953		
9	fluorine	F_2	molecules	1887	−220	−188
87	francium	Fr		1939		
79	gold	Au	giant atomic	ancient	1063	2707
2	helium	He	single atoms	1868	−270	−269
1	hydrogen	H_2	molecules	1766	−259	−253
53	iodine	I_2	molecules	1811	114	184
26	iron	Fe	giant atomic	ancient	1539	2887
36	krypton	Kr	single atoms	1898	−157	−153
103	lawrencium	Lw		1961		
82	lead	Pb	giant atomic	ancient	328	1751
3	lithium	Li	giant atomic	1818	181	1331
71	lutetium	Lu		1907		
12	magnesium	Mg	giant atomic	1808	650	1117
25	manganese	Mn	giant atomic	1774	1244	2041
101	mendelevium	Md		1955		
80	mercury	Hg		ancient	−39	357
10	neon	Ne	single atoms	1898	−248	−246
93	neptunium	Np		1940		
28	nickel	Ni	giant atomic	1751	1455	2837
7	nitrogen	N_2	molecules	1772	−210	−196
102	nobelium	No		1957		

fig 42

atomic number	name of element	formula	structure	date of discovery	m.p. in °C	b.p. in °C
8	oxygen	O_2	molecules	1774	−219	−183
15	phosphorus	P_4	molecules	1669	44	281
78	platinum	Pt	giant atomic	1735	1770	3827
94	plutonium	Pu		1940		
19	potassium	K	giant atomic	1807	63	766
61	promethium	Pm		1947		
91	protactinium	Pa		1917		
86	radon	Rn	single atoms	1900		
75	rhenium	Re		1925		
14	silicon	Si	giant molecular	1824	1410	2677
47	silver	Ag	giant atomic	ancient	961	2127
11	sodium	Na	giant atomic	1807	98	890
16	sulphur	S_8	molecules	ancient	119	445
43	technetium	Te		1937		
50	tin	Sn	giant atomic	ancient	232	2687
54	xenon	Xe	single atoms	1898		
30	zinc	Zn	giant atomic	1746	419	908

fig 42 continued

Questions

1 The elements marked 'ancient' in the 'Date of discovery' column were discovered before written records began.

● **a** Make a list of these elements. *(1)*

■ **b** What comment can you make about the majority of these elements? *(1)*

■ **c** Suggest an explanation for your answer to **b**. *(1)*

2 ● **a** Make a list of the elements discovered during the 20th century. *(1)*

■ **b** What do most of these elements have in common? *(2)*

◆ **c** Suggest why they were not discovered until this time. *(2)*

3 Look at the elements with a structure of single atoms.

● **a** To which Group of the Periodic Table do they belong? *(1)*

■ **b** Explain why the elements in this Group exist as single atoms. *(2)*

4 ● **a** Make a list of the elements with a structure of molecules. *(1)*

■ **b** In which part of the Periodic Table are these elements? *(2)*

■ **c** What do these elements have in common? *(1)*

◆ **d** What is common about the formula of these elements? *(2)*

5 Look at the elements with a giant molecular structure.

■ **a** In which part of the Periodic Table have these elements been placed? *(1)*

◆ **b** What is unusual about the properties of these elements? *(2)*

6 ● **a** Make a list of the elements which are gases at room temperature. *(1)*

■ **b** Where do these elements appear in the Periodic Table? *(2)*

■ **c** What types of structure do these elements have? *(1)*

◆ **d** Suggest a reason for their low melting and boiling points. *(2)*

◆ **7** Use graph paper to plot the melting points of the elements in Period 3 of the Periodic Table against atomic number.

a What pattern is shown by these melting points? *(2)*

b Suggest an explanation for this pattern. *(2)*

Questions on the Periodic Table

1 To which group of the Periodic Table do each of the following elements belong?

K   P   Xe   Sr   Al
Si   F   Tl   Fr   Po

(10)

2 Name the family of elements to which each of the following belongs.

Cl   Li   Ar

(3)

3 From the following descriptions, name each element and its Group in the Periodic Table.

a This red-brown liquid easily vaporizes. It reacts vigorously with sodium to form a salt. *(2)*

b This silver solid quickly goes dull when exposed to air. It reacts violently with water, producing a red flame. *(2)*

c This colourless gas does not react with other elements. If is used to fill light bulbs. *(2)*

4 The word periodic means 'occurring at regular intervals'. Explain why this word is used in the Periodic Table of elements. *(2)*

5 For each of the following pairs of elements, choose which is the more reactive and explain your choice.

a Sodium and caesium. *(2)*

b Chlorine and iodine. *(2)*

c Oxygen and sulphur. *(2)*

6 Except for helium, atoms in Group 0 have eight electrons in their outer shells.

a What is the characteristic chemical property of Group 0? *(1)*

b What is the connection between this chemical property and eight electrons in an outer shell. *(2)*

c How many electrons has helium in its outer shell? *(1)*

d Explain why helium is still included in Group 0 even though it does not have eight outer electrons. *(2)*

7 The element francium is at the bottom of Group 1 in the Periodic Table. It is immediately below caesium. Francium is a radioactive element. Its most stable isotope has a half life of 22 minutes.

a Make predictions about the chemical properties of francium. *(2)*

b Caesium has a melting point of 28.6 °C. Predict a melting point for francium (use the data on page 46). *(1)*

c Explain why a study of the chemistry of francium is difficult. *(1)*

d Write a symbol equation for the reaction of francium with water. *(2)*

8 The pairs of elements shown below are reacted together:
- lithium and iodine
- potassium and chlorine
- potassium and fluorine
- sodium and chlorine
- sodium and iodine.   *(4)*

a Place the pairs of elements in a list according to how vigorous their reactions are. Begin your list with the most vigorous reaction. *(4)*

b Explain the order of your list. *(2)*

9 A few drops of orange-red bromine water are added to a colourless solution of potassium iodide.

a What change would you see? *(1)*

b Write an equation for this change. *(2)*

c Explain why this change takes place. *(2)*

10 Two carbon rods are lowered into a beaker containing a concentrated solution of sodium chloride. A few drops of the indicator phenolphthalein are added to the solution. The carbon rods are used to pass an electric current. The following observations are made.

Around the positive electrode a green gas bubbles up from the solution.

Around the negative electrode the solution turns pink.

Explain these observations. *(4)*

11 When chlorine is dissolved in water some of the chlorine molecules react with water molecules. This reaction produces a mixture of hydrochloric acid and chloric(I) acid. Chloric(I) acid is a bleaching agent oxidising coloured dyes to colourless compounds.

a Write an equation for the reaction of chlorine with water. (2)

b A piece of blue litmus paper is dipped into a solution of chlorine in water. It first turns red, then white. Explain these observations. (4)

12 Mendeléev left gaps in his Periodic Table for elements which had not been discovered at that time. One of these he called eka-silicon. He made the following predictions for this element:

relative atomic mass half way between silicon and tin, 73.4

melting point higher than tin, perhaps around 800 °C

density 5.5 g/cm³

a Suggest why Mendeléev thought eka-silicon would have a relative atomic mass half way between those of silicon and tin. (1)

b Suggest why Mendeléev predicted eka-silicon would have a melting point higher than that of tin. (1)

c The element Mendeléev called eka-silicon is now called germanium. How close were Mendeléev's predictions? (2)

d Why did Mendeléev's Periodic Table not contain the noble gases? (1)

13 The following symbols represent atoms of the most common isotopes of magnesium and oxygen.

$$^{24}_{12}Mg \qquad ^{16}_{8}O$$

When magnesium burns in oxygen the compound magnesium oxide is formed. Magnesium forms ions with a +2 charge and oxygen forms ions with a −2 charge.

a What names are given to the numbers in the above symbols? (2)

b Work out how many protons, electrons and neutrons are in each of the above atoms. (3)

c Write symbols similar to those above for magnesium and oxygen ions. (2)

d Magnesium also has an isotope with 14 neutrons. Write the symbol for this isotope. (1)

e A sample of magnesium contains 85% ^{24}Mg and 15% ^{26}Mg. Work out the relative atomic mass of this magnesium. (2)

14 Potassium chloride contains potassium ions, K^+, and chloride ions, Cl^-. Argon contains argon atoms.

a Draw diagrams to show the arrangement of electrons in a potassium ion, a chloride ion and an argon atom. (3)

b What feature do these three particles have in common? (1)

c Potassium chloride is a very stable compound. Use your answers to a and b to suggest why. (2)

15 Use ideas about the structure of atoms and patterns in the Periodic Table to explain each of the following facts.

a As we move across Period 3 from sodium to argon the character of the elements changes from metallic to non-metallic. (3)

b As we move down Group 7 from fluorine to iodine the reactivity of the elements gets less. (3)

c As we move across Period 3 from sodium to argon the size of each atom, measured as the atomic radius, decreases. (2)

d As we move down Group 7 from fluorine to iodine the size of each atom increases. (2)

IDEAS AND EVIDENCE

16 Both Mendeléev and Newlands based their patterns for the elements on the idea of dividing them into eights. Newlands' ideas were ridiculed by other scientists, whereas Mendeléev's ideas quickly gained acceptance. Why was Mendeléev's arrangement of the elements so much more successful? (6)

Rates of reaction

fig 1 | Tombstones affected by acidic rain water

Introduction

All around us chemical reactions are taking place.

Some of these reactions happen so slowly we hardly notice them. We can only see that they have happened after many years. A good example of this is the attack made by acidic rain water on statues and gravestones. Acidic rain water reacts with limestone but this is a very slow reaction.

In industry it is important that the speed of chemical reactions is carefully controlled. Too slow and the product may be expensive to make; too fast and the process may become dangerous.

In this Teaching block we will see how the speed of chemical reactions can be measured, and how it can be changed.

Many reactions around us take place at a speed that is easy for us to follow. Frying an egg takes a couple of minutes, and we can see the change taking place.

Some reactions take place very quickly. In a limestone quarry the rock is blasted down using explosives. The chemical reaction in the explosion takes a tiny fraction of a second.

fig 2 | A fried egg

Check-up

a The list below gives some chemical changes and some physical changes. A physical change is a change which can be reversed, e.g. melting ice.

Put these into two lists – chemical changes and physical changes.

boiling an egg • burning natural gas • crystallizing a salt • digesting food • dissolving sugar • freezing water

b Place the following chemical reactions in order of the speed with which they take place. Write down the slowest first.

fireworks burning • iron rusting • milk going sour • rifles firing

• **rocks weathering • spaghetti cooking**

c When different metals are added to dilute hydrochloric acid and warmed, they react at different rates. This information can be used to place these metals in order of reactivity, as shown in fig 3.

We can also use ideas about the reactivity series of metals to predict how fast the metals will react.

Use these ideas to place the following metals in order of how fast they will react with warm dilute hydrochloric acid.

copper • iron • magnesium • zinc

If you have difficulty, ask your teacher for a Summary sheet.

very reactive

potassium
sodium
calcium
magnesium
aluminium
zinc
iron
tin
lead
copper
mercury
silver
gold

unreactive

fig 3 | Reactivity series of metals

Contents of the Teaching block

4.1 Following reaction progress

Reactions take place at widely different rates (speeds). The rate of a reaction can be found by measuring the disappearance of a reacting substance (reactant) or the formation of a new substance (product). Just like any other rate, the rate of reaction involves measuring time.

4.2 Faster and slower

The rate of a chemical reaction alters as other changes are made.

The rate of a reaction is affected by change in concentration, temperature and the size of any solid pieces.

Reactions involving gases are also affected by changes in pressure.

4.3 Catalysts

Some chemical reactions can be speeded up or slowed down by adding substances called catalysts.

Different chemical reactions need different catalysts to speed them up or slow them down.

4.4 Enzymes

Enzymes are biological catalysts produced by living things.

These enzymes are proteins. They are sensitive to change in temperature and pH.

Some industries such as brewing and cheese making use enzymes.

Links with other Teaching blocks

1.3 Equations
1.5 Acids
2.5 The transition metals
6.4 Catalytic cracking
8.1 The Haber process

4.1 Following reaction progress

Key points

- We can find how fast a reaction is going by measuring the disappearance of a reactant or the formation of a product.
- These measurements can be used to plot graphs.
- Finding the rate of a reaction also involves measuring time.

Disappearance of a reactant

As a reaction takes place the amount of each chemical reacting gets less. The amount of **reactant** in the mixture can be measured at intervals of time to find how the rate of reaction changes.

Marble chippings, which are made of calcium carbonate, react with dilute hydrochloric acid as shown by this equation.

$$CaCO_3 + 2HCl \rightarrow CaCl_2 + H_2O + CO_2$$

calcium carbonate + hydrochloric acid → calcium chloride + water + carbon dioxide

a What do you see as this reaction takes place?

As the calcium carbonate reacts carbon dioxide gas escapes from the reaction mixture.

The mass of the mixture decreases and this loss in mass can be measured using a balance, as shown in fig 4.

b Why does the flask have a cotton wool plug?

c Explain why the reaction mixture of marble chippings and hydrochloric acid loses mass.

The table in fig 5 shows how the mass decreases with time.

These results can be plotted on a graph (fig 6).

At first the mixture loses mass quickly. The steep slope between 0 and 50 s shows this.

During the reaction the slope gets less steep as the reaction rate slows down.

Eventually the reaction stops. The horizontal line on the graph shows this.

d At what time is the rate of reaction highest?

e Why does the rate of this reaction fall with time?

f Why does the reaction stop?

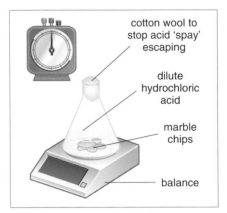

fig 4 | Measuring loss of mass during a reaction

time in s	mass in g	mass lost in g
50	82.00	1.20
100	80.80	1.75
150	80.25	2.05
200	79.80	2.20
250	79.75	2.25
300	79.75	2.25

fig 5 | Decrease in mass with time

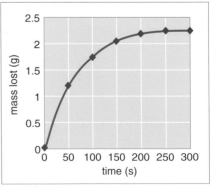

fig 6 | Graph to show mass lost with time

Formation of a product

Carbon dioxide is a **product** in the reaction. The volume of carbon dioxide gas given off can also be used to measure the rate of reaction. This can be measured using a gas syringe.

The volume of carbon dioxide given off is shown in the table in fig 8.

g Use graph paper to plot the results of this experiment. Draw a curve.

h How does your graph compare with that in fig 6?

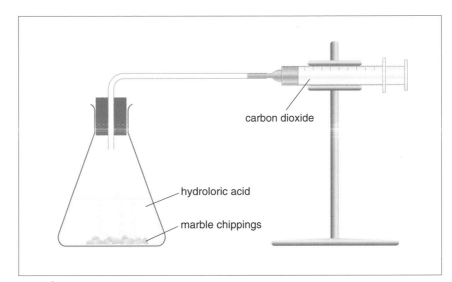
carbon dioxide

hydroloric acid

marble chippings

fig 7 | Using a gas syringe

The rate of a reaction can be calculated from the formula:
rate of reaction = change in mass ÷ time taken.

This gives the average rate of reaction over the time interval used.

From the mass measurements in fig 5 we can calculate the rate of reaction in the time interval from 50s to 100s.

Mass lost from 50s to 100s = 1.75 − 1.20 = 0.55 g

Average rate of reaction from 50s to 100s $\quad$ = 0.55 ÷ 50
$\qquad\qquad\qquad\qquad\qquad\qquad$ = 0.011 g/s.

i Use the volume measurements in fig 8 to calculate the rate of reaction in each 50 s interval. Include the units for your rate figures.

j Using the rates you have calculated, describe how the rate of this reaction changed with time.

time in s	volume of carbon dioxide in cm^3
50	288
100	420
150	504
200	528
250	540
300	540

fig 8 | Carbon dioxide evolved with lime

Thinking further

■ **1** Zinc reacts with sulphuric acid.

$$Zn + \quad H_2SO_4 \quad \rightarrow \quad ZnSO_4 \quad + H_2$$
zinc + sulphuric acid → zinc sulphate + hydrogen

a How can you measure the rate of this reaction?

b Why is it difficult to find the rate of this reaction by measuring the loss in mass?

◆ **2** A dry cell battery gives out electrical current as a chemical reaction takes place in the cell. With time the voltage of the cell falls. Use ideas about rate of reaction to explain this fall.

◆ **3** Excess calcium carbonate is added to 50 cm^3 of dilute hydrochloric acid. What will be the pH value of the mixture at the end of the reaction?

KEY WORDS
product • rate of reaction • reactant $\qquad$ *Measuring rates of reaction.*

4.2 Faster and slower

> ### Key points
>
> - The rate of a reaction is affected by change in concentration, temperature and the size of any solid pieces.
> - Pressure has an effect on the rate of reactions involving gases.

Concentration

Fig 9 shows a marble chip reacting in each of three different concentrations of hydrochloric acid.

a Which marble chip is reacting more quickly?

b Explain how you decided your answer to **a**.

In a low **concentration** of acid the particles are spread far apart. They only **collide** with the marble chip occasionally.

In a higher concentration of acid the particles collide with the marble chip more often. This increases the rate of reaction.

c Opening the air hole of a Bunsen burner lets more oxygen in. Explain why this makes the flame hotter.

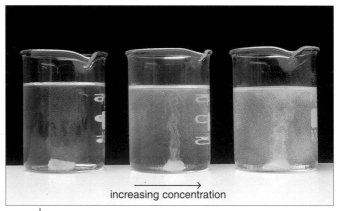

increasing concentration

fig 9 | Rate of reaction at different concentrations

Pressure

In reactions that involve gases the rate increases when the **pressure** is increased.

At higher pressures the particles are squashed closer together. They collide more often, and therefore react more quickly.

Temperature

The graph in fig 10 shows how the rate of a typical reaction changes as the temperature is increased.

d What effect does temperature have on the rate of reaction?

As the temperature is increased the particles move around more quickly. This causes them to collide more often, and therefore react more quickly.

This is one reason why reactions are faster at higher temperatures, but it is not the whole story.

When two particles collide they do not always react.

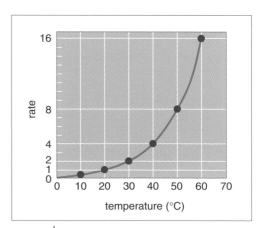

fig 10 | A typical rate/temperature graph

They must collide with enough energy to break their chemical bonds. They can then form new bonds to make the products of the reaction.

As the temperature increases the particles have more energy. More of the collisions produce products, so the rate is faster.

e Why does milk go sour quickly if left out in the sun, but slowly if it is kept in a refrigerator?

The size of solid pieces

In fig 11 the same mass of marble is being added to the same concentration of acid.

When the marble is in one large lump, the reaction is slow.

When the marble is powdered, the reaction is fast.

For the same mass, smaller lumps have a larger **surface area** for the acid particles to collide with. More collisions each second give a higher rate of reaction.

f An iron bar held in a Bunsen burner flame will not burn, but iron wool will. Explain this difference.

fig 11 | Effect of size of solid pieces on the rate of reaction

Thinking further

1 Some iron filings are added to dilute sulphuric acid. They react according to the equation:

$$Fe + H_2SO_4 \rightarrow FeSO_4 + H_2$$
iron + sulphuric acid → iron(II) sulphate + hydrogen

Some water is added to the reaction mixture and the experiment repeated.

a Describe the change you see after the water is added.

b Explain this change.

2 A piece of magnesium ribbon will burn in air with a bright flame. If burning magnesium ribbon is lowered into a gas jar of oxygen the flame becomes much brighter.

a Which piece of magnesium will go out quicker?

b Why is the flame brighter in oxygen?

3 Plants kept in a greenhouse grow more quickly than those outside. Explain why.

4 In a flour mill the finely powdered flour can float around in the air. Flour is not a substance we would normally think of as explosive, but in flour mills the flour and air mixture can explode.

a Explain why the flour can explode.

b Suggest what measures can be taken to reduce the danger of explosions in flour mills.

> **KEY WORDS**
> collide • concentration • pressure • surface area

 Rates of reaction: effect on temperature. *Rates of reaction: effect on concentration.*

 Effect of surface area on reaction rate. *Using a data logger to follow mass changes.*

4.3 Catalysts

Hydrogen peroxide decomposition

Hydrogen peroxide is widely used as a **bleach**. It turns wood pulp from brown to white so that it can be used to make paper. It is also used to bleach hair.

Hydrogen peroxide decomposes, giving off oxygen gas.

$$2H_2O_2 \rightarrow 2H_2O + O_2$$

hydrogen peroxide → water + oxygen

a How would you test the gas being given off in this reaction to show that it is oxygen?

b The **decomposition** of hydrogen peroxide is speeded up if the solution is exposed to sunlight. Bottles of hydrogen peroxide need to be kept in laboratories. How could the decomposition due to sunlight be reduced?

At room temperature, in the absence of sunlight, the reaction is very slow.

It would take many years for all of the hydrogen peroxide in a solution to react.

If a little powdered manganese(IV) oxide is added to a solution of hydrogen peroxide, the result is dramatic.

You can see this in fig 12.

All of the hydrogen peroxide reacts in a few seconds.

The manganese(IV) oxide does not disappear during the reaction.

c Briefly describe how you could show that the manganese(IV) oxide is not used up in the reaction.

The manganese(IV) oxide is a **catalyst**.

It has increased the rate of reaction breaking up the hydrogen peroxide, but has not been used up.

Different substances act as catalysts to different reactions. The table in fig 13 shows some catalysts and the reactions that they catalyse. You will meet some of these reactions elsewhere in this book.

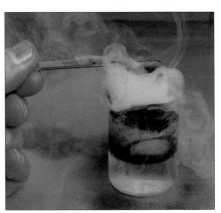

fig 12 | Adding manganese(IV) oxide to hydrogen peroxide

d Can you find something that all of the catalysts in the table have in common? (Hint: have a look at the Periodic Table of the elements on the back page.)

Some substances slow down the rate of chemical reactions. These are called negative catalysts or inhibitors. Glycerine is an **inhibitor** for the breaking up of hydrogen peroxide.

e Suggest how the use of glycerine to inhibit the decomposition of hydrogen peroxide could be useful.

catalyst	reaction
Titanium(IV) chloride	Polymerisation of ethene to make polythene
Vanadium(V) oxide	Contact process to make sulphuric acid
Iron	Haber process to make ammonia
Nickel	Hardening of vegetable oils to make margarine
Platinum	Manufacture of nitric acid from ammonia

fig 13 | Examples of catalysts

▷▷ Taking it further ▷▷

Car exhaust gases contain carbon monoxide and nitrogen monoxide. These gases cause city smog. The exhaust systems of modern cars are fitted with catalytic converters. They contain platinum and rhodium, which are catalysts.

fig 14 | The inside of a catalytic converter

In the catalytic converter carbon monoxide and nitrogen monoxide are converted into less harmful gases.

$$2CO + 2NO \rightarrow 2CO_2 + N_2$$

carbon + nitrogen → carbon + nitrogen
monoxide monoxide dioxide

Unfortunately many catalysts, including platinum and rhodium, are 'poisoned' by small quantities of other metals such as lead.

f A car with a catalytic converter must use unleaded petrol. Why is this?

g Besides helping to cause smog, what other harm may be caused by the release of carbon monoxide into the air in city centres.

Thinking further

■ **1** It is suggested that copper(II) oxide is also a catalyst for the decomposition of hydrogen peroxide.

   a How could you show that this is true?

   b Briefly describe how you could find out if it is a better or worse catalyst for this reaction than manganese(IV) oxide.

■ **2** Gardeners add fertilisers to the soil. This makes plants grow faster.

a Are fertilisers catalysts?

b Explain your answer to **a**.

■ **3** Different masses of manganese(IV) oxide are added to identical solutions of hydrogen peroxide.

   a Suggest what effect the mass of the catalyst might have on the reaction.

   b Explain your answer to **a**.

KEY WORDS

catalyst • decomposition • inhibitor • bleach

 Rates of reaction: effect of a catalyst.   *Which catalyst is best?*

5.1 Ions

Ions

Some atoms can lose electrons from their outer electron shell. Other atoms can gain electrons into their outer electron shell. Whenever this happens the atoms end up with a different number of electrons to protons. This means that the atom is no longer neutral but has an overall charge. Charged particles such as this are called **ions**.

a What is the relative charge of an electron and of a proton?

When atoms form ions, the loss or gain of electrons usually results in the ions formed having a full outer electron shell.

b What is the maximum number of electrons that the first and second electron shells can hold?

Positive ions

Atoms in Group 1 form positive ions by losing an electron from their outer shell.

c How many electrons are in the outer shell of any Group 1 element?

This loss of one electron forms an ion with a positive charge. For example, the sodium atom, Na, has 11 protons, 11 electrons and 12 neutrons. When this atom loses one electron the particle formed still has 11 protons but now only has 10 electrons. There is one more positive than negative charge, so the particle is now a sodium ion, Na^+.

d What is the electron arrangement of Na^+?

e What change takes place when a lithium atom turns into a lithium ion?

f What is the arrangement of electrons in a lithium ion, Li^+?

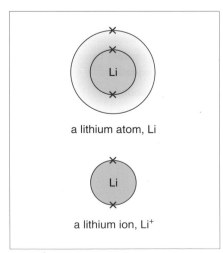

a lithium atom, Li

a lithium ion, Li^+

fig 2 | A lithium atom and a lithium ion

Atoms in Group 2 form positive ions by losing two electrons from their outer shell. This loss of two electrons forms an ion with two positive charges. For example, the calcium atom loses two electrons. This produces a particle with two more protons than electrons. This is a calcium ion, Ca^{2+}.

g How many protons, neutrons and electrons are present in a magnesium atom, Mg, and a magnesium ion, Mg^{2+}?

Negative ions

Atoms in Group 7 form negative ions by gaining an electron into their outer shell.

h How many electrons are in the outer shell of any Group 7 element?

This gain of one electron forms an ion with a negative charge. For example, the fluorine atom, F, has 9 protons, 9 electrons and 10 neutrons. When this atom gains one electron the particle formed still has 9 protons but now has 10 electrons. There is one more negative than positive charge, so the particle is now a fluoride ion, F^-.

i What is the arrangement of the electrons in an F^- ion?

j What change takes place when a chlorine atom turns into a chloride ion?

Atoms in Group 6 form negative ions by gaining two electrons into their outer shell. This gain of two electrons forms an ion with two negative charges. For example, the sulphur atom gains two electrons. This produces a particle with two more electrons than protons. This is a sulphide ion, S^{2-}.

k How many protons, neutrons and electrons are present in an oxygen atom, O, and a oxide ion, O^{2-}?

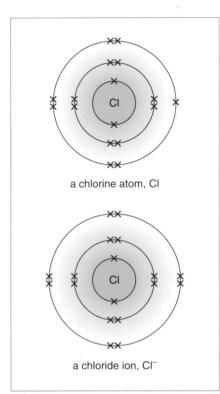

a chlorine atom, Cl

a chloride ion, Cl^-

fig 3 | Arrangement of electrons in a chlorine atom, Cl, and a chloride ion, Cl^-

Thinking further

■ **1** Two atoms X and Y form ions. X forms X^{2+}. Y forms Y^-.

 a In which group of the Periodic Table is X found?

 b In which group of the Periodic Table is Y found?

◆ **2** Aluminium and nitrogen can both form ions.

 a The table in fig 4 shows information about aluminium and nitrogen and the ions they form. Copy and complete the table.

particle	aluminium atom	aluminium ion	nitrogen atom	nitride ion
protons	13		7	
neutrons				
electrons				

fig 4

 b What are the charges on aluminium ions and nitride ions?

KEY WORDS

ion

5.2 Ionic bonding (1)

Ionic compounds

Elements in Groups 1 and 2 lose electrons when they form ions.

Elements in Groups 6 and 7 gain electrons when they form ions.

a How is the group number linked to the number of electrons lost or gained when atoms form ions?

Elements from Groups 1 and 2 react with elements from Groups 6 and 7. When they react, electrons transfer between atoms. Ions are formed.

Example 1

A sodium atom reacts with a chlorine atom.

b What are the symbols for a sodium atom, a sodium ion, a chlorine atom and a chloride ion?

In this reaction there is a transfer of an electron from the outer electron shell of the sodium atom to the outer electron shell of the chlorine atom.

c What are the electron arrangements of a sodium ion and a chloride ion?

Because one sodium atom transfers one electron to one chlorine atom, there must be the same number of sodium ions as there are chloride ions. The **ionic compound** sodium chloride has the formula NaCl.

Example 2

Magnesium reacts with fluorine. Magnesium is in Group 2. It loses two electrons when it forms an ion.

d What is the charge on a magnesium ion?

Fluorine is in Group 7. A fluorine atom gains one electron when it forms an ion.

e What is the charge on a fluoride ion?

One magnesium atom can transfer electrons from its outer electron shell to the outer electron shell of two fluorine atoms.

f What are the electron arrangements of a magnesium ion and a fluoride ion?

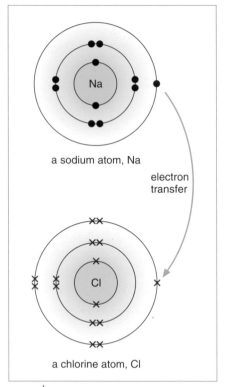

fig 5 | Electron transferring from a sodium atom to a chlorine atom

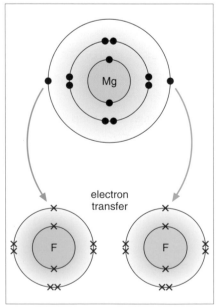

fig 6 | Electrons transferring from a magnesium atom to two fluorine atoms

Because one magnesium atom transfers an electron to each of two fluorine atoms, there must be two fluoride ions for every magnesium ion. The ionic compound magnesium fluoride has the formula MgF_2.

Example 3

Magnesium reacts with oxygen. Magnesium is in Group 2. It loses two electrons when it forms an ion. Oxygen is in Group 6. An oxygen atom gains two electrons when it forms an ion.

Because one magnesium atom transfers two electrons to each oxygen atom, there must be one oxide ion for every magnesium ion. The ionic compound magnesium oxide has the formula MgO.

Diagrams that show the transfer of electrons between atoms are sometimes called 'dot and cross' diagrams. Although the electrons from one atom are shown as different from the other (one is shown as a cross and one as a dot), this is only to help us see how they transfer. All electrons are the same really.

Example 4

Sodium reacts with oxygen. Sodium is in Group 1. It loses one electron when it forms an ion. Oxygen is in Group 6 and gains two electrons when it forms an oxide ion.

Because an oxygen atom gains two electrons there must be two sodium atoms for every oxygen atom. Each sodium atom transfers one electron. The ionic compound sodium oxide, Na_2O, is formed.

g Draw a dot and cross diagram to show the formation of sodium oxide, Na_2O.

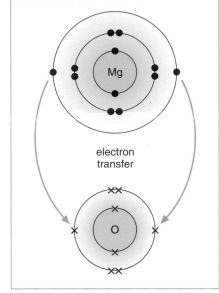

fig 7 | Electrons transferring from a magnesium atom to an oxygen atom

Thinking further

■ **1 a** Draw dot and cross diagrams to show the transfer of electrons between magnesium and chlorine atoms when they react.

b What is the name and formula of the product?

◆ **2** Find the elements strontium and bromine in the Periodic Table (see the back page). Strontium and bromine react to form strontium bromide. Predict the formula of strontium bromide. Explain how you reached your prediction.

┌─ **KEY WORDS** ─────────────
│ **dot and cross diagrams • ionic compound**
└─────────────────────────

5.3 Ionic bonding (2)

Attractions between ions

Opposite charges attract each other. When electrons transfer between atoms to form ions, the oppositely charged ions will attract each other. This is an **electrostatic attraction**. It is very strong. This electrostatic attraction is called an **ionic bond**. It extends throughout the whole structure of ions in the ionic compound.

a A sodium chloride crystal has 10 billion billion sodium ions, how many chloride ions will it have?

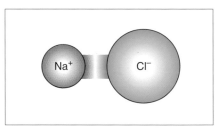

fig 8 | Attraction between oppositely charged ions

When ions attract each other in an ionic compound they do so in a way that produces a regular arrangement. This regular arrangement extends throughout the whole structure. This can be clearly seen for sodium chloride where the arrangement produces a regular cube structure. There is a cubic arrangement on the level of individual ions (see fig 9) as well as the larger scale of salt crystals themselves (see fig 10).

b Suggest why potassium chloride forms a similar cubic lattice to sodium chloride but magnesium chloride does not.

This regular arrangement of particles, such as the ions in ionic compounds, is called a **lattice**. As the strong ionic bonds extend throughout the structure, ionic compounds are also said to have a **giant structure**.

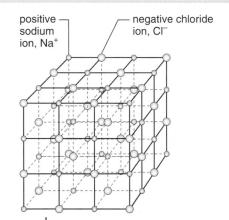

positive sodium ion, Na⁺ — negative chloride ion, Cl⁻

fig 9 | Cubic structure of NaCl at ionic level

Melting points and boiling points

When a solid melts, energy, usually in the form of heat, has to be provided to overcome the forces of attraction between particles in the solid state in order to separate them. In ionic compounds these forces are strong electrostatic forces and extend between all of the ions in the giant structure. A large amount of energy is needed. Ionic compounds therefore have relatively high melting points.

fig 10 | A crystal of sodium chloride

In the liquid state, although ions are now free to move, there are still forces of attraction between oppositely charged ions. These must be overcome when the liquid is turned into the gas state. Therefore ionic compounds also have very high boiling points.

The table in fig 11 shows the melting points of some ionic compounds. The melting point of magnesium oxide is much higher than the melting point of sodium chloride, although they are both ionic compounds with giant structures.

c What are the charges on sodium ions, magnesium ions, chloride ions and oxide ions?

d Which structure, NaCl or MgO, will have the stronger attractions between adjacent ions?

e Use your answers to **c** and **d** to explain why magnesium oxide has a higher melting point than sodium chloride.

When an ionic compound melts the ions become free to move about. This is important in electrolysis.

Solutions of ionic compounds

Some ionic compounds are soluble in water; some are not. In general, compounds of Group 1 elements are usually soluble.

When an ionic compound such as sodium chloride dissolves in water, the ions become separated and free to move about. You may meet this when you have to write **ionic equations**. If an ionic compound dissolves in water, simply represent the ions as separate particles. For example, when magnesium chloride, $MgCl_2$, dissolves, one magnesium ion, Mg^{2+} and two chloride ions, Cl^-, are formed for every $MgCl_2$ unit of structure.

$$MgCl_2 \rightarrow Mg^{2+} + 2Cl^-$$

substance	melting point in °C
lithium fluoride	848
sodium fluoride	996
magnesium fluoride	1248
lithium chloride	610
sodium chloride	801
magnesium chloride	714
lithium oxide	1570
sodium oxide	1132
magnesium oxide	2830

fig 11 | Melting points of some ionic compounds

Thinking further

■ **1** Lithium, Li, reacts with fluorine, F_2, to make lithium fluoride.

a Write word and symbol equations for the reaction.

b What groups are lithium and fluorine in?

c An electron transfers from lithium to fluorine in the reaction. What sort of bond will be present in lithium fluoride?

◆ **2** Suggest how the melting point of strontium oxide will differ from that of strontium chloride. Explain your answer.

▷▷ Taking it further ▷▷

A sodium chloride lattice breaks up when water is added. This takes place at room temperature. Water molecules have slight positive and negative charges.

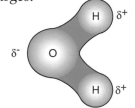

fig 12 | A polarised water molecule

KEY WORDS

electrostatic attraction • giant structure • ionic bond • ionic equations • lattice

5.4 Covalent bonding (1)

Covalent bonds

Hydrogen gas exists as molecules, H_2. The bond holding the two atoms of hydrogen together is not ionic because no electrons have passed from one hydrogen atom to the other. The sharing of the outer electron of each hydrogen atom forms the bond between the two atoms. We can represent this sharing of electrons as shown in fig 13.

Each hydrogen atom now effectively has a filled outer shell.

a What is the maximum number of electrons that the first electron shell can hold?

The shared pair of electrons holds the atoms together. It is called a **covalent bond**. Covalent bonds formed by shared pairs of electrons are strong. A large amount of energy is needed to break the hydrogen molecule into separate atoms.

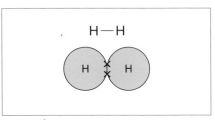

fig 13 | Bonding between two hydrogen atoms

Representing covalent bonds

We can draw covalent bonds by showing the shared pairs of electrons. However, chemists usually just represent a covalent bond by drawing a line between the atoms. Hydrogen would be represented as H—H. Questions will always tell you when they expect you to show the shared pairs of electrons. This will usually be in the form of dot and cross diagrams.

Molecules with covalent bonds

We have already come across the hydrogen molecule, H_2. Chlorine molecules also have a covalent bond holding two chlorine atoms together. Fig 14 shows the shared pair of electrons in a chlorine molecule.

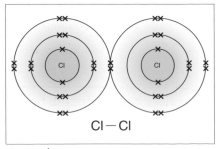

fig 14 | Bonding between two chlorine atoms

b How many electrons are in the outer shell of a chlorine atom? How many electrons are effectively in the outer shell of each of the atoms in a chlorine molecule?

Notice how each chlorine atom now has effectively given itself a full outer electron shell. This is very common when covalent bonds form.

So far we have looked at covalent bonds between two identical atoms. However, covalent bonds can also form between different atoms. Ammonia, NH_3, is an example.

c How many electrons are in the outer shell of a nitrogen atom?

d How many more electrons does a nitrogen atom need to make a filled outer shell?

Nitrogen forms covalent bonds with three hydrogen atoms, as shown in fig 15.

Notice that there is one pair of electrons in the outer shell of the nitrogen atom that has not been used in making bonds. It is shown as a pair of electrons on its own in the dot and cross diagram but is not shown on the simpler diagram.

Sometimes atoms can share more than one pair of electrons. Oxygen, O_2, is an example.

Each oxygen atom has shared two electrons with the other. Each oxygen now has effectively a full outer shell of eight electrons. As there are two shared pairs of electrons holding the atoms together, we show two lines between the oxygen atoms. This type of bond is called a **double bond**.

e Two nitrogen atoms are held together by a treble covalent bond. Draw a simple diagram to show this.

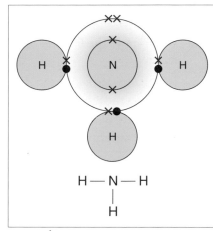

fig 15 | The bonding in ammonia, NH_3

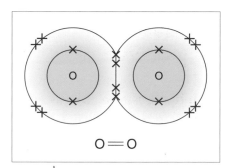

fig 16 | The bonding in oxygen, O_2

▷▷ Taking it further ▷▷

f Suggest the covalent bonding that would be present in a molecule of carbon dioxide, CO_2.

Thinking further

■ **1** A carbon atom has four electrons in its outer shell. A hydrogen atom has one. Draw a dot and cross diagram to show the covalent bonds in a methane molecule, CH_4.

■ **2** Draw a dot and cross diagram to show the bonding in a water molecule.

◆ **3** Suggest how the strengths of the bonds in hydrogen, oxygen and nitrogen molecules may be different.

— KEY WORDS —
covalent bond • double bond

5.5 Covalent bonding (2)

Key points

- Substances with covalent bonding are usually in the form of simple molecules.
- Although the bonds within the molecules themselves are strong, there are only very weak forces between the separate molecules.
- Simple molecular compounds are said to have molecular structures.
- Many substances with molecular structures are gases or liquids, though some are solids with low melting points.

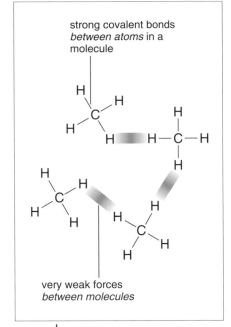

strong covalent bonds *between atoms* in a molecule

very weak forces *between molecules*

fig 17 | Molecules of methane, CH_4

Simple molecules

Substances such as hydrogen, H_2, or methane, CH_4, are described as being simple molecules. The covalent bonds within simple molecules are strong but the attraction between one molecule and another is very weak.

a Draw a diagram to show four molecules of ammonia. Indicate the relative strengths of the forces between atoms within the molecules and those between individual molecules.

Any compound that exists as simple molecules is said to have a **molecular structure**.

b Which of the following have molecular structures? NaCl, H_2O, O_2, MgO, Cl_2, H_2, LiF

c Explain how a molecular structure is different from a giant structure.

Melting points and boiling points

When a solid melts, energy, usually in the form of heat, has to be provided to overcome the forces of attraction between particles in the solid state in order to separate them. In compounds with molecular structures these forces are very weak. Very little energy is needed to separate one molecule from another. Compounds that have molecular structures therefore have relatively low melting points and boiling points. Many are gases or liquids at room temperature.

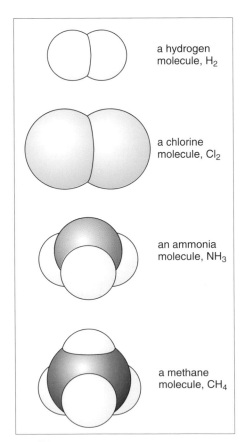

a hydrogen molecule, H_2

a chlorine molecule, Cl_2

an ammonia molecule, NH_3

a methane molecule, CH_4

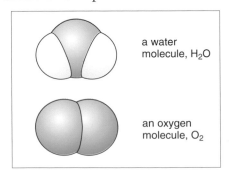

a water molecule, H_2O

an oxygen molecule, O_2

fig 18 | Space filling models of H_2O, O_2, H_2, Cl_2, NH_3 and CH_4

The table in fig 19 shows the melting and boiling points of some compounds that have simple molecular structures.

d Which substance has the lowest boiling point?

e Which substance has the highest boiling point?

f How do the values of the melting points suggest that some simple molecules have stronger forces of attraction between adjacent molecules than others?

	melting point in °C	boiling point in °C
hydrogen	−259	−252
chlorine	−101	−35
ammonia	−77	−33
methane	−183	−162
water	0	100
oxygen	−219	−183

fig 19

At low enough temperatures all simple molecules will condense (if they are gases) to a liquid and then freeze to the solid state. In this solid state they arrange themselves regularly in a lattice, but the structure is not 'giant' because strong bonds do not extend throughout the lattice. Simple molecules that do exist as solids at room temperature have stronger forces between adjacent molecules than those that are liquids or gases at room temperature. They usually melt easily and have lower melting points than ionic compounds.

Solubility of simple molecules

In general simple molecules are not particularly soluble in water. If they do dissolve, the solution formed does not contain ions. Compounds with molecular structures do not undergo electrolysis.

Thinking further

◆ **1** The table in fig 20 shows the melting points of some substances. State whether they have giant ionic structures or simple molecular structures.

substance	melting point in °C
titanium(IV) chloride	−23
rubidium chloride	715
benzene	5
nickel tetracarbonyl	−25

fig 20

◆ **2** The table in fig 21 shows the boiling points of chlorides of elements from Period 2 of the Periodic Table.

	lithium chloride	boron chloride	carbon chloride
boiling point in °C	1350	12	77

fig 21

Explain how the data shows that two of the chlorides have molecular structures but the other does not. Account for the difference in boiling points between these two substances and the third.

┌─ **KEY WORDS** ─────────┐
molecular structure
└──────────────────────┘

 Structures of substances.

5.6 Carbon

Key points

- Atoms that share electrons by covalent bonding can sometimes form giant structures.
- Examples include graphite and diamond, which are both forms of the element carbon.
- Substances that have a giant lattice of covalent bonds have high melting points and high boiling points.
- Recently chemists discovered that carbon atoms could also form molecules.

Carbon

Carbon, element 6 in the Periodic Table, is a non-metal.

a How many protons are in an atom of carbon?

b What is the arrangement of electrons in a carbon atom?

Carbon is an unusual element because it can exist in forms with different structures. Two of these are **graphite** and **diamond**.

Recently chemists discovered another form of carbon, which has been called buckminsterfullerene.

Diamond

Diamond contains only carbon atoms. Shared pairs of electrons attach each carbon atom to four others.

c Suggest why you would expect carbon to form four bonds to neighbouring atoms.

Each carbon atom is at the centre of a tetrahedron with four other carbon atoms at the corners of the tetrahedron.

All of the covalent bonds are very strong and extend throughout the structure. It is a giant structure. There are no weak points in the structure and the three-dimensional arrangement of the strong bonds makes the structure very strong indeed.

The strong bonds also mean that it is difficult to melt diamond. A vast amount of energy is needed to cause the carbon atoms to vibrate fast enough to separate from their neighbouring atoms.

Graphite

Graphite is another form of the element carbon. It, too, therefore contains only carbon atoms. The atoms are, however, arranged in a very different way to the atoms in diamond. The atoms are arranged in layers. Within each layer, each carbon atom forms covalent bonds with three neighbouring atoms. These are strong bonds.

fig 22 | Diamond-tipped drills were used to help construct the Channel Tunnel

fig 23 | Artists can use graphite for drawing

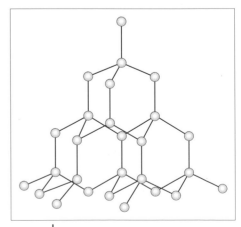

fig 24 | The structure of diamond

d Three electrons from each carbon atom have been used to form bonds. How many unused electrons remain on each carbon atom?

The unused electrons from each carbon atom hold the layers together. The force involved is much weaker than the covalent bonds within each layer. This is why graphite is such a good lubricant, the layers slide over each other very easily.

e Explain how the artist in fig 23 is using the weak forces that exist in graphite.

Graphite has a giant structure and has a high melting point.

fig 25 | The structure of graphite

Buckminsterfullerene

Chemists are always looking for new substances. They were very surprised and excited in 1985 when a new form of carbon was discovered. People had thought that they knew all of the forms of carbon. A form of carbon containing single molecules with 60 carbon atoms was made by electrically evaporating carbon electrodes in helium gas at low pressure.

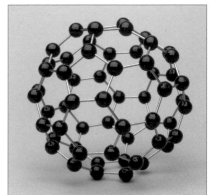
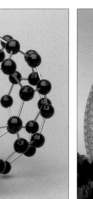

fig 26 | Buckminsterfullerine has the shape of a geodesic dome

The molecule was shown to have a shape similar to that of a geodesic dome (see fig 26) designed by the architect R. Buckminster Fuller. The new molecule was therefore named buckminsterfullerene after him.

Other molecules of carbon in the form of tubes have since been discovered. Scientists are now looking for ways in which the new molecules may be useful. One idea is that it may be possible to trap otherwise reactive atoms inside the cage of carbon atoms. Other possible uses being explored are as catalysts, lubricants and semi-conductors.

Thinking further

◆ **1** Chemists electrically evaporated carbon electrodes in an atmosphere of helium to make buckminsterfullerene. Explain why they could not use air or oxygen.

◆ **2** Explain why the combustion of diamond, graphite or buckminsterfullerene in a plentiful supply of air produces the same product. Name this product.

◆ **3** Buckminsterfullerene is soluble in solvents such as hexane. Diamond and graphite are not. Suggest why.

KEY WORDS
buckminsterfullerene • diamond • graphite

5.7 Formula calculations

Relative formula mass

In 3.1 Atomic structure, you found out that atoms of different elements have different masses. This is the relative atomic mass of that element.

a Which two particles in an atom make up most of its mass?

It is possible to use the values of relative atomic masses to compare the relative masses of compounds. This relative mass of a compound is called its **relative formula mass**. All that is required to calculate a relative formula mass is the formula of the substance and a list of relative atomic masses.

b Where would you find a list of all of the elements together with their relative atomic masses?

For example water, H_2O, contains two hydrogen atoms and one oxygen atom. Adding up the relative atomic masses, $1 + 1 + 16$ gives a total of 18. The relative formula mass of water is 18. In cases where the formula involves brackets make sure that all of the atoms are counted. For example, the formula mass of $Ca(OH)_2$ is $40 + 16 + 16 + 1 + 1 = 74$. Formula masses are given in units of grams.

c Calculate the formula mass of calcium carbonate, $CaCO_3$.

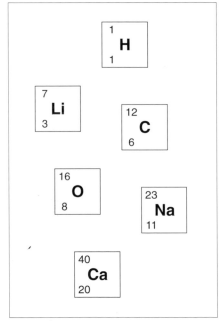

fig 27 The atomic numbers and relative atomic masses of some atoms

Percentage of an element in a compound

The percentage, by mass, of a particular element in a compound can also be calculated from a formula. For example, in carbon dioxide, CO_2, there is one carbon atom and two oxygen atoms. The relative formula mass is 44 g; 12 g of this is carbon. So the percentage by mass of carbon in carbon dioxide is $12/44 \times 100 = 27.3\%$.

d What is the percentage by mass of oxygen in carbon dioxide?

Calculations from equations

A balanced symbol equation shows the total numbers of particles involved in a chemical reaction. As mass cannot be lost in a chemical reaction, the relative formula mass of the products is the same as the relative formula mass of the reactants. For example:

$$C + O_2 \rightarrow CO_2$$

12 g of carbon react with 32 g of oxygen to produce 44 g of carbon dioxide. This ratio of masses is always the same; 1.2 g of carbon react with 3.2 g of oxygen to make 4.4 g of carbon dioxide.

e What mass of carbon dioxide is formed by the combustion of 120 tonnes of carbon?

This is of great use to chemists when they have to predict the mass of reactants necessary to make a certain mass of a product. For example, a fertiliser manufacture wishes to make 8000 tonnes of ammonium nitrate fertiliser from ammonia. How much ammonia is needed? The balanced equation is:

$$NH_3 + HNO_3 \rightarrow NH_4NO_3$$

This means that 17 g of ammonia is needed to make 80 g of ammonium nitrate. As the ratio is fixed 1700 tonnes of ammonia would be needed to make 8000 tonnes of the fertiliser.

f What mass of nitric acid would be needed?

Calculating the formula of a compound

The formula of a compound can be calculated, if the exact quantities of masses of reactants used to make it are known. For example, 4.8 g of magnesium burn in air to make 8.0 g of magnesium oxide.

g What mass of oxygen must have reacted with the 4.8 g of magnesium?

We can now calculate what fraction of the relative atomic masses of magnesium and oxygen have combined (see fig 28).

Mg	$\dfrac{4.8}{24} = 0.2$
O	$\dfrac{3.2}{16} = 0.2$

fig 28 Calculating the fractions of the relative atomic masses of magnesium and oxygen. This shows us that 0.2 formula units of magnesium combine with 0.2 formula units of oxygen. The ratio is 1:1 and so the formula of magnesium oxide is MgO

Thinking further

■ **1** Calculate the relative formula mass of each of the following.

HCl, CH_4, CuSO_4, H_2SO_4, Mg(OH)_2, (NH_4)_2SO_4

■ **2** Calculate the percentage of calcium, carbon and oxygen in calcium carbonate, CaCO_3.

◆ **3** What mass of calcium oxide is obtained by completely decomposing 300 tonnes of calcium carbonate?

◆ **4** 46 g of sodium react in oxygen to make 62 g of sodium oxide. Work out the formula of sodium oxide.

KEY WORDS

relative formula mass   *Determination of the formula of magnesium oxide.*

5.8 Energy changes

Key points

- Covalent bonds between different atoms require particular amounts of energy to break them.
- This is called the bond energy of that bond.
- Breaking of bonds requires energy and is endothermic.
- Making bonds releases energy and is exothermic.
- Overall energy changes for reactions can be calculated by considering bonds broken in the reactants and bonds formed in the products.
- Energy changes in reactions can be represented by energy level diagrams.

Average bond energies

Covalent bonds hold atoms together in molecular structures.

In order to separate atoms that are held together by electron sharing, energy must be put in. This means that bond breaking is an endothermic process. For example, to break up the formula mass of hydrogen molecules, H_2, into atoms, 436 kilojoules (kJ) of energy are needed. Notice how we quote a figure for the formula mass of bonds rather than just one bond.

a What would be the problem in giving an energy value to break the bond in one molecule of hydrogen?

The energy to split the bonds in one formula mass of hydrogen molecules is called its **bond energy**.

All covalent bonds have a certain bond energy. However, the precise bond energy for some bonds may slightly vary depending on the other atoms around it and in the rest of a molecule. To simplify this we give covalent bonds an **average bond energy**.

b Which of the bonds shown in fig 30 requires least energy to break?

c Suggest why N_2 needs the most energy to break.

Use of bond energies

Just as energy is needed to break covalent bonds apart, so that same amount of energy is released when covalent bonds form. Bond making is an exothermic process. Tables of average bond energies can be used to work out the energy change in a chemical reaction. The amount of energy needed to break bonds in the

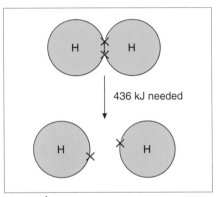

fig 29 Splitting a molecule of hydrogen into atoms

bond	average bond energy in kJ
H—H	436
C—H	412
C—C	348
Cl—Cl	242
O═O	496
O—H	463
H—Cl	431
C═O	743
N≡N	944
H—Br	366
Br—Br	193

fig 30

reactants can be calculated. The amount of energy released when the bonds in the products form can be calculated. For example, chlorine reacts with hydrogen to form hydrogen chloride.

$$H_2 + Cl_2 \rightarrow 2HCl$$

The equation is correctly balanced; this is important.

d How much energy is needed to break the bonds in one formula mass of hydrogen molecules and one formula mass of chlorine molecules?

e How much energy is released when two formula masses of hydrogen chloride molecules form?

f Show that 184 kJ more energy is released than is used up when the reaction takes place.

This reaction is exothermic. The excess energy is given out to the surroundings as heat.

Energy level diagrams

Energy level diagrams are used to show energy changes in reactions. For example, the combustion of hydrogen in oxygen to make steam is represented by the energy diagram shown in fig 32.

The balanced equation is: $2H_2 + O_2 \rightarrow 2H_2O$

The diagram shows that two formula masses of H—H bonds and one formula mass of O=O bonds must break. This requires a total of 1368 kJ. When the four O—H bonds form in water, 1852 kJ of energy is released. The overall energy change is 484 kJ of energy released.

g The reaction $C + CO_2 \rightarrow 2CO$ is endothermic. Sketch the shape of the energy level diagram.

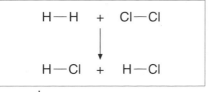

fig 31 | Bond breaking and bond making in the reaction

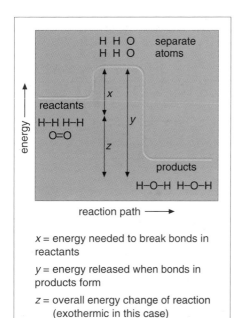

x = energy needed to break bonds in reactants

y = energy released when bonds in products form

z = overall energy change of reaction (exothermic in this case)

fig 32 | Energy level diagram for $2H_2 + O_2$. Notice how the product molecules of water are shown at a lower total energy than the reactant molecules. The lower axis shows the path of the reaction as it takes place

Thinking further

Use the table of average bond energies shown in fig 30 to answer these questions.

◆ **1** Calculate the overall energy change for the reaction:

$$H_2 + Br_2 \rightarrow 2HBr$$

Is the reaction above more or less exothermic than the reaction below?

$$H_2 + Cl_2 \rightarrow 2HCl$$

◆ **2** Fig 33 shows an energy level diagram for an endothermic reaction. Label the diagram to show the reactants, the products and the overall energy change for the reaction.

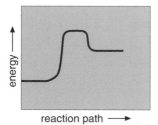

fig 33

◆ **3** Calculate the energy change for the combustion of methane, CH_4, in a plentiful supply of air. Use your answer to explain why methane is used as a fuel.

KEY WORDS
average bond energy • bond energy • energy level diagrams

 Exothermic and endothermic reactions.

Questions on structure and reacting quantities

If you need relative atomic masses to answer these questions refer to the Periodic Table on the back page.

● **1** Fig 34 shows the bonding in a molecule of ammonia.

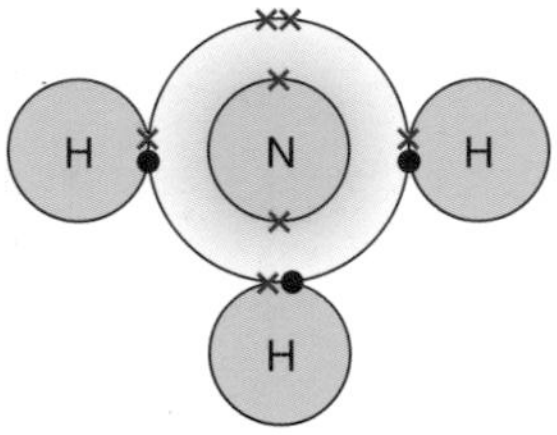

fig 34

a Copy the diagram. Put a ring around a pair of electrons that show a bond. *(1)*

b What sort of bonding is present in ammonia? *(1)*

c Write down the formula for a molecule of ammonia. *(1)*

● **2** Copy and complete these sentences. Choose words from this list:

covalent gain ionic share strongly weakly

When atoms lose or _____ electrons, ions form. These ions attract each other very _____ . The compound formed is said to be _____ . *(3)*

■ **3** Magnesium fluoride contains ionic bonding.

a Describe the changes that take place when magnesium and fluorine combine to form magnesium fluoride. *(5)*

b What sort of attraction exists between the particles in magnesium fluoride? *(1)*

c What is the formula of magnesium fluoride? *(1)*

■ **4** This question is about methane, CH_4.

a Draw a diagram to show the electron arrangement of a carbon atom. *(2)*

b Draw a diagram to show the electron arrangement of a hydrogen atom. *(1)*

c Draw a dot and cross diagram to show the bonding in methane. *(2)*

d What sort of bonding is present in methane? *(1)*

■ **5 a** Copy and complete the table in fig 35. *(4)*

	sodium atom	sodium ion	oxygen atom	oxide ion
protons	11			
neutrons	12			
electrons				

fig 35

b What is the formula of sodium oxide? *(1)*

◆ **6** This question is about the elements strontium and fluorine.

a What groups of the Periodic Table are these elements in:
  i strontium
  ii fluorine? *(2)*

b Atoms of strontium and fluorine react. When they do so electrons are transferred.
  i How will the electron arrangement of strontium change as this happens? *(1)*
  ii How will the electron arrangement of fluorine change as this happens? *(1)*
  iii Write down the symbols for the ions that will be produced by this electron transfer. *(2)*
  iv Write down the name and formula of the substance produced. *(2)*

c The melting point of the substance produced is very high. Suggest why. *(3)*

◆ **7** Fig 36 shows the structure of sodium chloride, NaCl, in the solid state. Only a few particles of the structure are shown.

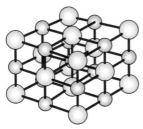

fig 36

a What sort of structure does sodium chloride have? *(1)*

b Explain why a crystal of sodium chloride measuring $1\,cm^3$ has a cubic shape. *(1)*

c Explain why the number of sodium ions, Na^+, is the same as the number of chloride ions, Cl^-. *(1)*

d Suggest why magnesium chloride, $MgCl_2$, has a different structure to sodium chloride. *(2)*

e Calculate the relative formula mass of magnesium chloride. Show your working. *(2)*

◆ **8 a** Draw a dot and cross diagram to show the bonding in a molecule of water. You must also show any electrons that are not involved in bonding. *(4)*

b The boiling points of some substances are shown in the table in fig 37.

substance	boiling point in °C
Water	100
Hydrogen	−252
Sodium chloride	1467

fig 37

Explain the differences in these boiling points. Use ideas about attractions between particles in your answer. *(6)*

◆ **9** The following equation is important in the manufacture of iron:

$$Fe_2O_3 + 3CO \rightarrow 2Fe + 3CO_2$$

a What is the relative formula mass of iron(III) oxide, Fe_2O_3? *(1)*

b Calculate the percentage by mass of iron in iron(III) oxide. *(2)*

c What mass of iron(III) oxide is needed to produce 100 tonnes of iron. Show your working. *(2)*

d Suggest why more iron ore than your answer to part **c** is usually needed by a manufacturer of iron. *(1)*

◆ **10** The data below is about two oxides of carbon.

Oxide A contains 12 g of carbon combined with 16 g of oxygen.
Oxide B contains 12 g of oxygen combined with 32 g of oxygen.

a What are the formulae of the two oxides? *(2)*

b Oxide A reacts with oxygen to form oxide B. Write a symbol equation for this reaction. *(2)*

◆ **11** The combustion of methane is represented by the following balanced equation:

$$CH_4 + 2O_2 \rightarrow CO_2 + 2H_2O$$

Use the table of average bond energies shown in

fig 38 to calculate the energy change for the combustion of one formula mass of methane.

bond	average bond energy in kJ
C—H	412
O=O	496
C=O	743
O—H	463

fig 38

a How much energy is required to break all of the bonds in the reactants? *(2)*

b How much energy is released when all of the bonds in the products form? *(2)*

c What is the overall energy change for the reaction? *(1)*

d Explain how the result shows that the reaction is exothermic. *(1)*

e Construct an energy level diagram to show the combustion of methane. *(3)*

IDEAS AND EVIDENCE

12 This question is about types of carbon.

a Name two forms of carbon that have giant structures. *(1)*

b In 1985 chemists discovered another form of carbon which they called buckminsterfullerene. *(1)*

i How do chemists publicise their discoveries?

ii Explain why it is important that others can repeat the original experiment. *(1)*

iii Buckminsterfullerene can be made by the action of laser beams on graphite or by electrically evaporating carbon electrodes in helium gas at low pressure. Suggest why diamond and graphite have been known for much longer than buckminsterfullerene. *(3)*

c One form of buckminsterfullerene has the formula C_{60}.

i What is its relative formula mass? *(1)*

ii Why was the molecule named after the architect R. Buckminster Fuller? *(1)*

iii Suggest why other chemists are looking to see what properties the C_{60} molecule has. *(1)*

d Write a balanced symbol equation for the combustion of C_{60} in a plentiful supply of oxygen. *(2)*

e Suggest whether you would expect C_{60} to have a higher or lower melting point than diamond. Explain your answer. *(2)*

Using crude oil

Introduction

Crude oil often appears in the news for the worst of reasons: a tanker sinking at sea and causing terrible pollution, oil spills into waterways or the pollution problems caused by using substances from crude oil as fuels. Yet without crude oil life today would be very different. Not only do we rely on chemicals from crude oil to use as fuels but also these same chemicals are vital for the manufacture of useful materials such as poly(ethene).

fig 1 | The positive side of using crude oil

Crude oil:

- was formed millions of years ago from the remains of dead plants and animals and the conditions needed for this were high temperatures and high pressures in the absence of air or oxygen
- is a fossil fuel
- is found trapped below layers of impermeable rock in the Earth's crust
- is called a non-renewable resource because it cannot be replaced in the foreseeable future
- is a finite resource because once it is used up there is no more.

fig 2 | The negative side of using crude oil

Check-up

a Name two other fossil fuels that are used as energy sources.

b Which object in the solar system is the source of the energy contained within these fuels?

c Name two renewable energy resources.

d Which one of the following gases is formed when fossil fuels burn?

carbon dioxide • nitrogen • oxygen

e Fossil fuels often contain a small amount of sulphur. What gas is produced when sulphur burns? What problem is caused when this gas dissolves in rain?

fig 3 | A badly weathered limestone building

Contents of the Teaching block

6.1 Crude oil

You already know that crude oil is an important fossil fuel. This section looks at the sort of substances present in crude oil and how these substances can be separated.

fig 4 | An oil well

6.2 Fuels

The substances in crude oil are used as fuels. Combustion in plenty of air produces carbon dioxide but in a restricted amount of air the poisonous gas carbon monoxide is produced.

6.3 Hydrocarbons

Hydrocarbons are compounds of carbon and hydrogen only. This section looks at two families of hydrocarbons called alkanes and alkenes. Alkenes are much more reactive than alkanes.

6.4 Cracking

Some hydrocarbons are in bigger demand than others. Scientists have found that they can break down larger, less useful, hydrocarbons into much more useful smaller ones by a process called cracking. This allows us to make maximum use of all of the fractions from the crude oil.

6.5 Polymers

There are many materials that people refer to as 'plastics'. However, a better name for these would be polymers. What are polymers, where do they come from and how do we make them? In this section you will find out how alkenes are vital for making polymers.

6.6 Using polymers

This section looks at the different polymers that are available. The use of a particular polymer depends upon its properties. There are problems disposing of polymers when we have used them.

6.7 The oil industry

The oil industry and oil-related industries often only appear on the news when there is a problem. Yet every day millions of tonnes of oil are transported and refined so that we can have the use of fuels and polymers. Many scientists are involved in providing us with these products.

Links with other Teaching blocks

6.1 Crude oil

> ### Key points
>
> - Crude oil is a mixture of many substances.
> - Most of the substances in crude oil are hydrocarbons.
> - Fractional distillation is used to separate the hydrocarbons into fractions, each with a different boiling point range.

What is in crude oil?

Crude oil is a very complex mixture of substances. Many of these substances belong to a family of chemicals called **hydrocarbons**. Hydrocarbons are substances that are made up from hydrogen and carbon atoms only.

a Which of these formulae show hydrocarbons?

$$CO_2 \quad CH_4 \quad C_2H_6 \quad C_2H_6O \quad CCl_4 \quad C_{50}H_{102}$$

Some of the substances in crude oil are **carcinogenic** and so it must be handled with care.

b Suggest what carcinogenic means.

There are a huge number of hydrocarbons. This is because carbon atoms have the ability to join up with one another and form very long chains of atoms. These chains may be thousands of atoms long in very big molecules.

The smallest hydrocarbon molecules with up to four carbon atoms are colourless gases at 20 °C and atmospheric pressure. Propane and butane, sometimes called Calor gas, are examples. Calor gas is used as heating gas in isolated houses and for camping.

fig 5 | Crude oil is a hazardous substance

fig 6 | Propane gas is used as a fuel

fig 7 | Petrol is obtained from crude oil

Hydrocarbons with between five and sixteen carbon atoms are liquids at 20 °C and atmospheric pressure. Octane, which is in petrol, is an example.

Much bigger hydrocarbon molecules are solids at 20 °C and atmospheric pressure. Candle wax is an example.

c Are the following solid, liquid or gas at 20 °C?

CH_4 $C_{40}H_{82}$ C_7H_{16} C_2H_6 $C_{33}H_{68}$

fig 8 | Candle wax contains hydrocarbons

Separating hydrocarbons

It is fortunate that hydrocarbons have different boiling points because this allows us to separate them. Separated hydrocarbons are much more useful than the mixture in crude oil. Crude oil is transported to oil refineries where this separation is carried out.

d What problems could occur when crude oil is transported?

At the refinery the crude oil is heated to evaporate it. The vapour is passed into a tower, called a fractionating column. Different parts of the column are at different temperatures. It is coldest at the top and hottest at the bottom. Because the different hydrocarbons have different boiling points, they condense at different positions in the column. Traps can then collect the liquids at each level. This method of separating a mixture of liquids is called **fractional distillation**.

e What two changes of state occur in fractional distillation?

The boiling point of a hydrocarbon depends on how many carbon atoms are in it. Smaller hydrocarbons have very low boiling points and this is why the very smallest are gases at 20 °C. As the size of the hydrocarbon increases, so does its boiling point.

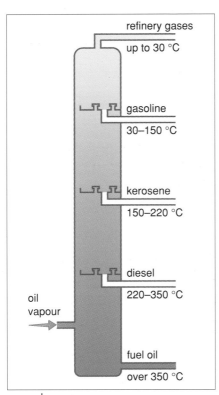

fig 9 | A simplified diagram of a fractionating tower

Thinking further

■ 1 The table in fig 10 shows the boiling points of hydrocarbons with up to seven carbon atoms.

number of carbon atoms	boiling point in °C
1	−162
2	−89
3	−42
4	0
5	36
6	
7	98

fig 10

Draw a chart with number of carbon atoms on the horizontal axis and boiling point on the vertical axis. Draw in the best curve to join the points. Predict the boiling point of the hydrocarbon with six carbon atoms.

■ 2 At the start of the fractional distillation process the crude oil has to be heated. Suggest where the refinery gets its fuel supplies from to do this heating.

◆ 3 Suggest why small alkanes are gases at 20 °C and ordinary pressure. Use ideas of forces between molecules in your answer.

KEY WORDS
carcinogenic • fractional distillation • hydrocarbon

6.2 Fuels

Hydrocarbons as fuels

Under the right conditions all hydrocarbons will burn in air or oxygen and all will release energy in the form of heat. This process is called **combustion**. Smaller hydrocarbon molecules are gases and these ignite very easily. Hydrocarbons with more than seventeen carbon atoms are solids and these require a much higher temperature before they will burn. The liquid hydrocarbons with between five and sixteen carbon atoms also show a steady trend in how easily they will ignite.

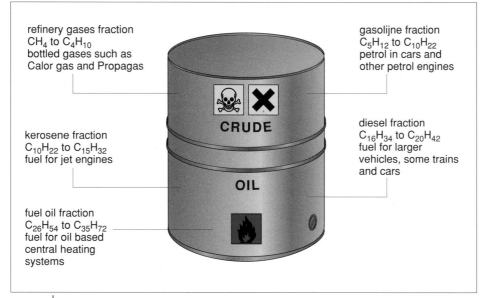

refinery gases fraction
CH_4 to C_4H_{10}
bottled gases such as
Calor gas and Propagas

kerosene fraction
$C_{10}H_{22}$ to $C_{15}H_{32}$
fuel for jet engines

fuel oil fraction
$C_{26}H_{54}$ to $C_{35}H_{72}$
fuel for oil based
central heating
systems

gasolijne fraction
C_5H_{12} to $C_{10}H_{22}$
petrol in cars and
other petrol engines

diesel fraction
$C_{16}H_{34}$ to $C_{20}H_{42}$
fuel for larger
vehicles, some trains
and cars

fig 11 | Uses of the hydrocarbons from crude oil

a Which hydrocarbon will catch fire more easily, C_8H_{18} or $C_{12}H_{24}$? Explain your choice.

The various uses of the hydrocarbons from crude oil as fuels are shown in fig 11.

b In which fuels might you find the following hydrocarbons?

C_8H_{18} $C_{15}H_{32}$ C_3H_8 $C_{10}H_{22}$

Burning hydrocarbons in a plentiful supply of air

All hydrocarbons produce carbon dioxide gas and water vapour when they burn, as long as there is plenty of oxygen. The carbon atoms in the hydrocarbon **oxidise** to carbon dioxide and the hydrogen atoms oxidise to hydrogen oxide (water). Carbon dioxide is a colourless gas but the water vapour may sometimes be seen as it condenses back to liquid water.

Example: CH_4 + $2O_2$ → CO_2 + $2H_2O$
methane + oxygen → carbon dioxide + water

c Write a word equation and a symbol equation for the combustion of propane in a plentiful supply of oxygen.

d Write a symbol equation for the combustion of C_8H_{18}, which is found in the petrol fraction, in a plentiful supply of air.

Burning hydrocarbons in a restricted supply of air

If oxygen is restricted hydrocarbons start to produce the poisonous gas carbon monoxide instead of carbon dioxide. This gas is particularly dangerous as it is colourless and has no smell. Badly serviced gas burners in homes may produce carbon monoxide if they cannot get enough oxygen to fully combust the hydrocarbon. This may happen if the carbon dioxide produced is not vented away properly. Water vapour is still formed in this reaction.

fig 12 | Petrol produces water vapour when it burns

Example: $CH_4 + 1\frac{1}{2}O_2 \rightarrow CO + 2H_2O$
methane + oxygen $\rightarrow$ carbon monoxide + water

e Write a word equation to show propane gas burning in a restricted supply of oxygen.

Thinking further

■ **1** Copy and complete the table in fig 13.

hydrocarbon formula	fraction it is found in	use
CH_4		household gas
		petrol engines
$C_{14}H_{30}$		

fig 13

KEY WORDS
combustion • oxidise

◆ **2** Balance the following equations.

a $C_5H_{12} + O_2 \rightarrow CO_2 + H_2O$

b $C_2H_6 + O_2 \rightarrow CO + H_2O$

6.3 Hydrocarbons

Alkanes

Alkanes are hydrocarbons containing only single covalent bonds between carbon atoms. We say they are **saturated**.

The simplest alkane is methane, CH_4. This contains one carbon atom covalently bonded to four hydrogen atoms.

The structure of methane can be shown by a **'displayed' formula**. This is shown in fig 15.

The next simplest alkane is called ethane. Its formula is C_2H_6. Its shape and displayed structure are shown in fig 16.

Notice each carbon atom has four single bonds to either a hydrogen atom or another carbon atom. Hydrogen atoms only ever have one bond.

a An alkane has the molecular formula C_3H_8. Draw its displayed formula.

b Predict the molecular formula of the alkane that has four carbon atoms. Draw its displayed formula.

Alkenes

Alkenes are another family of hydrocarbons. They differ from alkanes in that they have a double covalent bond between two of the carbon atoms in their structure. We say they are **unsaturated**. The simplest alkene is ethene, C_2H_4.

c Why is it impossible to have an alkene with one carbon atom in the structure?

The alkene C_3H_8 is called propene and its displayed structure is shown in fig 18.

Notice the double bond between two of the carbon atoms and how each carbon atom still has a total of four bonds to neighbouring atoms.

d Can you think of two different places to put a carbon to carbon double bond in the alkene called butene, C_4H_8?

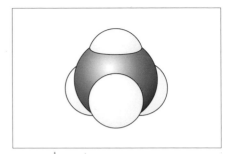

fig 14 | A model of a molecule of methane

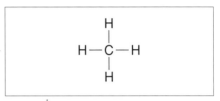

fig 15 | Graphical representation of CH_4

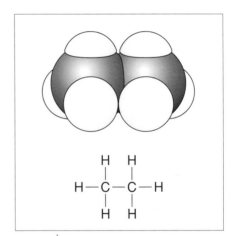

fig 16 | Two ways to represent ethane, C_2H_6

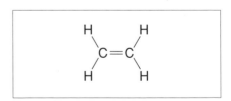

fig 17 | The structure of ethene, C_2H_4

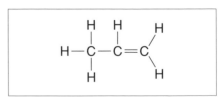

fig 18 | The structure of propene

Properties of alkanes and alkenes

Although alkanes are generally unreactive substances, they do burn in air or oxygen and release energy. This makes them good fuels.

Alkenes are much more reactive than alkanes. They burn in air in a similar way to alkanes. However, alkenes also undergo reactions that involve the breaking of one of the bonds in the double bond. Other atoms then 'add' to the carbon atoms that have lost the double bond. For example, ethene reacts with hydrogen, in the presence of a nickel catalyst, to form ethane.

$$C_2H_4 + H_2 \rightarrow C_2H_6$$
ethene + hydrogen → ethane

e Write the equation above using displayed formulae.

The reaction between alkenes and bromine (dissolved in water) is used to determine whether a substance is an alkane or an alkene, as shown in fig 19. Only alkenes will undergo an **addition reaction** with bromine.

f Describe the changes that can be seen when bromine is shaken with ethane or ethene. How does this help to tell them apart?

The reaction that takes place is:

$$C_2H_4(g) + Br_2(aq) \rightarrow C_2H_4Br_2(l)$$
ethene + bromine → dibromoethane

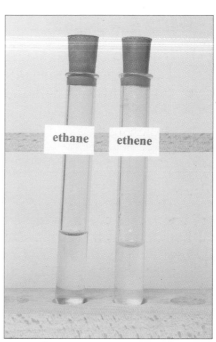

fig 19 | Bromine water is used to distinguish alkanes from alkenes

Thinking further

The table in fig 20 shows information about alkanes.

Use the table to answer questions 1 to 4.

name	formula	boiling point in °C	state at 20 °C
methane	CH_4	−162	gas
ethane	C_2H_6	−89	
propane	C_3H_8	−42	gas
butane	C_4H_{10}	0	gas
pentane		36	liquid
hexane	C_6H_{14}	68	
heptane		98	liquid

fig 20

● **1** What are the formulae for pentane and for heptane?

● **2** What are the states of ethane and hexane at 20 °C?

■ **3** What is the connection between the boiling point of an alkane and the number of carbon atoms in its structure?

■ **4** The next alkane in the series has eight carbon atoms. Predict its name, formula and state at 20 °C.

◆ **5** Ethene reacts with hydrogen bromide, HBr, in an addition reaction. Write an equation to show this using displayed formulae.

◆ **6** What will be the formula for the alkane containing n carbon atoms? What will be the formula for the alkene containing n carbon atoms? These are called their general formulae.

KEY WORDS

addition reaction • alkane • alkene • displayed formula • saturated • unsaturated

6.4 Cracking

Key points

- The fractions that are obtained from crude oil are not in equal demand from consumers.
- Smaller hydrocarbons are generally in greater demand than larger ones.
- Cracking breaks down larger hydrocarbons into smaller ones.

fig 21 | The ancient Greeks used crude oil in Greek fire. Greek fire was a mixture of crude oil, sodium nitrate and quicklime which ignited when added to water

Supply and demand

Although the ancient Greeks may have been the first to use crude oil over 2000 years ago in 'Greek fire', oil has only been exploited commercially during the last 100 years. Over the last 50 years the demand for oil-based substances has increased dramatically and continues to do so. The demand for the smaller hydrocarbons in particular has also become much greater than demand for the larger ones. This is shown in the table in fig 22.

fraction	approximate % in crude oil	approximate % demand
refinery gas	2	4
gasoline	20	27
kerosene	13	7
diesel oil	17	24
fuel oil and bitumen	48	38

fig 22

fig 23 | Today we use oil for many things

a Suggest uses for the three fractions that have a demand greater than the percentage present in crude oil.

b Which fraction is produced in the refinery in much larger quantities than is needed?

This situation could have left oil refineries with a large surplus of some fractions. Fortunately, scientists have found ways to change the larger, less useful molecules into smaller, more useful ones.

Cracking

Research chemists discovered how larger hydrocarbon molecules could be broken down into the more useful smaller ones.
This enabled oil refineries to allow supply to match demand.
It also enabled them to avoid having unsold reserves of the larger hydrocarbons that would be difficult to dispose of because of environmental considerations. In addition they would be able to

maximise profit by converting the less useful larger hydrocarbons into ones with a higher demand and therefore price.

The process discovered by scientists is called **cracking**.

Cracking alkanes literally means breaking them apart into smaller molecules. Heating the alkane to a very high temperature will do this. This is called **thermal cracking**. Alternatively, a lower temperature can be used together with a catalyst. The alkane is passed over a heated mixture of aluminium oxide and silicon(IV) oxide. This process is called **catalytic cracking**.

c Suggest why there is a cost advantage in using catalytic cracking compared to thermal cracking.

The products from cracking are smaller alkane molecules and alkenes. Hydrogen may also form. The products obtained from a particular cracking reaction consist of a mixture of gases and liquids. The composition of this mixture can vary greatly and depends very much on the exact conditions used.

d Name a process that could be used to separate the hydrocarbons produced from a cracking reaction.

When alkanes are heated they gain energy. Eventually the molecules can gain so much energy that they begin to break up. Fig 25 shows this happening to a molecule of decane.

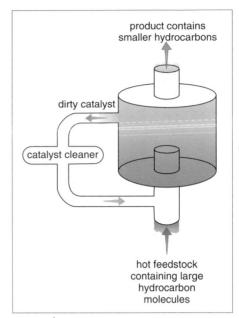

fig 24 | Simplified diagram of a catalytic cracker

The equation for this reaction is:

$$C_{10}H_{22} \rightarrow C_8H_{18} + C_2H_4$$
$$\text{decane} \rightarrow \text{octane} + \text{ethene}$$

Another typical cracking reaction is:

$$C_{12}H_{26} \rightarrow C_8H_{18} + 2C_2H_4$$
$$\text{dodecane} \rightarrow \text{octane} + \text{ethene}$$

e Which fraction is dodecane found in?

f Explain why this cracking reaction is economically important for an oil refinery.

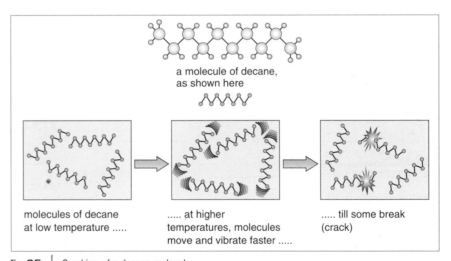

fig 25 | Cracking of a decane molecule

Thinking further

■ **1** Cracking alkanes produces alkenes. Describe a chemical test to show that an alkene is present.

◆ **2** Cracking of a hydrocarbon produces a mixture of saturated and unsaturated compounds. Explain the meaning of the words underlined.

◆ **3** Cracking decane can produce a mixture of butane and propene in the ratio 1:2 respectively. Write a balanced symbol equation for this reaction.

◆ **4** What are the values of x and y in the equation below?

$$C_xH_y \rightarrow C_{12}H_{24} + C_2H_4 + H_2$$

KEY WORDS
cracking • catalytic cracking • thermal cracking

 Cracking long chain alkalines.

6.5 Polymers

Key points

- Under suitable conditions alkene molecules join up with themselves to produce long chains of carbon atoms.
- The small alkene molecules that do this are called monomers.
- The long chain molecules that form are called polymers.
- The structure of a polymer is determined by the structure of the monomer.

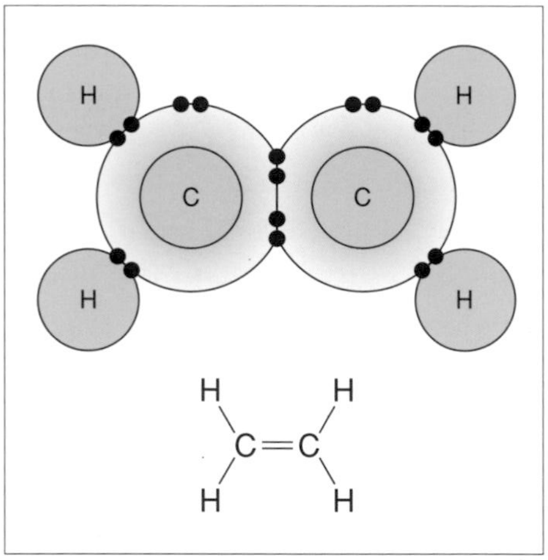

fig 26 | Bonding in a molecule of ethene

How polymers form

Alkenes have a double bond in their structure. This means that when one of these bonds breaks the carbon atoms have an extra pair of electrons that can be used for bonding to other atoms. It is these electrons that are used when one alkene molecule joins up with another.

a Why is it impossible for ethane to form a polymer?

Poly(ethene)

The simplest alkene is ethene.

When heat and pressure are applied to ethene gas, in the presence of a catalyst, electrons from the double bond move and form bonds with neighbouring ethene molecules. This process happens repeatedly between hundreds of ethene molecules forming chains up to thousands of atoms long. Fig 27 shows this happening to four ethene molecules.

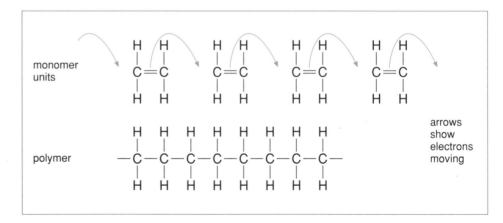

fig 27 | Ethene molecules join to form poly(ethene)

The product is called poly(ethene). This is sometimes abbreviated to 'polythene'.

b If the average relative formula mass of poly(ethene) is 140 000, how many ethene molecules must have made up the average chain?

Notice how the poly(ethene) does not have any carbon to carbon double bonds. It has become a long chain alkane.

c Which is more reactive, ethene or poly(ethene)? Why?

The small ethene molecules are called **monomers**. The product is an example of a **polymer**. Since the monomer units add together to form just one product, the reaction is described as **addition polymerisation**.

Writing equations for polymerisation

Writing equations for polymerisation may look difficult. However, there are some simple rules to follow.

For the polymerisation of ethene shown previously we write the equation as shown in fig 28.

The important points to notice are:

- The monomer has a double bond between two carbon atoms, the polymer does not.
- Instead of showing a particular number of monomer units joining up, we write that 'n' of them do. We then show the **repeat unit** of the polymer 'n' times.
- The bonds of the repeat unit pass through the edges of the square brackets.

It is not just ethene that will form an addition polymer. Any other substance with a carbon to carbon double bond in its structure can polymerise. For example, propene forms the polymer poly(propene) as shown in fig 30.

d Write down the name of the polymer formed from chloroethene.

It is always possible to work out the structure of an addition polymer if you know the monomer it is formed from. Conversely it is possible to work out the structure of the monomer if the structure of the polymer is known.

e The polymerisation of tetrafluoroethene, C_2F_4, produces a polymer that is used as the coating in non-stick frying pans. Name the polymer and write an equation for its formation.

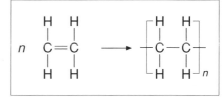

fig 28 | Polymerisation of ethene

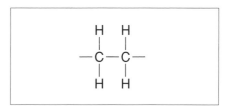

fig 29 | The repeat unit of poly(ethene)

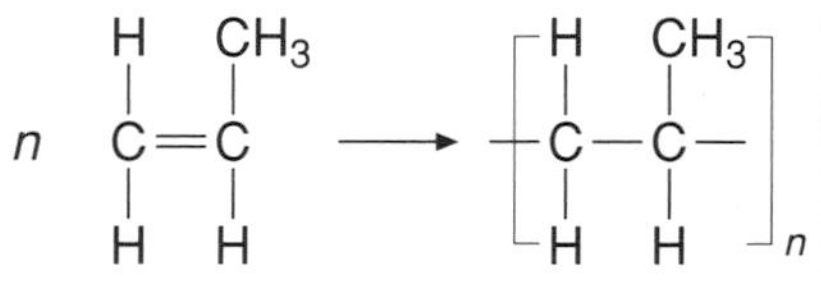

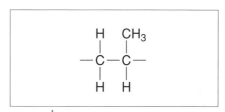

fig 30 | Polymerisation of propene

fig 31 | The repeat unit of poly(propene)

Thinking further

◆ **1** Copy and complete the table in fig 32.

◆ **2** There is only a small amount of ethene in crude oil. Describe the process that an oil refinery could use to supply enough ethene to a polymer manufacturer.

fig 32

name of monomer	formula of monomer	name of polymer	polymer repeat unit
chloroethene	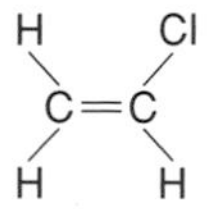		
		polystyrene	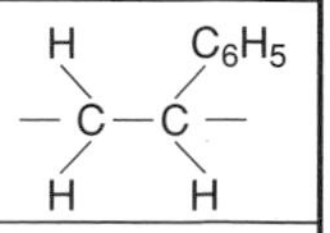
	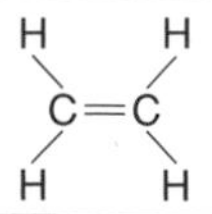		

6.6 Using polymers

> ### Key points
>
> - Polymers have many different uses.
> - The use that a particular polymer has depends directly on the properties of that polymer.
> - Scientists now try to make new polymers to fit particular needs.

fig 33 | We did not always wrap food in cling film

From crude oil to cling film

Cling film is made from poly(chloroethene). We take it for granted that it is available to wrap our sandwiches in. Yet polymers such as this were unknown to our grandparents who would have probably wrapped their sandwiches in 'grease-proof paper'.

a Name five more things that are now made from polymers but would not have been 60 years ago.

Even ideas about the structure of natural polymers such as rubber were not understood until 1922. Poly(ethene) itself was discovered by accident in 1933 by scientists who were attempting another experiment. They noticed a white waxy deposit in their reaction vessel. This was the first sample of poly(ethene) to be made.

b The following steps are involved in making cling film from crude oil. Put them in the correct order.

cracking • oil extraction • fractional distillation polymerisation • transport of crude oil

fig 34 | Poly(ethene) was discovered by accident when scientists were using this apparatus for another experiment

Properties and uses

Polymers are all very large molecules containing chains of carbon atoms. There are many different polymers that can be formed by having different atoms or groups of atoms attached to the double bond in the monomer. Even polymers formed from the same monomer may have different properties depending on the conditions used to carry out the polymerisation. One method of making poly(ethene) produces a more flexible type of poly(ethene) while another method produces a higher density, less flexible type of poly(ethene).

c What type of poly(ethene) is best for making buckets?

The uses that a particular polymer has depend on its properties.

Most addition polymers share some common properties. For example they do not corrode and are cheaper than natural

fig 35 | Poly(ethene) has many different uses

materials that could be used to do the same job. However, different polymers do have some individual properties that make them better for particular uses, as the table in fig 36 shows.

name of polymer	properties	uses
poly(ethene) low density	durable, flexible, water resistant	plastic bin bags and supermarket bags, squeezy bottles, cling film
poly(ethene) high density	tough, durable, easily moulded, water resistant	buckets, bowls, sandwich boxes
poly(propene)	more rigid than poly(ethene), tough, durable	crates, ropes, fibres in some carpets
plasticised poly(chloroethene) PVC	insulator, tough, water resistant, more easily coloured than poly(ethene)	covering on electrical wires, artificial leather for furniture, rainwear, cling film
unplasticised poly(chloroethene) uPVC	tough, water resistant, hard	drain pipes, gutters, CD discs

fig 36

d What advantages do gutters made from uPVC have over iron ones?

Disposal of polymers

The use of polymers has become more and more widespread over the last 50 years and the problem of their disposal is now a serious issue. This is because most polymers are not **biodegradable**.

e Explain what biodegradable means.

Recycling is not a particularly easy option because of the many different types of polymer. These would need separating. Polymer scientists are developing polymers that are biodegradable. These have small amounts of poly(ethene) with cellulose, a natural polymer that does biodegrade. Other polymers are changed into fuel pellets. This has the advantage that the fraction from crude oil has been used twice, once as a polymer and then as a fuel. However, great care has to be taken because some polymers release poisonous fumes if they are burned at too low a temperature.

Thinking further

● **1** Why is poly(propene) better than poly(ethene) for making crates?

■ **2** You are designing the hull of a new sailing yacht. You decide to use a polymer instead of wood. What properties do you require of the polymer?

■ **3** Give reasons why it is dangerous to burn polymers in a classroom laboratory.

◆ **4** Which polymer is likely to give of fumes of hydrogen chloride when it is burned?

◆ **5** The polymerisation of ethyne, H—C≡C—H, produces a polymer which retains a double bond. The polymer also conducts electricity. Name the polymer and suggest a use for it.

KEY WORDS

biodegradable

6.7 The oil industry

The importance of the oil industry

Life today would be very different without the products that we get from crude oil.

Fuels used in cars and lorries (petrol and diesel), kerosene (for jet aircraft) and fuel oil (for ships) all come from crude oil.

Some fuel oil is also used for electricity generation.

a What other fossil fuels are used to generate electricity?

b What 'alternative' fuels is it possible to use?

Fractions from crude oil provide the monomers to make polymers and materials to make drugs, paints and solvents.

c Why would it be short-sighted to carrying on using crude oil at an ever-increasing rate for use as fuels?

Care for the environment

Our reliance on crude oil must be carefully balanced with the need to conserve and protect our environment. Fragile ecosystems are easily damaged by both the disturbance caused by the extraction of crude oil and any crude oil spillage. These ecosystems are not easily replaced. Accidents at sea cause birds to be coated in oil and tourism to be affected on polluted coastlines. Crude oil can also poison the smallest marine life and this in turn affects the whole food chain.

d Suggest why French environmental health officers banned the sale of mussels from the Southern Brittany coast in 1999.

The increasing use of polymers has led to problems of disposal (see 6.6 Using polymers) and the carbon dioxide produced by the combustion of fossil fuels is thought to be causing global warming (see 7.4 Carbon dioxide).

There is a balance between the advantages and disadvantages of using crude oil.

I am a geologist. My job is to predict likely places where crude oil may be found in the Earth's crust. My team will then use seismic surveying to help find the exact location of the oil.

I am a polymer scientist. My job is to synthesise and research the properties of polymers. I also try to make new ones. We have recently made Kevlar which is, weight for weight, five times stronger than steel. This has sold well.

Sue

Dan

When the location of oil is suggested by the geologist I use my knowledge as an engineer to set up the equipment for the oil well to extract the oil from the below the Earth's crust.

My job as a fuel technologist not only involves making the most efficient use of the fuels we get from crude oil but also research for replacements for fossil fuels in the future, such as hydrogen cells. The polymer scientist says we should keep oil to make polymers and not just burn it all as fuels.

John

Ali

As a chemical engineer I supervise the fractional distillation of the crude oil at the refinery. I have to make sure that the conditions are correct for the efficient separation of the fractions in the oil. I also advise on the best conditions for cracking the heavier fractions.

I am an environmental scientist. It is my job to ensure that everything that is possible is done to minimise damage to the environment from the extraction, transport and refining of crude oil as well as the use of crude oil products.

Mel   Mike

fig 37 | The jobs of some scientists

Thinking further

● **1** Suggest why the development of biodegradable plastics would be useful.

◆ **2** The manager of an oil company has sent you to a small developing nation. The company believes that this nation has oil deposits very near its coastline and is rich in the lighter fractions.

   a Which scientists will you take with you on your first visit?

The nation is very poor and hopes the money it will get from selling its oil will pay off its debt and will improve the standard of living for its entire people. The population is hopeful that it will also provide many years of employment.

You have also been told that this section of coastline is an area of one of two remaining habitats of its kind in the world. Development could destroy it.

   b Which scientists will help advise you?

   c Write two reports, one to your manager and the other to the President of the country. Advise them of the issues and your opinion.

Questions on using crude oil

1 This question is about the fractions that can be obtained from crude oil. Use the table in fig 38 to help you answer the questions that follow.

name of fraction	formulae of hydrocarbons in the fraction	boiling point range of the fraction (°C)	use of the fraction
refinery gases	CH_4 to C_4H_{10}	up to 30	Calor gas
gasoline	C_5H_{12} to $C_{10}H_{22}$	30 to 150	
kerosene	$C_{10}H_{22}$ to $C_{15}H_{32}$	150 to 220	
diesel	$C_{16}H_{34}$ to $C_{20}H_{42}$	220 to 350	fuel for lorries
fuel oil	$C_{26}H_{54}$ to $C_{35}H_{72}$	over 350	fuel for heating systems

fig 38

a Copy and complete the table in fig 38. *(2)*

b In which fraction would you find the following hydrocarbons?

CH_4 $C_{12}H_{26}$ C_8H_{18} *(3)*

c Which fraction would ignite more easily, gasoline or diesel? *(1)*

d Which fraction is a gas at 20 °C and ordinary pressure? *(1)*

e What is the connection between the boiling point of a fraction and the number of carbon atoms in its molecules? *(1)*

2 The lists below show the names of some scientists' jobs and what they do for an oil company. Match up the scientist to what they do. *(4)*

chemical engineer	using ethene to make poly(ethene)
fuel technologist	locating oil reserves
geologist	separating fractions in crude oil
polymer scientist	making an efficient petrol engine

3 a What is a hydrocarbon? *(2)*

b **i** Name the process used to separate the mixture of hydrocarbons in crude oil into more useful substances. *(1)*

ii Explain the steps that are involved in this process. *(4)*

iii What property of the different hydrocarbons allows this separation to be carried out? *(1)*

4 Methane burns in air as shown below.

$$CH_4 + 2O_2 \rightarrow CO_2 + 2H_2O \ \Delta H = -890\,kJ$$

a How can you tell that the reaction is exothermic? *(1)*

b What is the relative formula mass of methane? *(2)*

c What is the relative formula mass of carbon dioxide? *(1)*

d A factory burns 100 tonnes of methane gas as fuel. What mass of carbon dioxide is produced? *(1)*

5 The table in fig 39 shows the density of some hydrocarbons. Use the data in the table to answer the questions that follow.

hydrocarbon	density in g/cm^3
pentane	0.626
hexane	0.659
heptane	0.684
octane	0.703
nonane	
decane	0.730

fig 39

a Plot a graph of density, on the vertical axis, against number of carbon atoms in the hydrocarbon, on the horizontal axis. Draw the best curve through the points that you have plotted. *(5)*

b Predict the density of the hydrocarbon with nine carbon atoms. *(1)*

c Describe the connection between density of a hydrocarbon and the number of carbon atoms it contains. *(2)*

d Why would you expect the density of the hydrocarbon with four carbon atoms to be much less than 0.626 g/cm³ at 20 °C and atmospheric pressure? *(1)*

◆ **6** The combustion of propane, C_3H_8, gives water vapour as one of the products. The other product of combustion may be either carbon dioxide or carbon monoxide (or a mixture of both) depending on conditions.

a Explain how the carbon-containing combustion product depends on conditions. *(2)*

b Suggest why using a poorly serviced propane burner could be dangerous. *(1)*

c Write balanced symbol equations to show:
i propane burning to form carbon dioxide and water *(2)*
ii propane burning to form carbon monoxide and water. *(2)*

◆ **7** Dibromoethane is produced when ethene reacts with bromine. It is sometimes called 1,2-dibromoethane. It has the displayed formula shown below.

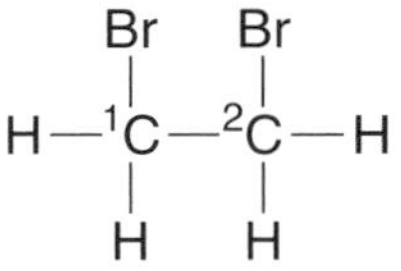

$$H-{}^{1}C-{}^{2}C-H$$

(with Br, Br above the two carbons and H, H below)

....
....

It is possible to draw another dibromoethane called 1,1-dibromoethane. Draw its displayed structure.
[Hint: notice that there are two carbon atoms, numbered 1 and 2.] *(1)*

◆ **8** Two types of plastics can be made from polymers. One type has long chains of polymer molecules with only weak forces between them (fig 40).

long chains

fig 40

The other type has strong covalent bonds holding neighbouring chains together (fig 41).

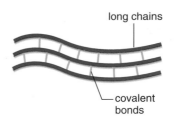

long chains

covalent bonds

fig 41

Suggest which plastic melts most easily. Explain your choice. *(1)*

IDEAS AND EVIDENCE

◆ **9** You are an adviser to an oil company. You are reviewing the choice of two types of crude oil (A and B) for use in the refinery. The refinery is about to place a very large order for crude oil. Each crude oil has a different composition. The table in fig 42 gives details of the fractions in each type of crude oil and also the demand of the refinery's customers for each fraction.

fraction	percentage in crude oil A	percentage in crude oil B	percentage demand
refinery gas	2	2	5
gasoline	18	24	29
kerosene	11	15	7
diesel	18	24	24
fuel oil	51	35	35

fig 42

a If both types of crude oil cost the same, advise the refinery manager which type you would recommend. Explain your choice. *(7)*

b Explain what the refinery will have to do to meet the demand for refinery gases. Which scientists will you have to consult about this? *(2)*

c You find that crude oil A is significantly cheaper than crude oil B and that there are far greater reserves of this type. Write a report suggesting how the choice of the cheaper oil may be to the refinery's advantage. The refinery has a full range of cracking facilities. *(7)*

Earth cycles

Introduction

About two and a half thousand years ago a Greek philosopher, called Empedocles, suggested that all matter consisted of four 'elements': air, earth, fire and water. Empedocles based his suggestion on those things that he saw around him. Although we now have a different understanding of what elements are, three of Empedocles' so-called 'elements' are involved in cycles that affect us all.

The balance of gases in the air depends on processes such as photosynthesis and combustion.

In the water cycle, water is evaporated from the seas to the atmosphere and condenses back again.

Rocks themselves are recycled but this takes long periods of time.

This chapter is concerned with these cycles and with how human activity may be affecting them.

Air, seawater and rocks are all mixtures. This means that the things that make them up (called constituents) are not combined.

Physical processes such as the 'freeze–thaw' mechanism can break down rocks.

Rocks are divided into three types depending on the processes involved in their formation:

* igneous rocks form when molten rock cools and crystallises
* sedimentary rocks form when rock fragments are deposited and compressed
* metamorphic rocks form when high pressure and/or high temperature affect any pre-existing rock.

fig 1 Empedoceles recognised four 'elements': air, water, fire and earth

Check-up

a Write down the names of the two most common gases in the air.

b Which gas do plants use to make food in photosynthesis?

c Which gas do plants make in photosynthesis?

d A white solid remains when seawater evaporates. What does this white solid mostly contain?

e What sort of rock, igneous, metamorphic or sedimentary, forms when:

  i lava from a volcano cools

  ii layers of shells are deposited on the sea floor

  iii some sedimentary rock is buried very deep underground?

If you have difficulty, ask your teacher for a Summary sheet.

Contents of the Teaching block

7.1 Air

You already know that air is a mixture of gases. This section looks at which gases are in air and how we can find out the percentage of oxygen in air. It also considers what gases may have been present in the atmosphere when it first formed from volcanoes.

7.2 The atmosphere

We know what gases are in today's atmosphere but how did the gases in the early atmosphere change to form the air we breathe today as well as our seas and oceans?

7.3 The oceans

An old fable asks the question 'how did the sea become salty'? In this section we will look at substances that have become dissolved in seawater and what factors allow the composition of seawater to remain constant.

7.4 Carbon dioxide

The amount of carbon dioxide in the atmosphere is increasing. There is also a rise in the Earth's temperature. What is likely to happen if this continues? Is there a link between the amount of carbon dioxide in the atmosphere and the Earth's temperature?

7.5 Rock formation

This section will show you how details within each rock can give useful evidence about how the rock itself was formed.

7.6 The rock record

The order in which rocks are laid down can give us evidence about their relative ages. Folds and faults in rock, caused by movement of the Earth's plates, give extra evidence about events in the past.

Links with other Teaching blocks

7.1 Air

Key points

- The present atmosphere has been much the same for the past 200 million years.
- Earth's atmosphere was probably formed about 4 thousand million years ago by volcanic activity.
- A pure sample of dry air in today's atmosphere contains about 80% nitrogen and 20% oxygen.

What gases are in air?

We now know that air is a mixture of gases. Yet just over 200 years ago people still believed air was an 'element' and not a mixture at all. Two scientists, Priestley and Lavoisier, did experiments to show that air was a mixture. Their ideas were not immediately accepted.

a New ideas are often rejected at first and sometimes even laughed at. Why is this?

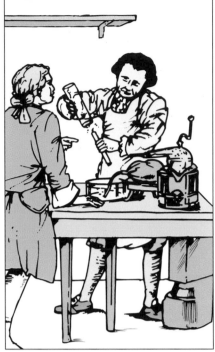

fig 2 Priestley was one of the first people to realise that air was not a single substance

Air is colourless. The table in fig 3 shows the approximate composition of a sample of dry air.

nitrogen	oxygen	argon	carbon dioxide
79%	20%	0.9%	0.04%

fig 3

b How does the table show that there are other gases in the air in addition to those named?

c Which of the gases shown consists of uncombined atoms?

d Older textbooks give a value for carbon dioxide of 0.03%. Why?

Pure air also contains traces of neon, krypton, helium and xenon. These are called noble gases.

e Which gas named in fig 3 is a noble gas?

f Which group of the Periodic Table are the noble gases in?

The Earth's atmosphere also contains other gases and most samples of air will contain variable amounts of different **pollutants.** Variable amounts of water vapour are also present. This is why we usually refer to pure, dry air in questions.

g Name two pollutants likely to be found in air near a busy road.

Finding the percentage of oxygen in air

Fig 4 shows apparatus that can be used in the laboratory to find the percentage of oxygen in a sample of air.

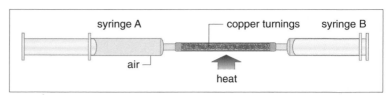

fig 4 | Apparatus to find the percentage of oxygen in a sample of air

Oxygen is removed from the air when it is passed over heated copper. Solid black copper(II) oxide is formed.

$$2Cu + O_2 \rightarrow 2CuO$$
copper + oxygen → copper(II) oxide

h The air is passed backwards and forwards over the heated copper. Suggest why.

i How will you know when all the oxygen has been removed?

j Which gas is left in the largest amount in the syringe at the end of the experiment?

Lavoisier called the gas left at the end of a similar experiment 'azote'. This means 'without life'.

k Why do you think he gave it this name?

Earth's early atmosphere

The very first 'atmosphere' around Earth was probably a mixture of hydrogen and helium but this would have disappeared into space.

The evolution of Earth's atmosphere as we see it today is thought to have started when volcanoes erupted and poured out gases. These gases were probably mostly carbon dioxide and steam, with smaller amounts of methane and ammonia.

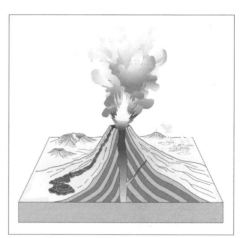

fig 5 | The volcano is erupting onto an Earth without life

Thinking further

■ **1** Fig 6 shows a candle burning under a bell jar. Suggest what would happen. How can you explain what would happen?

fig 6

bell jar

air

candle

water

■ **2** What sort of chemical change happens to copper when it reacts with oxygen?

■ **3** Two samples of air are tested using the apparatus shown in fig 4. One sample of air is taken from inside a room that has been full of students for an hour; the other sample is fresh air from outside. Suggest how the results may be different.

■ **4** Which of the gases formed by early volcanic activity on the Earth's surface would condense when the temperature fell below 100 °C?

◆ **5** Suggest why hydrogen in the earliest atmosphere would have escaped into space.

KEY WORDS
pollution

 What happens when copper is heated in air?

7.2 The atmosphere

- The composition of Earth's early atmosphere slowly changed over millions of years.
- Cooling of the Earth's surface allowed steam to condense to water and for the oceans to form.
- Evolution of photosynthesising organisms increased the amount of oxygen.
- Photosynthesis, the formation of fossil fuels and solution in the oceans decreased the amount of carbon dioxide.
- Ammonia was removed by bacteria and also by reaction with oxygen. This resulted in the formation of nitrogen.

Changes in the early atmosphere

Water vapour

The surface temperature of Earth remained over 100 °C for millions of years after Earth gained its first atmosphere. This meant that water was in the form of steam in the atmosphere. As the Earth's surface cooled, a point was reached when the temperature dropped below 100 °C. Steam began to condense as water, filling the lowest points on the Earth's surface. Oceans and seas began to form.

fig 7 | Oceans formed as steam condensed and fell as rain

Carbon dioxide

Scientists think that the early atmosphere contained large amounts of carbon dioxide gas, much like the surface of Venus today. Carbon dioxide is slightly soluble in water so that once the oceans formed some carbon dioxide would have dissolved in the water, reducing its concentration in the atmosphere. The evolution of simple plant life in the sea, about 3000 million years ago, resulted in carbon dioxide being used up as plants made food by **photosynthesis**.

a Which gas is produced when plants photosynthesise?

In time more plants and animals evolved. When these died, some were trapped in sedimentary rocks. In the absence of air, and under the right conditions of temperature and pressure, these deposits turned into fossil fuels. This meant that over millions of years there was a reduction in the amount of carbon dioxide in the atmosphere as the carbon atoms became locked up in the fossil fuels.

b Name two fossil fuels.

fig 8 | These trees may have been covered by sediment and, over millions of years, turned into coal

Shell formation also removed carbon dioxide from the atmosphere as calcium carbonate was formed. This is explained more fully in 7.3 The oceans.

Ammonia

Ammonia was present in the early atmosphere. Its removal from the air first depended on the evolution of life. Some organisms, called **nitrifying bacteria** were able to convert ammonia into nitrates. Other organisms, called **denitrifying bacteria**, were then able to change the nitrates into nitrogen. Once oxygen appeared in the atmosphere, it, too, would have reacted with the ammonia. Nitrogen and water are produced.

c   Write a word equation for the reaction of ammonia and oxygen.

Today the nitrogen cycle maintains the balance of nitrogen in the atmosphere.

Methane

Once oxygen was present in the atmosphere, any methane would have reacted with it to produce carbon dioxide and water.

d   Write a word equation for this reaction.

Oxygen

Oxygen may not have been present in the early atmosphere. It was formed by photosynthesis once plants evolved. Its presence in today's atmosphere remains a balance between processes which put it into the atmosphere and those that remove it.

Thinking further

■ **1** Name one process that increases the amount of oxygen in the atmosphere and two processes that reduce it.

■ **2** Land plants evolved about 400 million years ago. Animals evolved about 300 million years ago. Why was the evolution of plant life important for the evolution of animals?

■ **3** Write a word equation to show photosynthesis.

◆ **4** Write a balanced symbol equation for the reaction between methane and oxygen.

◆ **5** Balance this symbol equation:

$$NH_3 + O_2 \rightarrow N_2 + H_2O$$

◆ **6** Volcanoes produce vast quantities of carbon dioxide gas. Which substances produce carbon dioxide by thermal decomposition?

┌─ **KEY WORDS** ─────────────────────┐
│ denitrifying bacteria • nitrifying bacteria • photosynthesis │
└─────────────────────────────────────┘

 Gases from the air.   *Air pollution study.*

7.3 The oceans

> ### Key points
>
> - When the Earth formed the surface remained too hot for water to be present on the surface for hundreds of millions of years.
> - When the temperature became low enough for the water to condense, the oceans formed.
> - Water is a good solvent and dissolved some of the rocks it was in contact with.
> - Over millions of years the mineral composition of the oceans has become constant.

The oceans and seas

Although people have walked on the moon, no one has walked on the bottom of the deepest oceans. The oceans may still contain mysteries that we have yet to find out about. Recently, a live coelacanth, a fish thought to be extinct for the last 70 million years, was discovered. What else waits to be found?

We believe that the oceans formed when water vapour condensed as the Earth cooled. This water would have filled up the lowest points on the surface of the Earth and thus created the oceans. However, water is a solvent and it would start to dissolve substances it came into contact with on the Earth's surface. The more soluble the substance the more of it would dissolve. Often, when a substance dissolves in water it forms **ions**. Thus seawater became a solution containing ions of different elements.

a Which two ions are in greatest concentration in seawater?

Over hundreds of millions of years the composition of seawater became fairly constant over the entire globe. Although the actual concentration of ions varies from place to place, the ratio of each of the ions with respect to one another is the same. In places such as the Dead Sea the concentration of ions is five times higher than the concentration of ions in the Baltic Sea.

b What effect does the concentration of ions in seawater have on buoyancy?

Keeping the balance

Any change to a system that is balanced must have things added and taken away at the same rate. The oceans are no exception. Rainwater flowing over rocks will dissolve soluble material, usually as ions, and carry this to the sea.

fig 9 This fish is called a coelacanth; it was thought to have become extinct millions of years ago

fig 10 This person does not need to swim to stay afloat, because the concentration of dissolved substances in the water is very high

If a river flows over rock that contains particularly soluble constituents this will add more ions to the sea than a river that flows over rocks with less soluble constituents. As rivers continually flow into the seas and oceans, the concentration of ions in seawater should increase. However, the amount remains constant over long periods of time. There must therefore be processes that remove ions from seawater. There are three principal ways in which this happens.

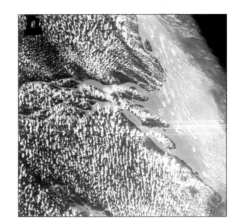

fig 11 | Besides deposited mud particles this river (photographed from space) adds a lot of dissolved substances to the sea

- When the concentration of some ions gets too high they may react. They may combine in **precipitation** reactions to form insoluble substances. These fall to the ocean floor and may, over millions of years, form sedimentary rocks. For example, calcium ions and sulphate ions forming calcium sulphate.

$$Ca^{2+}(aq) + SO_4^{2-}(aq) \rightarrow CaSO_4(s)$$

- Water may evaporate and leave behind dissolved substances. This process is taken advantage of in many countries where salt pans, small pools containing seawater, are allowed to evaporate. The sea salt is gathered up and marketed.

c Why is sea salt not pure sodium chloride?

- Marine animals, called molluscs, may use calcium ions from seawater to form shells. This involves the reaction between calcium ions and carbonate ions to form calcium carbonate.

$$Ca^{2+}(aq) + CO_3^{2-}(aq) \rightarrow CaCO_3(s)$$

fig 12 | These people have evaporated seawater to produce sea salt

The oceans and carbon dioxide

Carbon dioxide is partly soluble in water, especially under pressure.

There is a large surface area of water in contact with carbon dioxide in the air. How much carbon dioxide dissolves, and what happens to it, are not fully understood. Scientists are exploring this issue because it may have an important bearing on the 'greenhouse effect' (see 7.4 Carbon dioxide). Possibilities include: an increase in living organisms, called phytoplankton, which use carbon dioxide for photosynthesis, near the surface, an increase in shell formation or an increase in precipitation reactions. Scientists remain uncertain about the contribution of each effect and are researching the issue.

IDEAS AND EVIDENCE

d 'Scientists know the answer to every problem.' Give an example to show that this statement is not true.

Thinking further

■ **1** It is estimated that there are 9 million tonnes of gold in the oceans. What would be the main problem in extracting this gold?

◆ **2** Balance the equation below which shows a precipitation reaction that happens in the sea.

$$Fe^{3+} + OH^- \rightarrow Fe(OH)_3$$

KEY WORDS
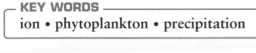
ion • phytoplankton • precipitation

7.4 Carbon dioxide

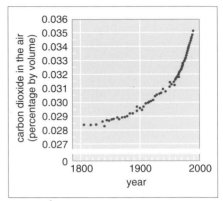

fig 13 | Changes in the percentage of carbon dioxide in the air

The issue

In 1997 there was a meeting in Rio de Janeiro of leaders of countries from all over the world. At this meeting they decided that the continuing rise in the levels of carbon dioxide in the atmosphere had to be reduced. There was increasing concern that carbon dioxide and other **greenhouse gases** are responsible for the rise in the temperature of the Earth's atmosphere, called **global warming**.

The evidence

Scientists have accurately recorded the percentage of carbon dioxide in the atmosphere for many years. They have also used bubbles trapped in ice cores from the Poles to measure the percentage present before systematic records began.

a What general trend does the graph in fig 13 show? Is there clear evidence that the amount of carbon dioxide is increasing?

Although a change from 0.029 to 0.036% may seem small, the actual change is a percentage increase of over 24%, which is huge. Similarly there is no disputing that the Earth's average temperature is increasing; this is called global warming.

The question that scientists are discussing is whether these two changes are linked.

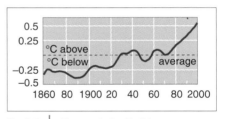

fig 14 | Changes in the Earth's average temperature since 1860

The mechanism

The Sun gives out energy in the visible and ultraviolet parts of the electromagnetic spectrum (see fig 15). Some of these rays are reflected off the atmosphere (A) while some penetrate the atmosphere (B). When these rays strike the Earth's surface they are absorbed and are changed into infra-red rays. Some of these are reflected back (C). However, infra-red rays are not able to pass back into space through the atmosphere. This is because gases such as carbon dioxide, methane and water

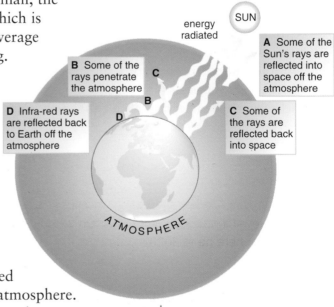

fig 15 | The greenhouse effect

vapour reflect the infra-red rays back to the Earth's surface (D). This process is called the **greenhouse effect** because it is similar to the process that takes place inside a greenhouse.

Without any greenhouse effect the Earth's surface would be about 30 °C cooler than it is today.

b What would the average UK summer temperature be without any greenhouse effect?

However, if there is too much carbon dioxide in the atmosphere then the Earth will warm up too much. There is a fine balance.

Possible consequences

There is mounting evidence that global warming is taking place. In August 2000, liquid water was seen at the North Pole, probably for the first time in millions of years.

Although a rising temperature may bring increased rainfall and crop yields to some areas, other areas that currently produce a lot of food will suffer from droughts. Scientists cannot be sure that the well-reported unusual weather patterns of recent years can be blamed on the greenhouse effect.

The balance

Carbon dioxide is removed from the atmosphere by photosynthesis and by solution in water. It is added by respiration, combustion and volcanic activity. In the last 100 years this balance has been upset by the burning of fossil fuels on an ever-increasing scale.

The future

World leaders are currently deciding whether to sign a declaration called the 'Kyoto protocol'. This would govern how much carbon dioxide particular countries are allowed to produce. Part of this agreement is that countries can produce more carbon dioxide than their allowance as long as they build forests to act as 'carbon sinks'. Scientists are unsure if this is a long-term answer.

c Suggest how forests act as 'carbon sinks'.

fig 16 | Liquid water was found at the North Pole in August 2000

IDEAS AND EVIDENCE

It has been suggested that burning grass as a fuel should be explored. Although it produces carbon dioxide, this carbon dioxide is used up as more grass grows. A new straw-burning power station in Cambridgeshire has recently started generating electricity.

IDEAS AND EVIDENCE

d Suggest why large forest fires would upset a country's calculations of its carbon dioxide 'quota'.

e Developing countries have a problem. If they are to develop they need energy. The easiest way to get this is from the burning of fossil fuels. Why is this a dilemma for the delegate from such a country at the meeting in Rio de Janeiro?

Thinking further

■ **1** It has been suggested that, at current rate of increase, the amount of CO_2 in the atmosphere will have doubled by 2020 compared to 1990. What will the percentage of carbon dioxide in the atmosphere be in 2020?

◆ **2** Carbon-containing compounds can decay in the absence of air to produce fossil fuels. Suggest how they decay in the presence of air. What contribution does this make to the carbon cycle?

KEY WORDS

greenhouse effect • greenhouse gases • global warming

7.5 Rock formation

Evidence from sedimentary rocks

Sedimentary rocks are made up from fragments of older rocks that have been **weathered**. They may also have formed from the remains of living organisms.

a Name a sedimentary rock formed from the remains of living organisms.

Fragments of **eroded** rocks are deposited in seas or lakes where, given sufficient time and the correct conditions, they turn into a sedimentary rock. Such rocks may form by:

- the action of pressure alone on the particles (e.g. mudstone)
- cementing of the particles together (e.g. sandstone).

Sedimentary rocks are often found in layers and these may give additional evidence about the conditions under which they formed.

- If the particles are large and coarse-grained they were probably deposited under active conditions, such as on a stormy beach.
- If the particles are smaller and fine-grained they were probably deposited under quiet conditions, such as in a lake or deep sea.
- Rocks may show evidence of wave ripples or current ripples on their surface.

b Under what different conditions would particles in rocks showing wave ripples or current ripples have been formed?

Evidence from igneous rocks

Igneous rocks form when molten rock cools. This cooling produces rocks that always contain crystals. The crystals interlock and are randomly arranged.

c Which part of the Earth does the molten rock come from?

The molten rock may break through the Earth's surface and form volcanoes. The **lava** that is produced cools quickly. This fast

fig 17 | Sandstone (top) and mudstone are both sedimentary rocks

fig 18 | Basalt (top) is an igneous rock containing very small crystals. These crystals can be seen in this photomicrograph

cooling produces fine-grained rocks with very small crystals, usually dark in colour. **They are called extrusive igneous rocks.** Basalt is an example.

Fine-grained extrusive igneous rocks also form from the ash that accompanies explosive volcanoes.

Sometimes molten rock from the mantle rises towards the surface but never breaks through the crust. This **magma** cools much more slowly underground. The rock that forms contains larger crystals that are visible without the aid of a lens.

They are called intrusive igneous rocks. Granite is an example.

d Granite 'tors' are found in Devon. Suggest why they are now on the surface of the Earth.

e Suggest why fossils are not found in igneous rocks.

Evidence from metamorphic rocks

Metamorphic rocks form when the material in pre-existing rocks recrystallizes. This recrystallization can be caused by high temperature alone. This can happen when an igneous intrusion bakes surrounding rocks and may cause them to recrystallize. This is called **contact metamorphism**. When the sedimentary rock mudstone is changed by contact metamorphism, the metamorphic rock formed still has randomly orientated crystals.

Most metamorphic rocks, however, are formed by the action of both high temperatures and high pressures. This occurs deep in the crust, often near plate boundaries. Rocks that recrystallize in this way have interlocking crystals that are aligned. The alignment gives evidence of the direction of pressure on the rock. When mudstone is metamorphosed in this way it first produces slate (low grade metamorphism), schist, and then gneiss (high grade metamorphism).

f Slate is used for roofing. Why?

Limestone metamorphoses to give a rock called marble.

fig 19 | Some volcanoes produce lots of ash and dust

fig 20 | The rock making up these granite tors in Devon was formed millions of years ago below the surface of the Earth

fig 21 | Slate is a metamorphic rock which cleaves easily

Thinking further

■ **1** Read the following descriptions and name each rock type.

a Large interlocking crystals, which are mainly light coloured, no fossils.

b Fine-grained particles, not interlocking, some graptolite fossils.

c Coloured crystals in layers, no fossils.

◆ **2** Slate, schist and gneiss are all metamorphic forms of mudstone. Suggest why fossils are only found in mudstone and slate, but not in schist and gneiss.

KEY WORDS
contact metamorphism • eroded • extrusive • igneous • intrusive • lava • magma • metamorphic • sedimentary • weathered

7.6 The rock record

fig 22 | This rock face contains layers of sedimentary rocks

Simple successions

Most of the time we are only aware of the surface of the Earth; we have little idea about the layers of rocks that lie beneath us. We may know that these layers must be solid 'rock' and that this solid crust is between 15 and 50 km thick.

a What name do we give to the rock that lies between the crust and the core?

If we drilled down we would pass through layer upon layer of rock and as we go deeper the rocks will become progressively older. We sometimes have a chance to look at some of these rocks in cliff faces.

b Geologists often visit quarries. Suggest why.

Interpreting sequences of rocks is not always easy. However, some are straightforward because the rocks lie in layers that are not broken or distorted in any way. Geologists call the order in which the rocks were deposited a succession. Fig 23 shows a sketch of a succession of three rock types.

c Which is the oldest rock type in this succession?

d Which is the youngest?

It is unlikely that an entire succession such as this will be visible, even on a cliff face. Geologists use evidence from other features to work out the order of succession for rocks that may be deep in the crust.

e Which industry would need to know the thickness of the sandstone layer in fig 23?

Sometimes a succession may be cut across by another rock, usually an igneous one. The rock that cuts across is always younger than the one it is cutting through.

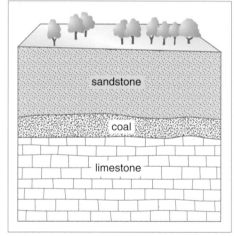

fig 23

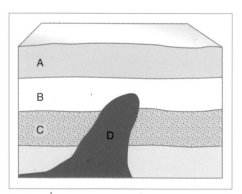

fig 24 | Igneous rock D is cutting through layers B and C. D is younger than C and B

Fossil evidence is very useful in helping to date rocks.

f Explain what a fossil is.

This can be especially useful when rocks are compared from two completely different locations, even from present-day different continents. Fossils that are used to help date rocks are called zone-fossils.

Faults and folds

The surface of the Earth is placed under stress by the movement of large pieces of crust. This movement can cause rocks to be pushed together causing layers to be buried deeper. The study of this movement is called **plate tectonics**.

Layers of rock may also be pushed together so that they **fold**. The layers may even crack so that they are broken and no longer in alignment. This is called a **fault**. Rock successions may show evidence of faulting and folding.

Folds and faults can help geologists to work out the order in which events occurred. Fig 25 shows a rock succession with a fault and a fold.

The fault must have occurred after the fold because the sandstone layer has been affected by the fault but not by the fold. Faults such as the one in fig 25 are called compression faults and are caused when plates are being pushed together. If the opposite occurs and plates are moving apart a different sort of fault, called a tension fault, is formed. This causes the formation of a rift valley, such as the Great Rift Valley in Africa.

g Suggest what might form in the Great Rift Valley in millions of years time.

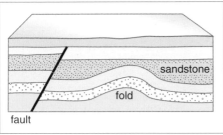
fig 25

Thinking further

■ **1** A fossil called didymograptus is found in shale rocks in North Wales. These rocks are 500 million years old. You find didymograptus fossils in some rock in Central Wales. What can you say about the rock you have found in Central Wales?

◆ **2** You are an adviser to a firm about to sink a coal mine. You have a geological map that shows the succession in fig 26.

Decide whether the mineshaft should be put at A, B or C. Explain your answer.

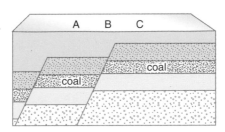
fig 26

KEY WORDS
fault • fold • fossil • plate tectonics • succession

IDEAS AND EVIDENCE

h William Smith's First Law states that a rock lower in a succession is older than one above it. What is the problem with this law in the highly distorted succession shown in fig 27?

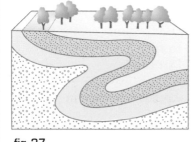
fig 27

Questions on earth cycles

● **1** The table in fig 28 shows the percentage of some ions present in seawater. Use the table to help you answers the questions that follow.

ion	symbol	%
calcium	Ca^{2+}	1
carbonate	CO_3^{2-}	1
chloride	Cl^-	54
magnesium	Mg^{2+}	4
sodium	Na^+	31
potassium	K^+	1
sulphate	SO_4^{2-}	8

fig 28

a Write down the symbols of the two most common ions in seawater. *(2)*

b Write down the formula of the main product when 1000 g of seawater is evaporated to dryness. *(1)*

c Which of the following best describes what remains when 1000 g of seawater is evaporated?
 • 540 g of a white solid
 • 35 g of a white solid
 • nothing remains *(1)*

● **2** The table in fig 29 shows the percentage of some gases in the air. Copy and complete the table by putting in the name of each gas. *(2)*

name of gas	approximate percentage in pure dry air
	78
	21
	1
	0.04

fig 29

■ **3** Mr Smith uses the apparatus shown in fig 30 to find the percentage of oxygen in some air from the bottom of a deep mine.

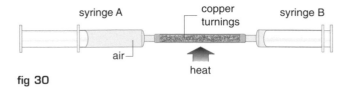

fig 30

a Before heating, he pushes all 200 cm³ of the air from syringe A into syringe B. The reading on syringe B now shows 200 cm³. What does this tell Mr Smith about the apparatus? *(1)*

b Mr Smith heats the copper bits and pushes air from syringe B back to syringe A. The copper bits turn black. Write an equation for the reaction that takes place. *(2)*

c Suggest why Mr Smith uses small bits of copper rather than one large piece. *(2)*

d The air is pushed repeatedly over the copper bits until the volume remaining stays constant. The final volume is 180 cm³. Copy and complete the table of results shown in fig 31. *(1)*

volume of air at start	200 cm³
volume of gas left at end	
volume of oxygen removed	

fig 31

e Calculate the percentage of oxygen in the sample of air. Show your working. *(2)*

f Suggest what this result tells you about this sample of air. *(1)*

■ **4** Choose labels from fig 32 to answer the questions that follow.

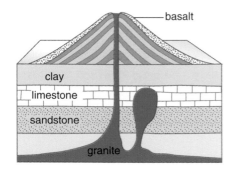

fig 32

Choose:

a the oldest sedimentary rock *(1)*

b an extrusive igneous rock *(1)*

c the layer in which marble may form *(1)*

d an intrusive igneous rock *(1)*

e a layer containing many shells of marine organisms *(1)*

5 Chalk is about 150 million years old. It was formed from the shelly remains of very small sea creatures that settled to the bottom of the sea.

a Suggest two conditions necessary for the formation of chalk from the shells. *(2)*

b What sort of rock is chalk: igneous, metamorphic or sedimentary? *(1)*

c What sort of rock would form after the action of high pressures and high temperatures on chalk? *(1)*

d Describe what you would see when dilute hydrochloric acid is added to chalk. Explain the observation *(3)*

6 The oldest rock so far discovered is 3 960 000 000 years old. It is a sedimentary rock.

a Explain why this rock would not have been the first rock on the Earth's surface. *(2)*

b Sedimentary rocks can contain fossils. Suggest, with a reason, whether this rock would contain fossils. *(2)*

7 Seawater contains dissolved solids. These are present in the form of ions. There is a balance between ions added to seawater and ions removed.

a Suggest one way that ions are added to seawater. *(2)*

b One way that ions are removed is by shell formation by some organisms. Write an ionic equation to show how these organisms use calcium ions and carbonate ions to make shells. You may use the table in fig 28 to help you. *(2)*

c Name two other processes that remove ions from seawater. *(2)*

8 Fig 33 shows a rock succession.

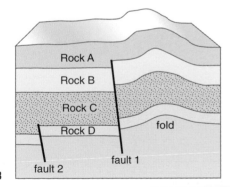

fig 33

Write down the order in which the folding and faulting occurred. Explain your answer *(6)*

IDEAS AND EVIDENCE

9 Read this passage from a geology textbook about how some ions are removed from seawater.

Precipitation reactions occur between ions in seawater. This occurs only when the concentration of an ion becomes greater than its solubility in water. Typically iron(III) ions precipitate out as iron(III) hydroxide. This process is also thought to remove traces of more soluble and toxic ions such as Cu^{2+} and Se^{2+}. These are thought to associate with the precipitate of iron(III) hydroxide as it deposits. This could explain the unusually low levels of Cu^{2+} and Se^{2+} in the seas compared to what we might expect from their input and solubility.

a Suggest why the removal of copper and selenium ions from the sea is important. *(2)*

b Which one of the following is least soluble? Explain your answer.

$Cu(OH)_2$ $Fe(OH)_3$ $Se(OH)_2$ *(2)*

c Suggest why geologists think it is unusual that the concentration of Cu^{2+} and Se^{2+} ions in seawater remains so low. *(2)*

d How much certainty does the passage contain about the explanation for the low level of copper and selenium ions in seawater? *(2)*

Equilibria and industrial processes

Introduction

Most of the chemical reactions that we study can only go in one direction. You can boil an egg but you cannot 'unboil' it. When a match burns you cannot turn it back into an unburned match.

Some reactions, however, are reversible. If blue crystals of copper(II) sulphate are heated they turn into a white powder. If water is added to this white powder it turns blue.

When the copper(II) sulphate crystals are heated, water contained within the crystal structure is driven off. The copper(II) sulphate becomes **anhydrous**.

$$CuSO_4.5H_2O \rightarrow CuSO_4 + 5H_2O$$
$$\text{blue} \qquad\qquad \text{white}$$

When water is added the anhydrous copper(II) sulphate becomes **hydrated**, and the blue colour returns.

$$CuSO_4 + 5H_2O \rightarrow CuSO_4.5H_2O$$
$$\text{white} \qquad\qquad \text{blue}$$

A reaction which can go in either direction is called a **reversible reaction.**

If hydrogen and iodine gases are mixed at 400 °C they slowly react to form hydrogen iodide. After about 80% of the two gases have reacted the reaction seems to stop. No more hydrogen iodide is formed. The hydrogen, iodine and hydrogen iodide have reached equilibrium.

$$\underset{\text{hydrogen}}{H_2} + \underset{\text{iodine}}{I_2} \rightleftharpoons \underset{\text{hydrogen iodide}}{2HI}$$

The double-headed arrow indicates a reversible reaction. As more hydrogen iodide is formed, more breaks up into hydrogen and iodine.

Eventually the rates of the forward and backward reactions become equal. This is **equilibrium**.

fig 1 | Once a match has burnt this change cannot be reversed

fig 2 | Water added to anhydrous copper(II) sulphate

Check-up

a Which of the following processes are reversible?

baking a cake · boiling liquid water into water vapour · dissolving sugar in water · melting ice · neutralization of an acid with an alkali · rusting iron

▶ Check-up (continued)

b Hydrated cobalt(II) chloride, $CoCl_2.6H_2O$, is purple. When heated it changes to blue anhydrous cobalt(II) chloride.

  i Write an equation for this reversible reaction.

  ii How can the reaction be reversed?

c Anhydrous copper(II) sulphate is used to test for water.

  i What do you see when anhydrous copper(II) sulphate is added to water?

  ii Explain how this test works.

d The photograph in fig 3 shows ammonium chloride being heated in a test-tube.

The white solid disappears near the bottom of the tube where it is hot and reappears further up the tube where it is cold. Explain these observations.

If you have difficulty, ask your teacher for a Summary sheet.

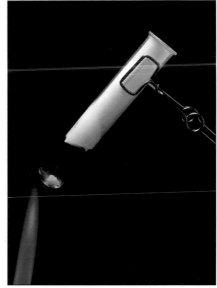

fig 3 | Ammonium chloride being heated

Contents of the Teaching block

8.1 The Haber process

Ammonia is made by the Haber process. This process involves an equilibrium reaction. Using the right conditions for the process improves the yield of ammonia.

fig 4 | Fritz Haber

8.2 Nitric acid

In industry nitric acid is made from ammonia. The ammonia is oxidised to form nitric acid. Nitric acid is used to make fertilisers and explosives.

8.3 Fertilisers

During the last century the need for nitrogen-containing fertilisers has risen. Fertilisers can be made by neutralising ammonia with nitric acid.

8.4 Fertiliser problems

Using too much nitrogen-containing fertiliser can cause eutrophication. Nitrogenous fertilisers can also contaminate drinking water.

Links with other Teaching blocks

8.1 The Haber process

Fritz Haber

Ammonia is made by reacting nitrogen with hydrogen.

$$N_2 \quad + \quad 3H_2 \quad \rightleftharpoons \quad 2NH_3$$
$$\text{nitrogen} + \text{hydrogen} \quad \rightleftharpoons \quad \text{ammonia}$$

a What does the sign $\rightleftharpoons$ show about this reaction?

This reaction presented several problems to chemists at the beginning of the twentieth century. They could not get it to make enough ammonia.

The first chemist to solve these problems was Fritz Haber.

Reaction conditions

Fritz Haber had discovered the reaction conditions needed to make ammonia from nitrogen and hydrogen on a large scale.

- A temperature of about 450 °C.
- A pressure of about 200 **atmospheres**.
- An iron catalyst.
- **Liquefy** the ammonia as it is made, and recycle the unused nitrogen and hydrogen.

A flow chart of the Haber process is shown in fig 6.

b Explain the advantage of using a catalyst.

c Describe how hydrogen can be obtained from oil.

d Hydrogen can also be obtained from natural gas, methane. Explain how.

e Suggest why air needs to be liquefied before nitrogen can be obtained from it.

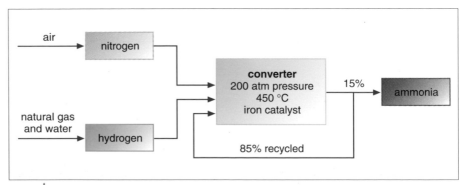

fig 5 | Flow chart of Haber process

Look carefully at the number of molecules on each side of the equilibrium sign in the Haber process reaction.

$$N_2 + 3H_2 \rightleftharpoons 2NH_3$$

Four molecules of gas on the left produce two molecules of gas on the right. This means that pressure will fall if the equilibrium moves to the right.

If pressure is increased this will make the equilibrium move to the right, so reducing the pressure.

A higher pressure makes more ammonia.

f Explain why fewer molecules cause a lower pressure.

As the equilibrium mixture is compressed ammonia condenses, leaving unreacted nitrogen and hydrogen to be returned to the reaction vessel.

As ammonia is removed, more nitrogen and hydrogen react to 'replace' this ammonia and so restore the equilibrium.

This increases the **yield** of ammonia.

g What advantage is gained by returning unreacted nitrogen and hydrogen to the reaction vessel?

The iron catalyst speeds up both directions of the equilibrium reaction. The mixture reaches equilibrium more quickly, but the percentage of ammonia produced remains the same.

The catalyst makes ammonia more quickly but does not give more ammonia.

h Small pieces of iron are used for the catalyst. What advantage is there in using small pieces of iron rather than large ones?

The equilibrium reaction used in the Haber process is exothermic from left to right. As the temperature is reduced the equilibrium position will move to the right.

At a low temperature more ammonia is made but the equilibrium is reached very slowly, even using a catalyst.

A compromise temperature of about 450 °C is used. This is hot enough to form the ammonia quickly, yet cool enough to give a reasonable yield of ammonia.

i Explain what is meant by the term exothermic.

j Why is the equilibrium reached slowly at low temperature?

Thinking further

1 In his laboratory apparatus Fritz Haber used a platinum catalyst. Suggest two reasons for the use of iron rather than platinum in the industrial process.

2 The Haber process is now carried out at about 200 atmospheres pressure.

 a What problems are likely at this pressure?

 b Suggest how these problems may be overcome.

◆ **3** Look at the equation shown above for the Haber process.

 a In what proportions, by volume, should nitrogen and hydrogen be mixed.

 b What would be the result of mixing the gases in different proportions?

┌─ **KEY WORDS** ─────────
atmospheres • liquefy • yield
└──────────────────────

 Ammonia production.   *Catalytic oxidation of ammonia.*

8.2 Nitric acid

Making nitric acid

Ammonia can be oxidised by oxygen in the air to produce nitrogen(II) oxide (nitrogen monoxide).

$$4NH_3 + 5O_2 \rightarrow 4NO + 6H_2O$$
ammonia + oxygen → nitrogen(II) + water
oxide

Nitrogen can form several oxides.

Nitrogen(II) oxide is very reactive, and quickly combines with more oxygen. This makes nitrogen(IV) oxide (nitrogen dioxide).

$$2NO + O_2 \rightleftharpoons 2NO_2$$
nitrogen(II)   oxygen   nitrogen(IV) oxide
oxide

This reaction can be carried out in the laboratory using the apparatus shown in fig 7.

The conical flask contains a concentrated solution of ammonia in water. A piece of platinum wire is heated until red hot in a Bunsen burner flame, and then lowered into the mixture of air and ammonia gas.

Ammonia gas is poisonous, so this reaction is usually carried out in a fume cupboard.

a What is the purpose of the platinum wire?

b Where does the ammonia gas come from?

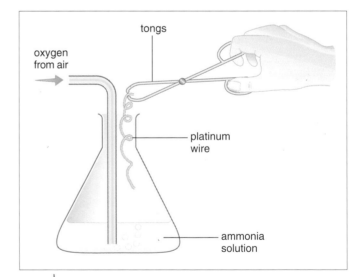

fig 6 | Apparatus for oxidation of ammonia

As the reaction takes place the platinum wire glows more strongly and brown fumes of nitrogen(IV) oxide can be seen, forming around the hot platinum wire.

c The oxidation of ammonia is an exothermic reaction. What observation suggests this?

In industry the nitrogen(IV) oxide produced by the oxidation of ammonia is dissolved in water to make nitric acid.

$$4NO_2 + 2H_2O + O_2 \rightarrow 4HNO_3$$
nitrogen(IV) + water + oxygen → nitric acid
oxide

The process is carried out on a large scale. A flow diagram of the industrial process is shown in fig 8.

d Care is taken that all impurities are removed from the air before it passes over the catalyst. Suggest a reason for this.

e The catalyst is at a temperature of about 900 °C. Why is the reaction carried out at such a high temperature?

f The mixture passing over the catalyst is about 90% air and 10% ammonia. Why are these proportions used?

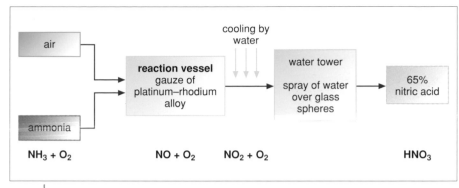

fig 7 | Flow diagram for nitric acid manufacture

Most of the nitric acid produced in industry is reacted with more ammonia from the Haber process to make ammonium nitrate fertiliser.

Another major use of nitric acid is in the manufacture of explosives such as dynamite and TNT.

Smaller quantities are used to make products such as nylon and dyes.

Thinking further

■ **1** A test-tube full of ammonia gas is turned upside down and lowered into a beaker of distilled water. The water quickly rises almost to the top of the test-tube. A piece of Universal Indicator paper dipped into the water turns blue. What do these observations tell you about ammonia?

■ **2** The catalyst used in the industrial oxidation of ammonia is a fine **gauze** of platinum and rhodium. Explain why the catalyst is used as a gauze.

◆ **3** Once the oxidation of ammonia has begun, the reaction vessel containing the catalyst stays at 900 °C with no further heating. Explain why no further heating is needed.

┌─ **KEY WORD** ─┐
gauze
└──────────────┘

8.3 Fertilisers

The need for fertilisers

Plants need nitrogen to grow. They use nitrogen to produce **proteins**. Nearly eighty per cent of the air is nitrogen, but plants are unable to use this.

a Fertilisers often have NPK values showing the proportions of the three important elements. Name these three elements.

Two hundred years ago the population of Europe was much smaller than it is today. Far less food needed to be produced by farmers. Less **intensive farming** methods could be used.

fig 8 | A horse-drawn plough

Farmers used animal **manure** as fertiliser, then sodium nitrate imported from Chile. As the population of Europe grew farmers had to use more fertilisers to increase the yield of their crops. By the start of the twentieth century a new source of nitrogen-containing fertiliser was needed.

The discoveries made by Fritz Haber made it possible to manufacture fertilisers.

Modern farmers use fertilisers such as ammonium nitrate, made by **neutralising** nitric acid with ammonia.

b Suggest why there is not enough animal manure to provide fertiliser for farming today.

c Why is so much nitrogen-containing fertiliser needed for modern farming?

fig 9 | Artificial fertilisers are used on modern farms

Neutralisation

Ammonia dissolves in water to form ammonium hydroxide.

$$NH_3 \quad + \quad H_2O \quad \rightarrow \quad NH_4OH$$
ammonia + water → ammonium hydroxide

Ammonium hydroxide is an alkali.

When an acid and an alkali are mixed they react.

acid + alkali → salt + water

This is called neutralisation.

d Suggest why this reaction is called neutralisation.

Ammonium hydroxide will neutralise nitric acid.

$$HNO_3 + NH_4OH \rightarrow NH_4NO_3 + H_2O$$
nitric + ammonium → ammonium + water
acid   hydroxide   nitrate

The salt formed is ammonium nitrate.

e Salts are ionic compounds. They contain positive and negative ions. The ammonium ion is NH_4^+. What is the charge on the nitrate ion?

Ammonium hydroxide will also neutralise sulphuric acid.

$$H_2SO_4 + 2NH_4OH \rightarrow (NH_4)_2SO_4 + 2H_2O$$
sulphuric + ammonium → ammonium + water
acid   hydroxide   sulphate

This time the salt formed is ammonium sulphate.

f Why are there two ammonium ions in the formula for ammonium sulphate, but only one ammonium ion in the formula for ammonium nitrate?

Fertilisers

A good nitrogen-containing fertiliser must contain a lot of nitrogen and must be soluble in water. Both ammonium nitrate and ammonium sulphate are used as fertilisers.

Many commercial fertilisers also contain phosphate and potassium compounds.

g Explain why a good nitrogen-containing fertiliser must be soluble in water.

Thinking further

■ **1** Two hundred years ago farmers often left fields unused for one year in three to allow nitrogen compounds to build up in the soil. Where did these nitrogen compounds come from?

■ **2** State one advantage of using manure as a fertiliser and one advantage of using ammonium nitrate.

◆ **3** For the same mass, which fertiliser provides the most nitrogen – ammonium nitrate or ammonium sulphate?

KEY WORDS

intensive farming • manure • neutralising • proteins

Making a fertilizer.

8.4 Fertiliser problems

Eutrophication

Using fertilisers containing nitrogen makes green plants grow better. Farmers use them to grow more crops, but they can cause problems.

If too much **nitrogenous** fertiliser is used serious pollution can occur. One kind of pollution is called **eutrophication**.

This happens in a number of steps. Each step follows on from the one before.

fig 10 | An algal bloom

1 Excess fertiliser dissolves in rain water. As the water drains into streams, rivers and lakes the nitrogen compounds go with it. This is called **leaching**.

2 Nitrogen compounds promote growth of plants in rivers and lakes.

3 There is a huge increase in the numbers of microscopic plants called algae. This is called an **algal bloom**.

4 Algae block sunlight from all but the top few centimetres of the water. Plants further down cannot carry out photosynthesis. These plants die.

5 Bacteria and other **decomposers** feed on the dead plants. These bacteria increase in number.

6 Decomposers use up all of the oxygen dissolved in the water.

7 Without a supply of oxygen fish and other organisms living in the water die.

a Farmers pay close attention to weather forecasts. If rain is forecast they delay using fertilisers. Suggest why they do this.

b Why do plants die if they cannot carry out photosynthesis?

Contamination of drinking water

Large quantities of water are taken from rivers, lakes and boreholes. After purification this water is supplied to houses.

Nitrates may be dissolved in this water. They are not removed by normal purification processes.

The level of nitrates in drinking water has been monitored for the past twenty years. It has increased steadily.

The World Health Organization recommends a limit of 10 mg/dm^3 of nitrates in drinking water.

In some places nitrate levels are even greater than the European Union maximum level of 50 mg/dm^3.

In the body nitrates may be converted into nitrosamines. These are **carcinogenic**.

It has also been suggested that small babies are particularly sensitive to high levels of nitrates in drinking water. The action of haemoglobin in their blood may be reduced.

Even breastfed babies can have nitrate ions passed to them in their mother's milk.

c Suggest why the level of nitrates in drinking water has increased over the past twenty years.

d How might a baby be affected by a reduction in the action of haemoglobin?

e Water supply companies can remove suspended clay from water, but not nitrate ions. Why is this?

fig 11

Thinking further

■ **1** Nitrate pollution would almost completely stop if farmers did not use nitrogen-based fertilisers. Why is this not a sensible suggestion?

■ **2** All nitrates are soluble in water, but many other nitrogen-containing compounds are far less soluble. Using these instead of nitrates would reduce pollution. Why are these compounds not used in fertilisers?

◆ **3** Many animals living in water use some of the dissolved oxygen. Under normal conditions the oxygen level of the water is kept in balance.

a Suggest two ways that oxygen may dissolve into the water.

b Mountain streams usually contain more dissolved oxygen than slower moving rivers. Suggest why.

┌─ **KEY WORDS** ─────────────────────────────────
algal bloom • carcinogenic • decomposers • eutrophication • leaching • nitrogenous
└───

Questions on equilibria and industrial processes

● **1** A reaction takes place when water is added to sodium metal. A reaction also takes place when water is added to anhydrous copper(II) sulphate.

Use these examples to explain the difference between reversible and non-reversible reactions. *(4)*

● **2** Copy and complete these sentences.

Ammonia is made by the _____ process. Nitrogen from the _____ and _____ made from oil or natural gas are reacted together. The process uses an _____ catalyst. A temperature of _____ and a pressure of _____ are used.
Most of the ammonia is used to make _____. Some of the ammonia is made into _____ acid. This is then reacted with more ammonia to make _____ _____ which is used as a _____ containing fertiliser. Ammonia is also used to make _____. *(12)*

■ **3** 1 dm³ each of hydrogen and iodine gases are sealed in a container. 2 dm³ of hydrogen iodide is sealed in a second container. Both containers are kept at 400 °C for several hours.

a Write an equation for the equilibrium formed in each of the containers. *(2)*

b What difference, if any, is there in the amounts of each gas in each container at equilibrium? *(1)*

c Explain your answer to **b**. *(2)*

■ **4** The graph in fig 13 shows the yield of ammonia in the Haber process under different conditions.

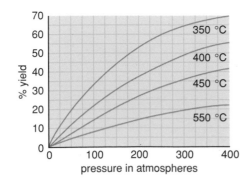

fig 12

a From the graph find the yield of ammonia at 200 atmospheres pressure at 350 °C and at 450 °C. *(1)*

b What effect does temperature have on the yield of ammonia? *(1)*

c Why is a temperature of 450 °C used in the Haber process? *(2)*

d How is the yield of ammonia affected by pressure? *(1)*

e The pressure used is about 200 atmospheres. Why is a higher pressure not used? *(2)*

f What yield would you expect under the conditions normally used for the Haber process? *(1)*

■ **5** The apparatus used to demonstrate the Haber process in a school laboratory is shown in fig 14.

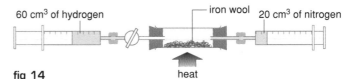

fig 14

The gas syringes are used to pass nitrogen and hydrogen backwards and forwards over heated iron wool.

a What is the job of the iron wool? *(1)*

b Why is iron wool used rather than pieces of iron? *(1)*

c This demonstration gives a very low yield of ammonia. Explain why. *(1)*

d Why are 60 cm³ of hydrogen and 20 cm³ of nitrogen used? *(1)*

e How could you show that ammonia is produced? *(2)*

■ **6** Manure is often spread on fields as a slurry. This is a thick liquid mixture of manure and water. If too much of this slurry is used, water containing soluble nitrogen compounds can run off the fields into surrounding ditches. Eventually this will be washed into rivers.

What effect might this have on wildlife in the area? *(6)*

■ **7** The following paragraph is an extract from a newspaper article.

LAST WEDNESDAY a malfunction in the local sewage works caused untreated sewage to be pumped into the river. On Friday several people walking along the path beside the river reported that the water had turned green. Alarmed residents living in Riverside Gardens telephoned this newspaper on Friday, saying that they had seen many dead fish floating in the river.'

a What type of compound in the sewage could have caused this disaster? *(1)*

b Suggest why the river turned green. *(2)*

c Explain how the leak of untreated sewage into the river caused the fish to die. *(3)*

◆ **8** Ammonium sulphate for use in fertilisers can be made by reacting ammonia gas with sulphuric acid.

$$2NH_3 + H_2SO_4 \rightarrow (NH_4)_2SO_4$$

a What mass of ammonium sulphate can be made from each tonne of ammonia gas? *(3)*

b What is the percentage by mass of nitrogen in ammonium sulphate? *(3)*

◆ **9** Sulphuric acid is manufactured by the Contact process. Sulphur dioxide is oxidised to sulphur trioxide.

$$2SO_2(g) + O_2(g) \rightleftharpoons 2SO_3(g)$$

The sulphur trioxide is combined with water to make sulphuric acid.

The oxidation of sulphur dioxide is an exothermic process.

Sulphur dioxide and oxygen are passed over granules of vanadium(V) oxide.

a Suggest, with reasons, what temperature should be used for this process. *(3)*

b Suggest, with reasons, what pressure should be used for this process. *(3)*

c Suggest why vanadium(V) oxide is used in the process. *(2)*

◆ **10** In some parts of Africa and South America farmers cannot afford to buy fertilisers. They often use a form of agriculture called 'slash and burn'. A farmer clears an area of forest and grows crops on this ground for a few years. When the supply of nitrogen compounds in the ground has been exhausted the farmer leaves this ground and clears another area of forest.

a What problems are caused by 'slash and burn' agriculture? *(2)*

b What action could be taken to prevent these problems? *(2)*

┌─ **IDEAS AND EVIDENCE** ─────────

11 Fritz Haber is regarded by most scientists as a hero. In 1918 he was awarded a Nobel prize for his work.

As a result of his discoveries farmers are able to produce enough food for the very large populations of Europe and North America.

Ammonia made by the Haber process is also used to make explosives. Some explosives have peaceful uses, such as quarrying. However, most of the munitions used in the First and Second World Wars were manufactured using explosives made from ammonia.

During the First World War Fritz Haber also devised and manufactured poison gases, which he described as 'a higher form of killing'.

a Write an account giving your opinion of how 21st century students should regard the work of Fritz Haber. *(6)*

b What controls do you think there should be on how the work of scientists is used for good or bad purposes? *(2)*

A1 Water

Links to Double Award

3 Atomic structure and the Periodic Table

5 Bonding, structure and reacting quantities

7 Earth cycles

8 Equilibria and industrial processes

Introduction

Water covers over 71% of the Earth's surface. The human body contains about 60% water by mass. Most of the reactions in animals and plants take place in solution in water. Water is obviously a very important compound.

Each molecule of water contains one oxygen atom and two hydrogen atoms, joined by covalent bonds. The oxygen 'end' of the molecule is slightly positive and the hydrogen 'end' is slightly negative.

These positive and negative charges on the water molecule attract the positive and negative charges on the ions of ionic compounds. Most ionic compounds dissolve in water.

The sea is a complex mixture of dissolved salts. It is an important source of many compounds and a reserve of carbon dioxide, present as dissolved molecules and ions.

Crystals contain water as part of their structure. The formula for crystals of copper(II) sulphate is $CuSO_4.5H_2O$.

If this water is taken away, the blue crystals turn into white powder. If water is added to this white powder it turns blue again.

In living organisms water is the environment in which most reactions take place. A person can go without food for many weeks, but will die in a few days without water.

Water is sometimes described as 'the universal solvent'. It does not dissolve every solute, but will dissolve a very large number. Plants absorb minerals from the soil in solution in water.

Water can become contaminated with dissolved materials. In the 1950s in the sea near Minamata, Japan, dissolved mercury salts polluted the water, making the fish poisonous to eat.

fig 1 | Water covers 71% of the Earth's surface

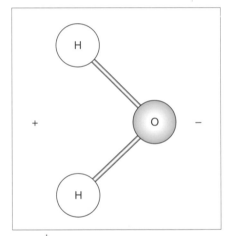

fig 2 | A water molecule

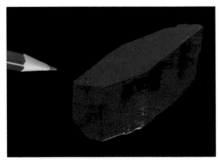

fig 3 | A large crystal of copper(II) sulphate

Check-up

1 Which of the following compounds are very soluble in water?

calcium carbonate • candle wax • carbon • copper(II) sulphate • sodium chloride

2 Describe how you could prove that a sample of colourless liquid contains water.

3 Name two solvents other than water.

4 Carbon disulphide, CS_2, does not dissolve in water. Explain why.

5 Why does water dissolve most ionic compounds?

6 Water has been described as the 'universal solvent'. How far do you think this description is true? Explain your answer.

7 You are given three solutions:
   silver nitrate
   sodium hydroxide
   hydrochloric acid

Briefly describe how you could make a solid sample of each of the following salts by using any two of these solutions:

a sodium chloride

b silver chloride.

Contents of the Teaching block

A1.1 Water as a solvent

Sea water contains dissolved sodium chloride and other salts. Different salts dissolve in different quantities in the same volume of water. This solubility of salts in water can be measured. For most substances solubility increases with increase in temperature.

A1.2 Water hardness

Hardness in water is caused by dissolved calcium and magnesium salts. Different salts cause temporary or permanent hardness. Hardness can be removed from water in several ways.

A1.3 Water hardness problems

Soap solution can be used to measure the amount of hardness in water. Using a supply of water with a high level of hardness can have both disadvantages and advantages.

IDEAS AND EVIDENCE

Nitrogen-containing fertilisers are essential to enable farmers to grow enough food for the large population in this country.

Too much nitrate, washed into rivers from fertilisers applied to fields, causes eutrophication, killing fish and aquatic animals.

Imagine that a local newspaper is printing a series of articles about water pollution.

a Write an article from the chairperson of the local environmental protest group.

b Write a second article from a local farmer who uses fertiliser on his fields.

You will find more information to help you on pages 136–7.

A1.1 Water as a solvent

> ### Key points
>
> - Sea water contains dissolved sodium chloride and other salts.
> - The solubility of salts in water can be measured.
> - For most substances solubility increases with increase in temperature.

Salty water

Water is a very good **solvent** for many ionic substances. Tap water contains a number of dissolved salts. Pure water is often called distilled water because it is made by distillation.

Sea water, or brine, contains 2.8% dissolved sodium chloride. This is about 30 g in each kilogram of brine.

Sea water also contains about 1% of other dissolved salts. These include salts of magnesium, calcium and potassium, and bromide, iodide and hydrogencarbonate.

Sodium chloride can be obtained directly from sea water. In many hot countries sea water is trapped in shallow 'pans'.

The sun evaporates the water, leaving impure sodium chloride. This can be purchased in supermarkets as 'sea salt'.

fig 4 | Evaporating sea water

a Sea salt is described as 'impure' sodium chloride. Explain this statement.

b A packet purchased in a supermarket contains 500 g of sea salt. How much sea water was evaporated to get this?

Solubility

When salt is added to water and the mixture stirred, the salt dissolves. We can continue to add salt and stir, until no more salt will dissolve.

The water has dissolved the maximum amount of salt possible at this temperature.

The **solution** made is called a **saturated solution**. The amount

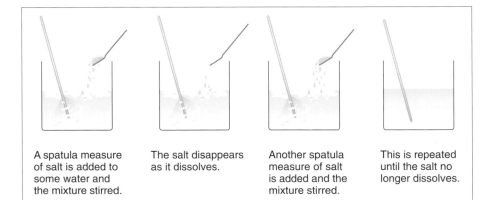

A spatula measure of salt is added to some water and the mixture stirred.	The salt disappears as it dissolves.	Another spatula measure of salt is added and the mixture stirred.	This is repeated until the salt no longer dissolves.

fig 5 | Salt added to water

of the salt that has dissolved is called the solubility of the salt in water. The **solubility** of substances is usually written as the mass of the substance that dissolved in 100 g of water.

c The solubility of sugar (sucrose) at 20 °C is 204 g in 100 g of water. What is the maximum mass of sugar that will dissolve at 20 °C in a cup containing 350 g of water?

Solubility curves

For most substances, solubility in water increases with increase in temperature. Fig 6 shows the solubility of some salts in water at different temperatures.

On graph paper use the same set of axes to plot solubility (vertical axis) against temperature (horizontal axis). Draw a smooth best-fit curve for each salt. The curves you have drawn are called **solubility curves**.

d Which of the three salts is the most soluble at 15 °C?

e Which of the three salts is the most soluble at 55 °C?

f At which temperature do sodium chloride and potassium nitrate have the same solubility?

Some substances dissolve less as the temperature increases. An example is oxygen.

g Sometimes on very hot summer days fish in pools can be seen at the surface 'gasping' for air. Suggest why.

temperature in °C	solubility in g per 100 g		
	sodium chloride	copper(II) sulphate	potassium nitrate
10	38	18	20
20	38	20	30
30	38	24	44
40	38.5	28	60
50	38.5	34	80
60	39	42	104
70	39	50	152

fig 6 | The solubilities of some salts in water

Thinking further

■ **1** Solubility values always give the temperature at which they apply. Explain why.

■ **2** A saturated solution of copper(II) sulphate at 70 °C is cooled to 20 °C.

  a What would you see as the solution cooled?

  b What mass of copper(II) sulphate would no longer be dissolved at 20 °C?

◆ **3** Suggest why the solubility of most salts increases with increase in temperature. Use ideas about particles in your answer.

┌─ **KEY WORDS** ──────────────────
saturated • solubility • solubility curves • solution • solvent
└──────────────────────────────

Solubility of potassium chlorate.

A1.2 Water hardness

Causes of water hardness

Water hardness is caused by dissolved calcium and magnesium salts.

Many rocks contain calcium and magnesium salts. Although most of these salts are only slightly soluble in water, as rain water soaks through the rocks small quantities of the salts dissolve. These dissolved salts include calcium sulphate and magnesium sulphate.

Carbon dioxide from the air dissolves in rain water. This makes the water slightly acidic.

$$H_2O \ + \quad CO_2 \quad \rightleftharpoons \quad H_2CO_3$$
water + carbon dioxide $\rightleftharpoons$ carbonic acid

This acid reacts with the calcium and magnesium carbonate contained in some rocks. This produces hydrogencarbonates, which are soluble in water.

$$H_2CO_3 \ + \ CaCO_3 \quad \rightleftharpoons \quad Ca(HCO_3)_2$$
carbonic + calcium $\rightleftharpoons$ calcium
acid   carbonate   hydrogencarbonate

a List the four salts that cause water hardness.

b Write an equation to show the formation of magnesium hydrogencarbonate by the action of carbonic acid on rocks.

The salts dissolved in hard water are the cause of stalactites and stalagmites in caves.

As water drops seep through the roof of the cave some of the water evaporates. The remaining water in each drop cannot hold all of the dissolved salts in solution, so some are precipitated. Though only tiny quantities of the salts are released from each drop, the solid builds up over millions of years to form fantastic shapes.

c Caves are usually found in areas of limestone rock. Suggest why.

fig 7 Stalactites and stalagmites in a cave

Removal of water hardness

Dissolved calcium and magnesium hydrogencarbonates cause **temporary hardness** in water. This can be removed by boiling the water. The hydrogencarbonates are decomposed to carbonates, which are insoluble in water.

$$Ca(HCO_3)_2 \rightleftharpoons CaCO_3 + H_2O + CO_2$$

| calcium hydrogencarbonate | calcium carbonate | water | carbon dioxide |

d Explain how the thermal decomposition of calcium hydrogencarbonate removes hardness from water.

e Write an equation for the decomposition of magnesium hydrogencarbonate by boiling water.

Permanent hardness in water is caused by calcium and magnesium sulphates. These salts are not decomposed when water is boiled.

Water softeners remove both temporary and permanent hardness in water. The cheapest of these is sodium carbonate, sometimes called washing soda. This reacts with the salts in hard water to form sodium sulphate or sodium hydrogencarbonate.

These sodium salts are soluble, but do not cause the water to be hard. The calcium and magnesium ions are precipitated as insoluble calcium and magnesium carbonates.

f Write equations for the reaction of sodium carbonate with calcium sulphate and with calcium hydrogencarbonate.

Another method that removes both temporary and permanent hardness in water is the use of an **ion exchange resin**.

This resin is made of polystyrene that has been treated so that it is negatively charged. When ready for use the resin contains positive sodium ions.

Positive calcium and magnesium ions change places with sodium ions on the resin. This removes the calcium and magnesium ions from the hard water, replacing them with sodium ions that do not cause water hardness.

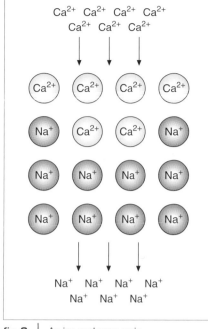

fig 8 | An ion exchange resin

Thinking further

■ 1 a How can you show that a solution of carbon dioxide in water is acidic?

  b Soft drinks contain dissolved carbon dioxide to give the 'sparkle'. Explain how it is safe to drink a solution containing acid.

■ 2 Suggest why some areas of the UK have soft water whilst others have hard water.

◆ 3 After use for a long time, an ion exchange resin has exchanged all of its sodium ions for calcium and magnesium ions. Suggest how sodium chloride can be used to recharge this resin for continued use.

--- KEY WORDS ---
ion exchange resin • permanent hardness • temporary hardness • water softeners

A1.3 Water hardness problems

Key points

- Soap can be used to measure the amount of hardness in water.
- Hard water can have both disadvantages and advantages.

Measurement of water hardness

A simple way to measure the amount of hardness in a sample of water is to use soap solution.

Soap reacts with the calcium and magnesium salts dissolved in the hard water. Only when all of these salts have reacted does the soap form **lather**.

The volume of soap solution needed to form lather in a sample of hard water gives a measure of how hard the water is.

The table in fig 10 shows the volume of soap solution needed to form lather with three samples of water.

water sample	volume of soap solution in cm^3
A	6.5
B	0.2
C	3.7

fig 10 | Volume of soap solution needed to form a lather

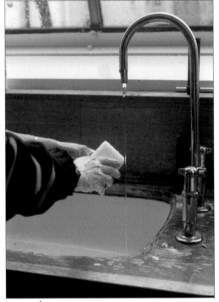

fig 9 | Soap forms a lather with water

a For the three samples to be compared everything in this test must be kept the same, except for the volume of soap solution used. Name two things that must be kept the same.

b Which of the water samples has the most water hardness?

c Which of the water samples could be distilled water?

Advantages and disadvantages of hard water

To get a lather with hard water needs more soap than it does with soft water. Hard water therefore wastes soap.

When soap reacts with the calcium and magnesium salts in hard water, it forms an insoluble precipitate called **scum**. This scum forms an unsightly deposit on clothing that has been washed, and forms a ring around the bath tub.

When water containing calcium hydrogencarbonate is boiled, solid calcium carbonate is formed.

This forms a deposit in articles such as kettles, washing machines and dishwashers. The deposit is called **lime scale**. The scale forms around the heating element. This can cause the element to overheat and fail.

In industry, deposits of scale can block the pipes in boilers. This is a safety hazard as it could cause pressure to build up until there is an explosion.

d Suggest the name of the compound that is contained in lime scale.

e Write an equation for the formation of lime scale when hard water is boiled.

Hard water does have advantages as well as disadvantages.

Calcium and magnesium salts improve the taste of water. Distilled water is tasteless and quite unpleasant to drink.

Calcium is also essential for the growth of bones and teeth.

In some places old lead pipes are used for water supply. Lead is very poisonous, and a little can dissolve into soft water. Hard water forms a coating of lead sulphate or lead carbonate that prevents the lead dissolving.

In recent years it has also been suggested that drinking hard water helps to prevent heart disease.

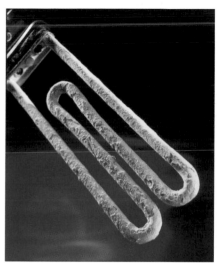

fig 11 Lime scale on the heating element of a kettle

Thinking further

■ **1** The following solutions are tested by adding a little soap solution and shaking the mixture.

sodium chloride   calcium chloride

magnesium nitrate   potassium sulphate

a Suggest which solutions do not form a lather.

b Explain your answer.

■ **2** Detergent powders often contain phosphates. These will react with calcium ions to form calcium phosphate. Suggest why phosphates are added to detergent powders.

◆ **3** A sample of the water supplied to a town was found to contain the substances shown in fig 12.

substance	Mass in each tonne of water in g
calcium sulphate	75
calcium hydrogencarbonate	3
magnesium sulphate	38

fig 12 Substances present in a water sample

a Suggest whether this water would need to be softened before it could be safely used in an industrial boiler.

b Explain your answer.

KEY WORDS

lather • lime scale • scum

 Determination of water hardness using soap solution.

Questions on water

● **1** Describe what is meant by each of the following terms. Use an example to help with each definition.
dissolve • solute • solution • solvent (4)

2 A spatula measure of common salt, sodium chloride, is added to 100 cm³ of water at room temperature in a beaker. The water is stirred with a glass rod until all of the salt disappears. This process is repeated until no more salt will dissolve.

● **a** How can you show that the salt that has disappeared is still in the water? (1)

■ **b** Explain where the salt has gone to. Use ideas about particles in your answer. (2)

■ **c** Eventually no more salt dissolves. Explain why. (1)

● **d** What term is used to describe the solution that is formed at the end of this experiment? (1)

This solution was heated up to 50 °C. Another spatula measure of salt was then added and the mixture stirred.

● **e** Describe what you would see. (1)

■ **f** Explain your answer to e. (2)

3 The table in fig 13 shows the solubility of two salts at different temperatures.

temperature in °C	solubility in g per 100 g	
	copper(II) sulphate	potassium sulphate
10	18	8
20	20	10
30	24	12
40	28	13
50	34	15
60	42	16
70	50	18

fig 13

■ **a** Use the data in fig 13 to plot solubility curves for the two salts. (3)

● **b** What is similar about the way that the solubility of the two salts changes with temperature? (1)

● **c** How does the solubility of the two salts differ? (1)

● **d** What is the solubility of each salt at 45 °C? (2)

A beaker containing 100 cm³ of water is heated to 60 °C. Copper(II) sulphate is dissolved in the water until no more will dissolve. Excess copper(II) sulphate is filtered off. The solution is then cooled to 20 °C. Crystals of copper(II) sulphate form in the beaker.

■ **e** Explain why crystals of copper(II) sulphate form in the beaker. (2)

■ **f** What mass of copper(II) sulphate is left in the solution after this cooling? (1)

■ **g** What mass of copper(II) sulphate crystals is in the beaker? (1)

4 Washing soda can be added to water to remove hardness. It contains crystals of sodium carbonate.

■ **a** Write the formula for sodium carbonate. (1)

■ **b** Describe how sodium carbonate softens water. (2)

■ **c** What is the formula mass of sodium carbonate? (1)

◆ **d** Write a symbol equation for the reaction between sodium carbonate and calcium sulphate. (2)

◆ **e** A sample of water contains 25 mg calcium sulphate per dm³. How much sodium carbonate would be needed to soften 50 dm³ of this water? (2)

5 A water softener fitted to the water supply of a house uses an ion exchange resin to remove hardness from tap water.

■ **a** Describe what the ion exchange resin is made of. (2)

■ **b** Which ions are removed from the tap water by the resin? (1)

■ **c** Which ions leave the resin and go into the water? (1)

■ **d** Explain why this exchange of ions takes place. (1)

e The tap water contains some nitrate ions, NO_3^-. Describe and explain what happens to these ions as the water passes through the resin. *(2)*

■ **6** The table in fig 14 shows results from an experiment to find the solubility of carbon dioxide in water at different temperatures.

temperature in °C	solubility in g per 100 g water
10	0.24
20	0.17
30	0.12
40	0.10
50	0.07

fig 14

a Use graph paper to plot a solubility curve for carbon dioxide. *(3)*

b Describe how the solubility of carbon dioxide changes with an increase in temperature. *(1)*

c How is this different from the way that the solubility of copper(II) sulphate (see question **3**) changes with an increase in temperature? *(1)*

Fizzy drinks are carbonated, that is they contain dissolved carbon dioxide. This comes out of solution to give bubbles – the fizz.
Use information from fig 14 to explain the following statements.

d A bottle of fizzy lemonade burst after being left for several hours on the seat of a car next to a window on a hot, sunny day. *(2)*

e The makers of a home drinks machine advise that water should be cooled in a refrigerator before being carbonated in the machine. *(2)*

■ **7** Water from an area where the rocks are made of limestone is found to be very hard. Water from an area where the rocks are made from granite is found to be very soft. Explain this difference. *(4)*

■ **8** A 1 dm³ sample of hard water is boiled. A precipitate is filtered off and is found to have a mass of 0.025 g.

■ **a** Suggest the name of the solid in the precipitate. *(1)*

◆ **b** Write an equation for the formation of this solid as the water boils. *(2)*

◆ **c** How much temporary water hardness does this water have? Give your answer in parts per million. (Hint: parts per million is grams in 1 000 000 g of water.) *(3)*

Another sample of 1 dm³ of this hard water is boiled to dryness. The mass of solid residue remaining is 0.032 g.

◆ **d** Why is this mass higher than the mass obtained when the water was boiled? *(1)*

◆ **e** Suggest two substances that form most of this extra mass. *(2)*

◆ **9** Samples of water from three different sources were analysed. The mass of each of the salts dissolved in the water samples is shown in the table in fig 15.

source of sample	mass in mg per dm³	
	calcium hydrogencarbonate	calcium sulphate
A	23	2
B	5	27
C	3	4

fig 15

a Water from which source would be least suitable for use in an industrial boiler? *(1)*

b Explain your answer to **a**. *(2)*

c Water from which source would be most suitable for this use without any softening? *(1)*

d Explain your answer to **c**. *(2)*

A sample of water from each source is boiled for three minutes.

e Water from which source would have the least hardness after boiling? *(1)*

f Explain your answer to **e**. *(2)*

A house is supplied with water from source B.

g Is the kettle in this house likely to become 'furred up'? *(1)*

h Explain your answer to **g**. *(2)*

i Suggest the best method for the owner of this house to use for softening the water supply. *(1)*

j Explain your choice in **i**. *(2)*

A2 Acids, bases and salts

Links to Double Award

1 Chemical reactions

8 Equilibria and industrial processes

Introduction

Acids have been known for thousands of years but they have not always been called 'acids'. The first property of acids that people recognised was that they had a sharp taste. This sharp taste was noticed in wine that came into contact with air as it was fermenting. We now know that this was ethanoic acid (vinegar) forming. Other substances that had a similar property were the juice from lemons and the product of sour milk.

It was the chemist Lavoisier, who lived over 200 years ago, who first put forward the idea of 'acids'. He believed that all acids contained the element oxygen.

fig 1 | Lavoisier at work

a Write down the names and formulae of two acids that would fit in with Lavoisier's theory.

b Why did the discovery of hydrochloric acid upset Lavoisier's theory of acids?

As more properties of acids became known the Swedish chemist Svante Arrhenius made the deduction that all acids seemed to contain hydrogen atoms that could be replaced. He decided that when an acid is dissolved in water it releases hydrogen ions. He could explain the reactions of acids using this model and it is still accepted today, although other models do exist.

The reaction between acids and alkalis to make a class of substances called salts has provided us with useful substances. One of the most important of these is the reaction between ammonia and acids such as nitric acid or sulphuric acid. These neutralisation reactions produce the salts ammonium nitrate and ammonium sulphate, which are important fertilisers.

As chemists gained a systematic knowledge of the properties and reactions of acids, bases and salts they were able to use this knowledge to identify the ions present in unknown substances.

Check-up

1 We can use indicators, such as litmus, to show if a compound is acidic or alkaline. What property of litmus allows us to do this?

2 Universal Indicator is used to determine the strength of an acid or alkali. What colour is Universal Indicator in each of the following:

  a a strong acid

  b a weak acid

  c a neutral solution

  d a strong alkali?

3 What is the approximate pH of the solutions in each of 2a, 2b, 2c and 2d?

4 Magnesium oxide is a base but sodium hydroxide is an alkali. What property of sodium hydroxide allows us to call it an alkali?

5 Slaked lime is often added to acidic lakes. What sort of reaction happens between the slaked lime and the acidity in the lake?

6 Name the products formed when each of the following pairs of substances reacts:

  a magnesium and hydrochloric acid

  b sodium hydroxide and sulphuric acid

  c calcium oxide and nitric acid

  d magnesium carbonate and hydrochloric acid.

7 Write balanced symbol equations for the reactions in question 6.

Contents of the Teaching block

A2.1 Acids and alkalis

There is an important difference between a strong acid and a concentrated acid. The strength of an acid depends on how many of the acid molecules split up into ions. There are various ways of following the progress of neutralisation reactions between acids and alkalis. Neutralisation reactions are often represented by ionic equations.

A2.2 Salts

A salt is formed whenever an acid reacts with a metal, a base, an alkali or a carbonate. The salt formed depends on the acid used and the metal or metal ion in the substance the acid has reacted with. Some salts are soluble in water and may be obtained by crystallisation.

A2.3 Precipitation

Some salts are insoluble and are made by precipitation methods. It is possible to identify many ions present in aqueous solutions by chemical tests, some of which involve precipitation.

A2.1 Acids and alkalis

Key points

- The characteristic feature of an acid is that it contains a hydrogen atom that is replaceable.
- When acids dissolve in water they produce hydrogen ions, H^+.
- The strength of an acid depends on the extent to which it produces H^+ ions when it is dissolved in water.
- The concentration of an acid depends on the amount of it that is dissolved in water.
- The strength of an alkali depends on the extent to which it produces OH^- ions when it is dissolved in water.

Hydrogen ions

All acids contain hydrogen atoms.

a Write down the formulae for hydrochloric acid, nitric acid and sulphuric acid.

These hydrogen atoms are all replaceable and it is this feature that makes some substances containing hydrogen atoms acidic. Some molecules contain hydrogen atoms that are not replaceable, for example methane, CH_4. Methane is not an acid. Other substances contain some hydrogen atoms that are replaceable and some that are not.

b Look at the displayed structure of ethanoic acid (fig 2). One of the hydrogen atoms is replaceable and three are not. Which hydrogen atom is replaceable?

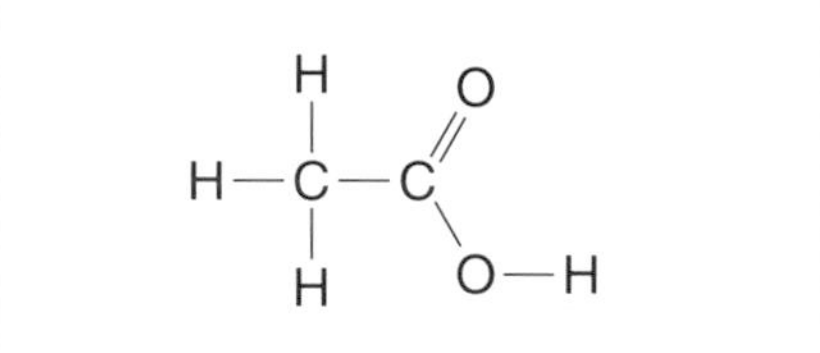

fig 2 Structure of ethanoic acid

Water has an important role to play in acidity. When substances with replaceable hydrogen atoms are dissolved in water they form ions. In particular the hydrogen atom in the molecule ends up as a hydrogen ion, H^+. An example of this is the covalent substance hydrogen chloride, HCl.

c Draw a dot and cross structure showing the bonding in a molecule of hydrogen chloride.

When hydrogen chloride dissolves in water, hydrogen ions, H^+, and chloride ions, Cl^-, form.

$$HCl(g) \rightarrow H^+(aq) + Cl^-(aq)$$

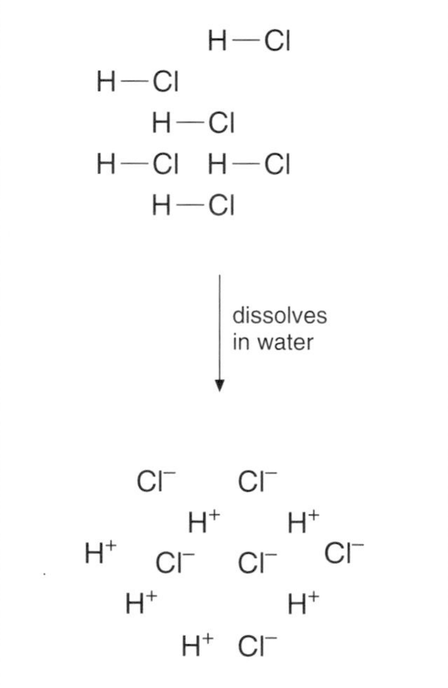

fig 3 Hydrogen chloride forms ions when dissolved in water

The (g) shows that hydrogen chloride is a gas and the (aq), which is short for aqueous, shows that the ions are dissolved in water.

Strength of an acid

When hydrogen chloride forms ions in water, almost all of the molecules of HCl split up into ions. This means that a lot of hydrogen ions are present and this makes the acid a **strong acid**. Sulphuric acid and nitric acid are also strong acids.

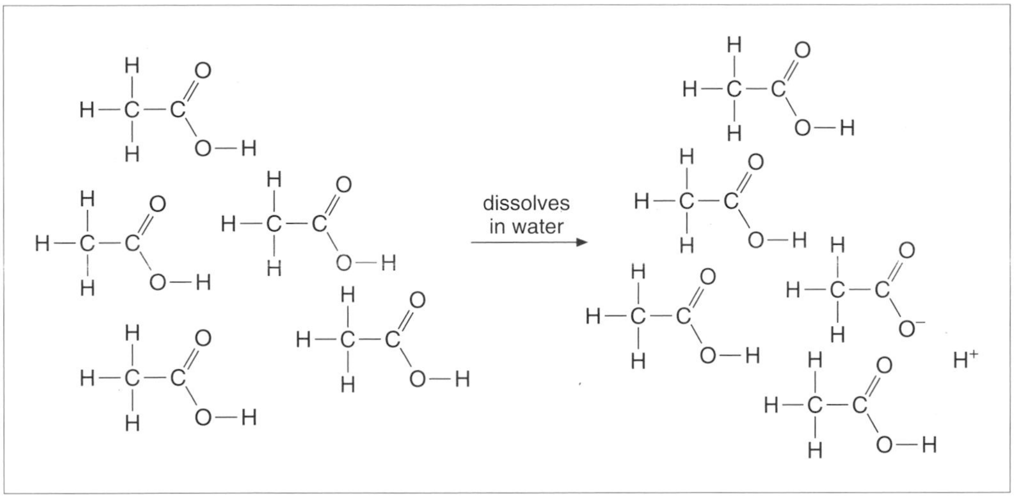

fig 4 | Ethanoic acid only produces a few ions in water

d Write an equation for the ionisation of nitric acid, HNO_3, to form hydrogen ions and nitrate ions.

Not all molecules with replaceable hydrogen atoms completely split up into ions, however. Ethanoic acid, for example, only partly splits up (see fig 4). We show it as a reversible reaction.

$$CH_3COOH \rightleftharpoons H^+ + CH_3COO^-$$

Very few hydrogen ions form. Ethanoic acid is a **weak acid**.

Concentration of an acid

There is an important difference between the strength of an acid and its **concentration**. The strength of an acid depends only on the degree of ionisation of the acid in water. The concentration of an acid depends on how much of the acid is dissolved in a given volume of water. If a lot of acid is dissolved in water then the acid is concentrated. If a small amount of acid is dissolved in a given volume of water, then the acid is dilute.

Alkalis

Alkalis are bases that dissolve in water. Sodium hydroxide, NaOH, and ammonium hydroxide, NH_4OH, are both alkalis.

Alkalis can also be strong or weak depending on how much they ionise when they dissolve in water. Sodium hydroxide is a strong alkali, and it dissolves in water and completely splits up into ions.

$$NaOH(s) \rightarrow Na^+(aq) + OH^-(aq)$$

Ammonium hydroxide is a weak alkali, however.

e Write an equation for the ionization of ammonium hydroxide into ammonium ions, NH_4^+, and hydroxide ions.

Alkalis can also be concentrated or dilute, the concentration only depends on the amount of the alkali dissolved in water.

KEY WORDS
concentration • strong acid • weak acid

Thinking further

■ **1** Calcium hydroxide is a weak alkali.

 a Name the ion that causes the substance to be called an alkali.

 b Calcium hydroxide is not very soluble in water. Explain why it is only possible to have dilute solutions of calcium hydroxide.

■ **2** Explain why a dilute solution of hydrochloric acid may contain more hydrogen ions than a concentrated solution of ethanoic acid.

◆ **3** Write an equation to show the ionisation when methanoic acid, HCOOH, dissolves in water to form methanoate ions, HCOO⁻, and hydrogen ions.

A2.2 Salts

- Acids and alkalis react together in neutralisation reactions.
- The progress of a neutralisation reaction can be followed by the change in heat evolved, conductivity or colour of an indicator as the reaction takes place.
- Neutralisation reactions can be used to make salts.

Neutralisation

An acid is **neutralised** when it reacts with a base. The only products are a salt and water.

a Name the products formed when magnesium hydroxide reacts with sulphuric acid.

When the base is soluble in water it is called an alkali. The reaction between alkalis and acids can be followed using Universal indicator. A few drops of indicator are added to a certain volume of alkali, for example, sodium hydroxide solution.

b What is the colour of the indicator?

Drops of acid, for example hydrochloric acid, are added to the alkali, usually using a **burette**. The acid is added to the alkali until the solution turns green. At this point the solution is neutral.

c What would you see if too much acid is added?

The exact amount of acid needed to neutralise the alkali is now known. The experiment can be repeated mixing the exact quantities of acid and alkali but without the indicator. To obtain crystals of the salt it is necessary to allow the water to evaporate. Warming the solution on a water bath to evaporate some of the water and allowing it to finish evaporating in the laboratory produces crystals of the salt. Sodium chloride can be produced by this method.

$$NaOH + HCl \rightarrow NaCl + H_2O$$

The change in pH when an acid reacts with an alkali can also be followed by using a **pH meter**. The meter gives a reading of pH 7 when the solution is neutral. It is also possible to measure the **conductivity** of the solution as the acid is added to the alkali. In acid or alkali the conductivity is high because ions are present. As neutralisation takes place, ions are removed and the conductivity falls. It will be at its lowest at the neutral point.

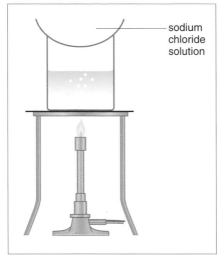

sodium chloride solution

fig 5 Using a water bath to gently evaporate water from sodium chloride solution

Ionic equations

When sodium hydroxide and hydrochloric acid dissolve in water they are fully ionised. The reaction is therefore between ions.

$$Na^+ + OH^- + H^+ + Cl^- \rightarrow Na^+ + Cl^- + H_2O$$

d Two of the ions are unchanged in the reaction. They are called **spectator ions**. Which ions are they?

The reaction that has taken place is that between hydrogen ions and hydroxide ions only.

$$H^+ + OH^- \rightarrow H_2O$$

This reaction happens in all acid–alkali reactions.

e The reaction between hydrogen ions and hydroxide ions is exothermic. Suggest how this could also be used to help follow the course of a neutralisation reaction.

Making soluble salts

Salts are also formed when a metal, metal oxide or carbonate reacts with an acid.

f What gas is produced when a metal reacts with an acid?

g What gas is produced when a carbonate reacts with an acid?

The practical procedure used is to add either a metal or an oxide or a carbonate to the acid until all of the acid has been neutralised.

h How will you be able to tell when all of the acid has been used up in these reactions?

Any excess metal, metal oxide or carbonate is then removed by filtering and the solution is allowed to crystallise. Zinc sulphate can be made by the reaction between zinc and sulphuric acid.

$$Zn + H_2SO_4 \rightarrow ZnSO_4 + H_2$$

i Name another substance that will react with sulphuric acid to form zinc sulphate.

Magnesium chloride can be made by the reaction between magnesium carbonate and hydrochloric acid.

$$MgCO_3 + 2HCl \rightarrow MgCl_2 + CO_2 + H_2O$$

j Write an equation for the formation of magnesium chloride from magnesium oxide and hydrochloric acid.

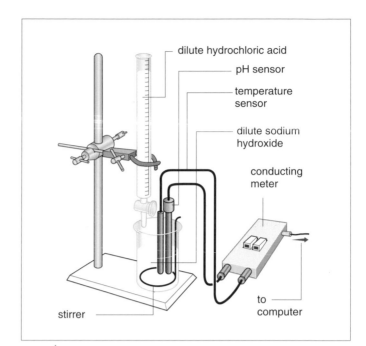

fig 6 | Using a data logger to measure conductivity

Labels: dilute hydrochloric acid; pH sensor; temperature sensor; dilute sodium hydroxide; conducting meter; to computer; stirrer

Ionic equations

It is possible to write equations for the reaction between a carbonate and an acid that do not include spectator ions. The reaction between magnesium carbonate and hydrochloric acid is represented as:

$$CO_3{}^{2-} + 2H^+ \rightarrow CO_2 + H_2O$$

Thinking further

1 Name three substances that each could be added to sulphuric acid to make magnesium sulphate.

2 Explain why the reaction between potassium hydroxide and hydrochloric acid is essentially the same as the reaction between sodium hydroxide and hydrochloric acid.

3 Sodium hydroxide reacts with sulphuric acid to make sodium sulphate, Na_2SO_4.

a Write a balanced symbol equation showing all of the reactants and products.

b Write an ionic equation ignoring all spectator ions.

KEY WORDS

burette • conductivity • neutralisation • pH meter • spectator ions

A2.3 Precipitation

- Some salts are insoluble in water.
- Insoluble salts are made by precipitation.
- Precipitation reactions can be used to identify some ions.

Insoluble salts

Salts of sodium or potassium are always soluble in water.

Some salts do not dissolve in water, however. These include silver chloride, barium sulphate and calcium carbonate. If a substance has a solubility of less than 1 g in 100 g of water it is insoluble.

Insoluble salts cannot be made by using the reactions shown on pages 154–155. To make an insoluble salt it is necessary to mix two soluble substances that contain the ions present in the insoluble salt. For example, to make barium sulphate we can add a solution of sodium sulphate to a solution of barium hydroxide. The sulphate ions from the sodium sulphate react with the barium ions from the barium hydroxide and the white, insoluble salt barium sulphate precipitates.

To obtain a pure dry sample of the insoluble salt it must be filtered, washed with distilled water and allowed to dry (fig 7).

a Why is it necessary to wash the precipitate?

Silver chloride can be made by mixing a solution of silver nitrate with a solution containing chloride ions.

b Name an acid that contains chloride ions.

Calcium carbonate can be made by mixing a soluble calcium salt, such as calcium chloride, with a solution containing carbonate ions.

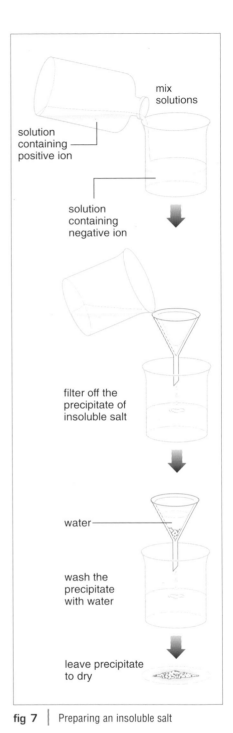

fig 7 | Preparing an insoluble salt

Identifying ions in aqueous solution

Precipitation reactions can be very useful. As certain ions give a characteristic precipitate of an insoluble salt when they are mixed, we can use this knowledge to tell us when one of these ions is present in a solution.

name	appearance
silver chloride	white precipitate
silver bromide	cream precipitate
silver iodide	pale yellow precipitate

fig 8 | The colours of halide precipitates

Chloride, bromide and iodide ions

The test for these ions is to add a few drops of nitric acid, followed by a few drops of silver nitrate to an aqueous solution. If the solution contains one of these halide ions a precipitate forms.

A typical reaction would be to show that chloride ions are present in sodium chloride solution. Silver chloride appears as a white precipitate and so proves that chloride ions were present.

Sulphate ions

Barium sulphate is insoluble. This is important in the test for sulphate ions. If a solution contains sulphate ions it will give a white precipitate when a few drops of hydrochloric acid, followed by a few drops of barium chloride, are added. The white precipitate is barium sulphate.

fig 9 | Tubes containing precipitates of Cu^{2+}, Al^{3+}, Fe^{3+} and Fe^{2+} hydroxides

c Write a word and balanced symbol equation for the reaction between sulphuric acid and barium chloride, $BaCl_2$.

The purpose of the hydrochloric acid is to prevent unwanted precipitates from spoiling the test.

Metal ions

It is possible to use precipitation reactions to show the presence of some metal ions in aqueous solution. The hydroxides of some metals are insoluble. Adding sodium hydroxide solution to a soluble salt of one of these metals gives a precipitate with a characteristic colour. Four of these are shown in fig 9.

d Describe the colours of the hydroxide precipitates in fig 9.

Carbonate ions

The presence of a carbonate ion, CO_3^{2-}, is proven by adding dilute hydrochloric acid. If a substance fizzes and gives off a gas that turns limewater cloudy, then the substance is a carbonate.

Ammonium ions

If a substance contains ammonium ions, NH_4^+, then it will give off ammonia gas, NH_3, when it is warmed with sodium hydroxide solution. The ammonia gas can be detected because it turns moist litmus paper blue. For example, ammonium chloride reacts with sodium hydroxide.

$$NH_4Cl + NaOH \rightarrow NH_3 + NaCl + H_2O$$

Ionic equations

All of the reactions above can be represented by ionic equations as well as by balanced symbol equations. Examples are:

halide ions, e.g. iodide
$$Ag^+ + I^- \rightarrow AgI$$

sulphate ions
$$Ba^{2+} + SO_4^{2-} \rightarrow BaSO_4$$

metal ions, e.g. Fe^{2+}
$$Fe^{2+} + 2OH^- \rightarrow Fe(OH)_2$$

carbonate ions
$$CO_3^{2-} + 2H^+ \rightarrow CO_2 + H_2O$$

ammonium ions
$$NH_4^+ + OH^- \rightarrow NH_3 + H_2O$$

In each case the spectator ions have been missed out.

Thinking further

1 When sulphuric acid is added to limestone, $CaCO_3$, there is a small amount of fizzing which quickly stops. A white powder coats the limestone. Explain these observations.

◆ **2** Write balanced symbol and ionic equations for the reaction between iron(III) chloride solution and sodium hydroxide solution.

Questions on acids, bases and salts

● **1** The table in fig 10 shows some information about the solubility of salts at room temperature.

metal	chloride	sulphate	carbonate
sodium	s	s	s
potassium	s	s	s
calcium	s	i	i
barium	s	i	i
silver	i	i	i

fig 10 | Solubility of salts (s = soluble, i = insoluble)

a Name an insoluble calcium salt. *(1)*

b Name a soluble salt of a Group 1 metal. *(1)*

c Name the only insoluble chloride shown. *(1)*

d How does the solubility of the Group 1 sulphates differ from the solubility of the Group 2 sulphates? *(1)*

e Which of the following will form an insoluble precipitate when they are mixed?

sodium sulphate and barium chloride
sodium sulphate and calcium chloride
potassium chloride and sodium carbonate
potassium carbonate and calcium chloride *(2)*

■ **2** The following passage describes the preparation of the salt potassium chloride. Read the passage and answer the questions that follow.

Put 25 cm³ of hydrochloric acid into a beaker. Add potassium carbonate a small amount at a time until the reaction stops. Filter and then evaporate the solution carefully on a water bath to remove some of the water. Leave the concentrated solution to crystallise.

a What is seen as the potassium carbonate is added to the hydrochloric acid? *(1)*

b How do you know when all of the acid has been used up? *(1)*

c What is removed by filtering? *(1)*

d Why is it important to evaporate some of the water away using a water bath? *(1)*

e There are three products in this reaction. Water is one of them. Write a word equation for the reaction. *(1)*

f Write a balanced symbol equation for the reaction. *(3)*

g Finish and balance the ionic equation for the reaction:
$$CO_3^{2-} + H^+ \rightarrow$$ *(2)*

h Why should you not use the reaction between potassium and hydrochloric acid to make potassium chloride? *(1)*

i Suggest another substance that you use in the laboratory to make potassium chloride by adding it to hydrochloric acid. *(1)*

■ **3** Name the products of the following reactions:

a sodium hydroxide and sulphuric acid *(2)*

b magnesium and hydrochloric acid *(2)*

c zinc oxide and sulphuric acid *(2)*

d calcium carbonate and hydrochloric acid *(3)*

◆ **4** Write balanced symbol equations for the following reactions.

a potassium hydroxide + sulphuric acid *(3)*

b zinc + hydrochloric acid *(3)*

c copper(II) oxide + sulphuric acid *(2)*

d magnesium carbonate + hydrochloric acid *(3)*

◆ **5** Finish and balance, where necessary, the following ionic equations.

a $H^+ + OH^- \rightarrow$ *(1)*

b $Mg + H^+ \rightarrow$ *(2)*

c $CO_3^{2-} + H^+ \rightarrow$ *(2)*

◆ **6** A student is testing aqueous solutions of five sodium compounds A, B, C, D and E. The results of the tests are shown in the table in fig 11.

	add hydrochloric acid	add nitric acid, then silver nitrate	add hydrochloric acid, then barium chloride
A	no reaction	no reaction	white precipitate
B	fizzing	fizzing	fizzing
C	no reaction	white precipitate	no reaction
D	no reaction	cream precipitate	no reaction
E	no reaction	pale yellow precipitate	no reaction

fig 11

The student knows the names of the sodium compounds but not which one is which. The names are shown below. Use the results to identify which letter represents:

a sodium bromide

b sodium carbonate

c sodium chloride

d sodium iodide

e sodium sulphate. *(5)*

◆ **7** The apparatus shown in fig 12 was used to follow the reaction between barium hydroxide and sulphuric acid.

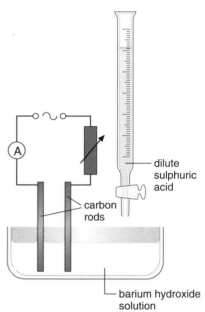

dilute sulphuric acid

carbon rods

barium hydroxide solution

fig 12

As the sulphuric acid was added the reading on the ammeter was recorded. The results are shown in the graph in fig 13.

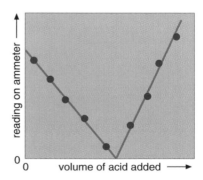

fig 13

a How does the reading on the ammeter show that the conductivity decreases as the sulphuric acid is added? *(1)*

b Balance the symbol equation for the reaction.

$$Ba(OH)_2 + H_2SO_4 \rightarrow BaSO_4 + H_2O \qquad (1)$$

c Look at the equation in part **b**. Explain why the conductivity falls to zero at the neutral point. *(3)*

d Explain why the conductivity starts to increase as more sulphuric acid is added after the neutral point. *(3)*

e Write an ionic equation for the reaction between barium ions, Ba^{2+}, and sulphate ions to make barium sulphate. *(1)*

◆ **8** A substance X contains one positive ion and one negative ion. When a solution of X is added to aqueous sodium hydroxide a green precipitate appears. When a few drops of hydrochloric acid are added to a solution of X, followed by a few drops of barium chloride, a white precipitate is formed.

a Name the green precipitate. *(1)*

b Name the white precipitate. *(1)*

c Write down the formula of the positive ion in X. *(1)*

d Write down the formula of the negative ion in X. *(1)*

e Name X and write down its formula. *(2)*

f Write an ionic equation for the reaction between the positive ion in X and hydroxide ions. *(2)*

--- **IDEAS AND EVIDENCE** ---

9 Both ammonium carbonate, $(NH_4)_2CO_3$, and sodium hydrogencarbonate, $NaHCO_3$, can be used as raising agents in baking.

You can assume that sodium hydrogencarbonate reacts in similar ways to sodium carbonate. Use your knowledge of the reactions of carbonates to answer these questions.

a You have two containers. One contains ammonium carbonate and the other contains sodium hydrogencarbonate. Describe a test, and the results of the test, that you could carry out to show that both substances are carbonates. *(3)*

b Suggest why these substances are used as raising agents in baking. *(1)*

c Assuming that your test in part **a** was successful, explain why it would not be safe to use the results of this test alone to say that the substances are safe to use in baking. *(1)*

A3 Metals and redox reactions

Links to Double Award

1 Chemical reactions
2 Metals
3 Atomic structure and the Periodic Table

Introduction

We use individual metals for a variety of purposes, for example copper is used for electrical wiring and aluminium for cooking foil. Sometimes a mixture of metals, called an alloy, is more suitable for a particular use. Coins are made from alloys.

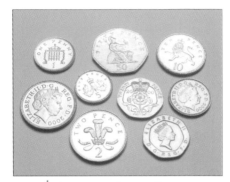

fig 1 | Coins are made from alloys

In this teaching block you will learn more about alloys.

Iron is the most used metal in the world, mainly in the form of steel. It is strong and cheap to produce. Unfortunately it also rusts.

Rusting is a major problem, causing millions of pounds worth of damage each year.

In this teaching block you will look at ways to prevent iron from rusting.

When magnesium burns in air the metal is oxidised.

$$2Mg + O_2 \rightarrow 2MgO$$

magnesium + oxygen → magnesium oxide

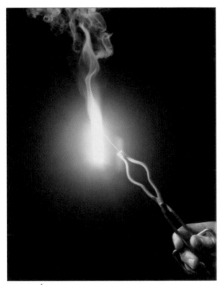

fig 2 | Burning magnesium

It is easy to recognise this as an oxidation reaction, as the magnesium gains oxygen to form magnesium oxide.

Other oxidation reactions are less easy to recognize.

In this Teaching block you will study some of these reactions, and see how oxidation can take place without oxygen.

Reactivity of metals

The commonly used metals can be placed in a list, in order from the most reactive to the least reactive. This list is called the reactivity series, and is shown in fig 3.

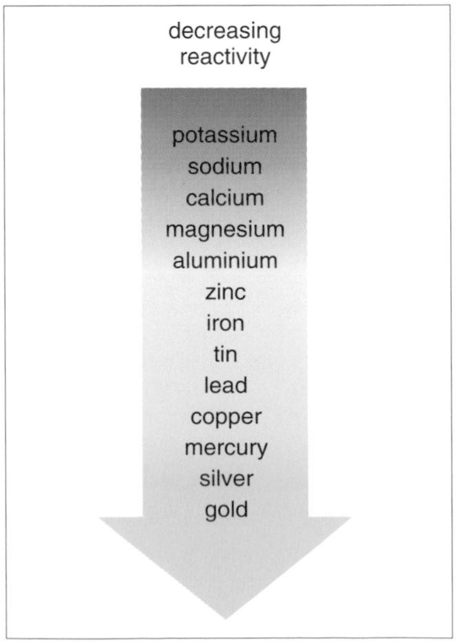
decreasing reactivity
potassium
sodium
calcium
magnesium
aluminium
zinc
iron
tin
lead
copper
mercury
silver
gold

fig 3 | Reactivity series of metals

If a metal higher up in the reactivity series is placed in a solution containing ions of a metal lower in the reactivity series, the more reactive metal takes the place of the less reactive metal.

Atoms of the more reactive metal become ions and enter the solution. The less reactive metal ions become atoms and leave the solution.

Check-up

1 When iron wire is heated with chlorine gas it glows red as the metal and non-metal react to form iron(III) chloride. Use the reactivity series to predict what you see, and what is made, when the following metals are heated with chlorine gas:

  a potassium   b zinc   c gold.

2 The uses of a metal are often related to its position in the reactivity series. For each of the following statements explain why one of the metals is used for the job but the other is not.

  a Copper for water pipes, but not iron.

  b Nickel for coins, but not calcium.

  c Gold for jewellery, but not magnesium.

3 The reactivity series shown in fig 3 does not contain carbon and hydrogen, because they are not metals. Explain why it would be useful to have these non-metals in the reactivity series.

4 Gold is found 'native'. This means that the ore contains gold that is not combined with any other element.

  a Explain why gold is found native, but not zinc.

  b Suggest two other metals that are likely to be found native.

Contents of the Teaching block

A3.1 Alloys

A mixture of metals is called an alloy. Alloys have different properties to the individual pure metals that they are made of. This often means that an alloy is better suited to a particular use than any of the metals it contains. Alloys have a range of uses related to their properties.

A3.2 Rusting

Iron must be in contact with both oxygen and water to rust. Rusting can be prevented in a number of ways. If iron is prevented from coming into contact with either water or oxygen it will not rust.

A3.3 Redox

A redox reaction involves both reduction and oxidation. Redox reactions can involve the transfer of electrons. When this transfer takes place, oxidation is a loss and reduction is a gain of electrons. Displacement reactions of halogens and metals are redox reactions.

A3.1 Alloys

What is an alloy?

An **alloy** is formed when two or more metals are mixed together. The mixture has different properties from each of the individual metals used to make the alloy.

Alloys are often stronger than the original metals. They also have different melting points and densities.

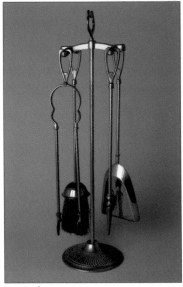

fig 4 | Fire implements made of brass

Brass

Brass is an alloy of copper with about 30% zinc. Brass is much harder than pure copper, and has the colour of gold. This alloy is useful for making articles that need to be used, but also have a decorative function, e.g. fire tongs and pokers.

a Suggest how a fire poker made from brass is better than a fire poker made from copper.

fig 5 | Solid state electrical circuits

Solder

A mixture of tin and lead in approximately equal quantities is called **solder**. The alloy has a much lower melting point than either metal. It is used to make joints in electrical circuits.

b Why would an alloy with a low melting point be useful for connecting the components in a solid state circuit?

Mild steel

This is a mixture of iron and carbon. Although carbon is a non-metal, **steel** is still classed as an alloy. It is much stronger and harder than iron. Steel is used to make cars, bridges and as a reinforcing material in concrete buildings.

c Name two household articles that are made from steel.

d For each of the articles you named in **c**, explain how steel is a better metal than pure iron.

fig 6 | Steel reinforcements in concrete

Fig 8 shows the arrangement of particles in a pure metal and in an alloy containing a second metal.

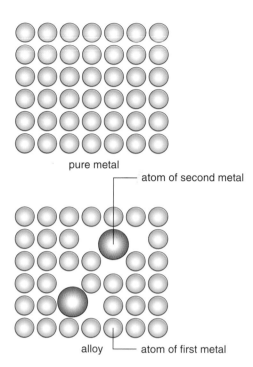

fig 8 | Structure of a pure metal and of an alloy

In the pure metal layers of atoms slip over each other. This makes the metal easy to bend or dent.

In the alloy movement of the layers is prevented by the different sized atoms of the second metal. This makes the alloy harder and stronger than the pure metal.

e Use the diagrams in fig 8 to explain why the alloy has a lower melting point than the pure metal.

Fig 9 shows how the properties of brass vary with composition.

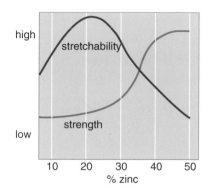

fig 9 | Graph to show how the properties of brass vary

f Choose which composition of brass you would use for each of the following and explain your choice:
 • The links of a chain.
 • The casing for a bullet.

Thinking further

1 Which of the following are alloys?

aluminium • brass • bronze • copper • duralumin • iron • magnesium • solder • steel • tin

2 Why are alloys often more useful than pure metals?

3 A period of history, the Bronze Age, is named after an alloy. Bronze is a mixture of copper and tin. Weapons such as swords and axes were made from bronze.

a Why is a bronze axe better than a copper axe?

b Suggest why bronze was so important that a whole period of history is named after it.

4 The table in fig 7 shows the composition of a number of samples of brass.

sample of brass	percentage of metal	
	copper	zinc
A	71	29
B	75	25
C	67	33

fig 7

Use the information in fig 7 to explain why brass is an alloy and not a compound of copper and zinc.

KEY WORDS
alloy • brass • solder • steel

 Making and testing alloys of lead and tin.

A3.2 Rusting

Conditions for rusting

When iron is left in contact with water and oxygen (or air) it reacts to form **hydrated iron oxide**. This is rust.

The conditions needed for iron to rust can be shown by a simple experiment, indicated in fig 10.

In fig 10, only the iron nail that is in contact with both water and air rusts.

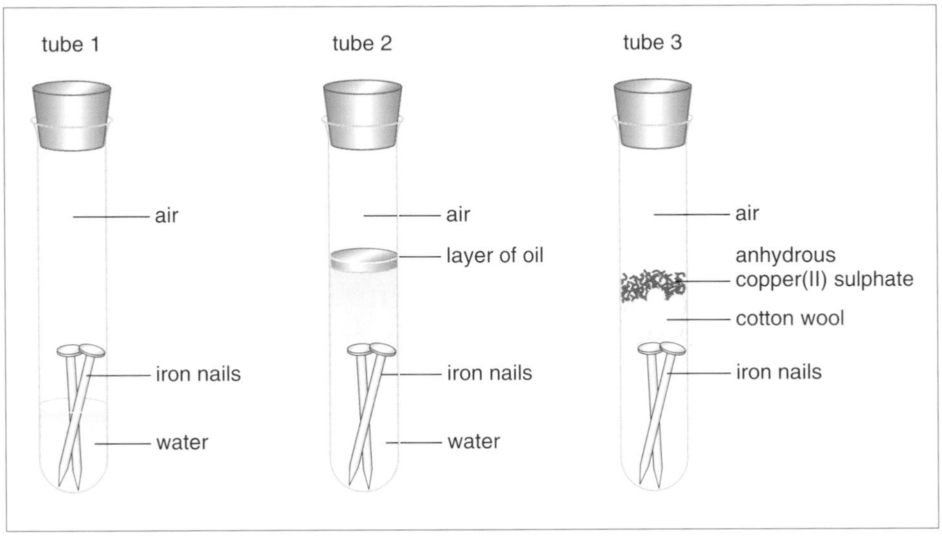

a What is the purpose of the anhydrous copper(II) sulphate in tube 3?

b What is the purpose of the layer of oil in tube 2?

tube 1 — air — iron nails — water

tube 2 — air — layer of oil — iron nails — water

tube 3 — air — anhydrous copper(II) sulphate — cotton wool — iron nails

fig 10 | Conditions needed for rusting

For iron or steel to be used out of doors it must be protected from rusting. Without this the iron will rust until it has so little strength that it breaks.

Prevention of rusting

Most methods used to prevent iron, or steel, from rusting are designed to stop either water or air, or both, from touching the iron.

Painting

Painting the iron article creates a waterproof and airproof cover over the surface of the iron. As oxygen and water cannot reach the iron, it does not rust.

fig 11 | Steel rusts when exposed to air and water

c What will happen to the iron if the paint is chipped or scratched?

Oiling and greasing

A covering of oil or grease wiped over the iron will form a protective layer. This will keep out air and the water vapour it contains.

This method is a good one for tools such as spades, when they are put away for winter storage.

d Why would this be a poor method of protection from rusting for an article such as a bicycle?

Galvanising

When an iron or steel article is dipped into molten zinc and then removed, it becomes coated with a thin layer of zinc. The zinc forms a protective coat over the surface of the iron. This process is called **galvanising**, and is used for dustbins, barbed wire and motorway crash barriers.

e Zinc is a more reactive metal than iron. Suggest why it does not corrode in damp air.

fig 12 | Galvanised dustbins

Sacrificial protection

If the protective layer of zinc is chipped or scratched the iron beneath it does not rust. This is therefore a good method for articles that will be banged or scratched in use.

Zinc is more reactive than iron, and will corrode away instead of the iron. This is called **sacrificial protection**. The method works with other metals which are more reactive than iron, e.g. magnesium.

It is not necessary to cover the whole surface of a steel article with the more reactive metal for sacrificial protection to work. A ship may have magnesium blocks riveted to its hull every few metres to prevent rusting of the whole hull.

fig 13 | Magnesium blocks on a ship's hull

Alloying

When iron is mixed with much less reactive metals such as nickel and chromium, it forms an alloy called **stainless steel**.
This alloy does not rust. It also has a very attractive appearance. Stainless steel is used to make cutlery and kitchen equipment.

f Suggest why this alloy is called *stainless* steel.

fig 14 | Stainless steel kitchen equipment

Thinking further

■ **1** Choose the best method to protect each of the following steel articles from rusting. For each give reasons for your choice.

　a a metal bucket

　b a saw

　c a steel coffee pot

　d a car exhaust

■ **2** If the body of a car is made from stainless steel it will never rust. Suggest why few cars have bodies made from stainless steel.

◆ **3** Tin cans used to package foods such as baked beans are really made of steel. They are covered with a thin layer of tin.

　a Explain how the tin prevents the steel rusting.

　b If the tin is scratched the steel rusts more quickly than it would with no tin. Explain this.

◆ **4** Many modern cars have engines made from aluminium. These engines are not bolted directly onto the steel shell of the car. Suggest why

KEY WORDS

galvanising • hydrated iron oxide • sacrificial protection • stainless steel

A3.3 Redox

> ### Key points
>
> - A redox reaction involves both reduction and oxidation.
> - Redox reactions can involve transfer of electrons.
> - Oxidation is loss of electrons and reduction is gain of electrons.
> - Displacement reactions are redox reactions.

Reduction and oxidation

In simple terms **oxidation** can be the addition of oxygen and **reduction** the removal of oxygen.

When a metal burns in oxygen, an oxide is formed.

$$4Fe \ + \ 3O_2 \ \rightarrow \ 2Fe_2O_3$$
iron + oxygen → iron(III) oxide

The iron has gained oxygen, so it has been oxidised.

In the blast furnace iron(III) oxide reacts with carbon monoxide.

$$Fe_2O_3 \ + \ 3CO \ \rightarrow \ 2Fe \ + \ 3CO_2$$
iron(III) + carbon → iron + carbon
oxide   monoxide   dioxide

In this reaction oxygen is removed from the iron, so the iron has been reduced.

a What has been oxidised in this reaction?

Oxidation and reduction also take place in reactions that do not involve oxygen. Oxidation can be a loss of electrons and reduction a gain of electrons.

When chlorine gas is bubbled through a solution containing iron(II) ions, iron(III) ions are formed.

$$Fe^{2+} \ \rightarrow \ Fe^{3+} \ + \ e^-$$
iron(II) → iron(III) + electron

This is an oxidation reaction.

b Why does an iron(II) ion get an extra positive charge when it loses an electron?

Chlorine gas forms chloride ions.

$$Cl_2 \ + \ 2e^- \ \rightarrow \ 2Cl^-$$
chlorine + electrons → chloride

This is a reduction reaction.

fig 15 | Iron wool burning in a Bunsen flame

Reduction and oxidation always take place in the same reaction. The overall reaction is described as a **redox** reaction. The two **ionic half equations** can be combined, and balanced.

$$2Fe^{2+} + Cl_2 \rightarrow 2Fe^{3+} + 2Cl^-$$

In this reaction chlorine is the **oxidising agent** because it has oxidized the iron(II) ions. Iron(II) is the **reducing agent** because these ions have reduced the chlorine.

An easy way to remember the transfer of electrons in a redox reaction is to use the mnemonic OILRIG. This stands for 'oxidation is loss and reduction is gain' of electrons.

Displacement reactions

When bromine is added to a solution of potassium iodide, iodine is produced. The bromine displaces the iodine from the solution.

c Write a symbol equation for this reaction.

d In this reaction what has been oxidised and what has been reduced?

When an iron nail is added to copper(II) sulphate solution the copper is displaced from the solution and sticks to the nail.

fig 16 | An iron nail placed in copper(II) sulphate solution

The overall equation for the reaction is:

$$Fe + CuSO_4 \rightarrow Cu + FeSO_4$$

e Write ionic half equations for this reaction.

f What has been reduced in this reaction?

Thinking further

■ **1** In each of the following reactions, what has been oxidised and what has been reduced?

a $2Mg + O_2 \rightarrow 2MgO$

b $Zn + 2HCl \rightarrow ZnCl_2 + H_2$

c $Ca + 2H_2O \rightarrow Ca(OH)_2 + H_2$

d $Cl_2 + 2KI \rightarrow 2KCl + I_2$

◆ **2 a** Write ionic half equations for the reaction in 1d.

b What is the oxidising agent in this reaction?

◆ **3** Magnesium powder is stirred into a solution of copper(II) sulphate.

a What would you see?

b Write ionic half equations for the reaction.

c Explain how this is a redox reaction.

┌─ **KEY WORDS** ─────────────────────────────────
│ ionic half equations • oxidation • oxidising agent • reducing agent • redox • reduction
└──

Questions on metals and redox reactions

● **1** A door knocker is made from the alloy brass.

  a What is an alloy? *(1)*

  b Which metals are contained in the alloy brass? *(1)*

  c Why is a brass door knocker better than one made of copper? *(1)*

2 When left in damp conditions mild steel rusts.

● **a** Which element in the mild steel reacts when it rusts? *(1)*

■ **b** Name the compound formed when mild steel rusts. *(2)*

● **c** Name the two substances needed for mild steel to rust. *(2)*

■ **d** Describe an experiment you can use to prove that these two substances are required for rusting to take place. *(3)*

■ **3** For each method of rust prevention given below,

  • give one advantage

  • give one disadvantage

  • give one example of an article protected by this method.

  a painting *(3)*

  b greasing *(3)*

  c galvanizing *(3)*

  d sacrificial protection *(3)*

  e alloying *(3)*

■ **4** An old piece of plated steel is found in a scrap-yard.

  a How can you tell if it is plated with tin or zinc? *(2)*

  b Explain your answer to **a**. *(2)*

  c Suggest why a mild steel can used to store baked beans is covered with a layer of tin rather than a layer of zinc. *(2)*

■ **5** A car exhaust system made from mild steel will rust. With average use the system will last about two years before it is so badly rusted that it has to be replaced.

An exhaust system made from stainless steel costs twice as much as one made from mild steel. It will never rust.

Write an advertisement to encourage motorists to buy your company's stainless steel exhaust systems. *(4)*

■ **6** Solder is an alloy of lead and tin. The table in fig 17 shows how the melting point of solder varies with the percentage of tin by mass.

percentage of tin	melting point in °C
0	327
20	280
40	230
60	185
80	209
100	232

fig 17

  a Use graph paper to plot the percentage of tin against melting point. Draw a smooth curve. *(3)*

  b Use the shape of your graph to explain why a mixture of lead and tin is used for solder, rather than either pure metal. *(2)*

  c For joining solid state electrical circuits solder with the lowest melting point is needed. What composition should this solder have? *(2)*

7 The company you work for has decided to sell a new product to stop car bodies rusting. Small blocks of zinc are bolted onto the underside of the car.

■ **a** Write an advertisement for the new product. *(2)*

◆ **b** Write a short article about the new product, to be printed in a scientific magazine. *(4)*

◆ **8** Bronze is an alloy of copper and tin. Bronze is much stronger than copper. Use ideas about the arrangement of particles in metals, and the sizes of copper and tin atoms, to explain this fact. *(4)*

◆ **9** In the Thermit reaction aluminium powder is mixed with iron(III) oxide. A burning magnesium fuse is used to start a highly exothermic reaction in which the aluminium displaces the iron.

$$2Al + Fe_2O_3 \rightarrow 2Fe + Al_2O_3$$

a Write ionic half equations for this reaction. *(2)*

b Use the mnemonic OILRIG to explain how aluminum is oxidised and iron reduced in this reaction. *(2)*

c Name the reducing agent in this reaction. *(1)*

d Why would this not be a good reaction to use for the large scale production of iron? *(1)*

e To weld together two rail lines requires 1.5 kg of iron. What mass of aluminium and iron(III) oxide should be mixed to produce this mass of iron? *(3)*

◆ **10** For each of the following reactions say which element is oxidised and which element is reduced.

a $CuO + H_2 \rightarrow Cu + H_2O$ *(2)*

b $Br_2 + 2NaI \rightarrow I_2 + 2NaBr$ *(2)*

c $Mg + Zn(NO_3)_2 \rightarrow Mg(NO_3)_2 + Zn$ *(2)*

d $Zn + 2HCl \rightarrow ZnCl_2 + H_2$ *(2)*

◆ **11** Aluminium metal is produced by electrolysis. Carbon electrodes are used in a solution of aluminium oxide, Al_2O_3, in cryolite. At the negative electrode aluminium is produced, and at the positive electrode oxygen is evolved.

a Write ionic equations for the reactions at the two electrodes. *(2)*

b At which electrode does oxidation take place? *(1)*

c Explain your answer to **b**. *(2)*

12 Aluminium bronze is an alloy of copper and aluminium. The table in fig 18 shows how the strength of this alloy varies with the percentage of aluminium added to the copper.

percentage of aluminium	relative strength of alloy
0	1.0
2	1.1
4	1.3
6	1.6
8	2.0
10	3.0
12	2.4
14	1.9

fig 18

■ **a** Use graph paper to plot the percentage of aluminium against the relative strength. Draw a curve. *(3)*

■ **b** At what composition does this alloy have maximum strength? *(1)*

◆ **c** The strength of this alloy increases with percentage of aluminium until a maximum strength is reached, then with higher aluminum content the strength falls. Use ideas about the arrangement of particles in metals and the relative sizes of aluminium and copper atoms to explain why this happens. *(3)*

◆ **13** A solution of potassium iodide is added to a solution of iron(III) sulphate. The mixture forms a brown solution. When a few drops of starch solution are then added, a deep blue/black colour is formed.

a What product of the reaction between potassium iodide and iron(III) sulphate is responsible for both the brown solution and the blue/black colour. *(1)*

b Write an ionic half equation for the formation of this product. *(1)*

c Write an ionic half equation to show what has happened to the iron(III) ions. *(1)*

d What has been reduced in this reaction? *(1)*

A4 Carbon chemistry

Links to Double Award

Biology 3 **Respiration**

5 **Bonding, structure and reacting quantities**

6 **Using crude oil**

Introduction

Carbon is a most unusual atom. It has the ability to join up to itself and form very long chains of atoms. Without this ability life on Earth would not exist because the molecules that make up our bodies contain mostly long chains of carbon atoms.

As a consequence of its ability to form chains of atoms, and for other atoms or groups of atoms to be attached to these chains, there are a huge number of carbon-containing compounds. There is a whole branch of chemistry, called organic chemistry, which is dedicated to carbon and its compounds.

fig 1 | Society today depends heavily on organic chemistry

All living things contain carbon compounds. Raw materials such as oil and coal, derived from living things, are also based on carbon. Our modern society is very dependent on organic chemistry to make the fuels and materials that we use every day of our lives. In particular, polymers, large molecules obtained from alkenes, have very widespread use. Without alkanes from crude oil our transport system would grind to a halt.

There are millions of carbon-containing compounds. In order to simplify the study of these compounds, chemists have grouped them into families. The members of each family have characteristic chemical properties and graded physical properties, such as boiling point. The difference in boiling point is essential for the process of separating the hydrocarbons in crude oil by fractional distillation.

Although polymers contain chains of many thousands of carbon atoms, the smaller carbon-containing compounds consist of simple molecules. There are only very weak forces of attraction between neighbouring molecules. This means that little energy is needed to separate them and so they exist as gases, liquids or solids with low melting points at room temperature.

Scientists continue to research the properties of carbon-containing compounds and to make new ones. Without this research our advances in the treatment of illnesses would be hindered.

fig 2 | The work of research scientists is vital

Check-up

1 Name two elements present in a hydrocarbon.

2 Name the products for the combustion of any alkane in:

a a plentiful supply of air

b a limited amount of air.

3 Name the substance with the formula CH_4.

4 Write down the formula of the alkane with two carbon atoms.

5 Explain how the structure of an alkene is different to that of an alkane.

6 Describe a test, and the result of the test, that you could use to tell an alkane from an alkene.

7 How is a simple molecule different to a giant structure?

8 Why is methane a gas but sodium chloride a solid at room temperature?

Contents of the Teaching block

A4.1 Carbon compounds

Carbon compounds can exist in the form of branched chains and rings as well as straight chains of atoms. Families of compounds are recognised by having a general formula. The boiling point and melting point of a particular compound in a family are linked to the size of its molecule.

A4.2 Isomerism

It is sometimes possible for there to be more than one way of arranging atoms in a carbon compound with a particular molecular formula. When this happens the two arrangements are structural isomers of each other.

A4.3 Ethanol

Ethanol, commonly referred to as 'alcohol', has many uses. It is made on a large scale. There are two main methods of manufacture and the method used depends on the intended use of the ethanol. Ethanol can be dehydrated to make ethene.

A4.1 Carbon compounds

Key points

- Carbon atoms can join up in long chains; these chains can have branches.
- Carbon atoms can also join up in rings.
- Families of compounds, such as the alkanes, which have a general formula, are part of a homologous series.
- Alkenes and alcohols form homologous series.
- Compounds in a homologous series have increasing boiling points and melting points as their molecular mass increases.

Types of carbon compounds

Carbon atoms have the unique ability to join up in chains, which can be many thousands of atoms long. This means that there are millions of possible carbon compounds depending on the length of the chain, what is attached to it and where. To add to the possibilities, carbon atoms themselves can form branches on the chains. They can even join up in rings of atoms. The rings of atoms may also have branches.

a Write down the molecular formulae for the compounds shown in fig 3.

All of these structures are stable and so it becomes clear why there are millions of carbon-containing compounds known and many more yet to be discovered. This area of chemistry is still referred to as **'organic chemistry'**.

b The term organic chemistry was originally used because carbon compounds were thought to come from living things. Why was the word 'inorganic chemistry' used for substances obtained from minerals?

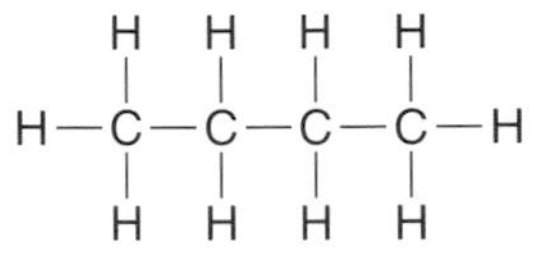

butane

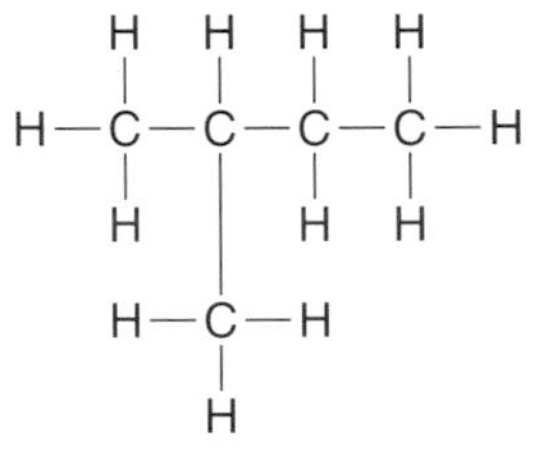

2-methylbutane

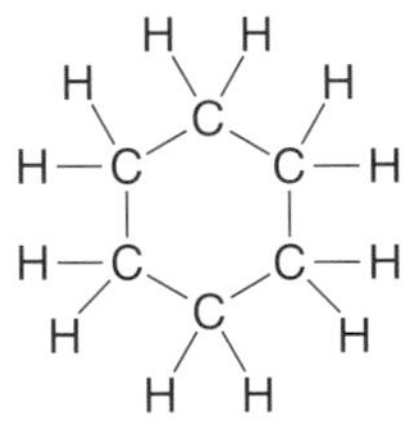

cyclohexane

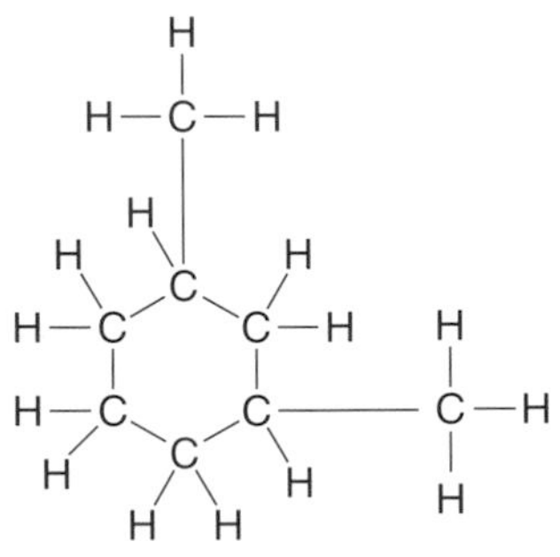

1,3-dimethylcyclohexane

fig 3 Displayed formulae of butane, 2-methylbutane, cyclohexane, 1,3-dimethycyclohexane.

Homologous series

In order to simplify the vast number of carbon-containing compounds, chemists have grouped together those with similar properties into families. Alkanes and alkenes are two of these families. One of the characteristic features of such a family is that they are part of a series. This series has a **general formula**. The family is called an **homologous series**. Any compound in an homologous series has a formula that can be expressed in general terms.

For example, the compounds with the formulae CH_4, C_2H_6, C_3H_8, C_4H_{10} and C_5H_{12} are all part of the alkane family. Their general formula is C_nH_{2n+2}. This general formula can be used to work out the formula of any other alkane if we know the number of carbon atoms.

c What are the formulae of the alkanes with 10 carbon atoms, 18 carbon atoms and 49 carbon atoms?

Grouping organic substances into families not only helps with the prediction of formulae but also helps to predict their chemical reactions. Compounds in the same family have similar chemical reactions, although the rate of a reaction may vary.

d What is the general formula for these alkenes?

C_2H_4 C_3H_6 C_4H_8 C_5H_{10}

Another family of organic substances is called the **alcohols**. The term 'alcohol' is often used to refer to one particular member of the family, called ethanol. This has many uses including as a solvent and in 'alcoholic' drinks.

The formulae for the first three alcohols of the family are written as CH_3OH, C_2H_5OH, and C_3H_7OH.

e What is the noticeable common feature of an alcohol from its formula?

f What is the general formula for an alcohol?

Boiling point and melting point

While compounds in the same family have similar chemical properties, their physical properties, such as boiling point and melting point, show gradual trends. The larger the molecule, the higher the boiling point or melting point. This is because bigger molecules will have more attraction to neighbouring molecules than smaller ones. More energy will be needed to separate them and so the boiling point or melting point will be higher.

fig 4 | All of these contain ethanol

▷▷ Taking it further ▷▷

There are many more families of organic compounds. Can you work out what the general formula of each of the following families will be?

Aldehydes family: the first two are methanal, CH_2O and ethanal, C_2H_4O.
Carboxylic acids family: the first two are methanoic acid, HCOOH, and ethanoic acid, CH_3COOH.

Thinking further

■ 1 Copy and complete the table in fig 5 to show the correct homologous series for each formula. One has been done for you.

◆ 2 The boiling point of ethanol is 78 °C, whereas the boiling point of methanol is 64 °C. Explain this difference. Use the figures to predict the boiling point of propanol, the next in the series.

formula	alkane C_nH_{2n+2}	alkene C_nH_{2n}	alkyne C_nH_{2n-2}
C_2H_2			✓
C_5H_{10}			
$C_{16}H_{34}$			
$C_{20}H_{40}$			
C_4H_6			

fig 5

KEY WORDS

alcohols • general formula • homologous series • organic chemistry

A4.2 Isomerism

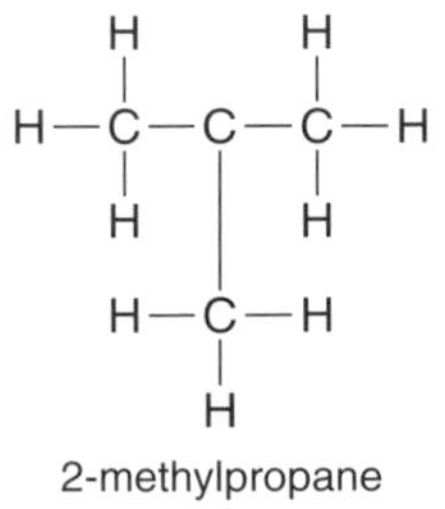

fig 7 | Displayed structure of 2-methylpropane

Key points

- Carbon chains can have branches.
- This means that it is possible for two different structures to have the same molecular formula.
- When two different structures have the same molecular formula they are called structural isomers of each other.

Structural isomerism

Alkanes

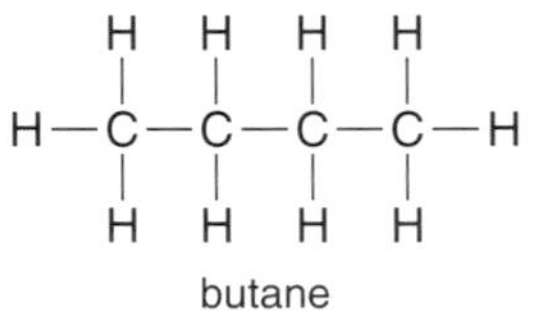

Butane has the formula C_4H_{10}. Its structure consists of four carbon atoms in a straight chain. Each carbon atom has four bonds, attached to other carbon atoms and hydrogen atoms.

fig 6 | Displayed structure of butane

a How is the number of bonds that carbon forms linked to the number of electrons in its outer shell?

As carbon chains can have branches it is possible to form another structure which has the formula C_4H_{10}. This structure has a straight chain of just three carbon atoms but there is a side chain on the middle carbon atom (see fig 7).

Adding up the number of atoms shows that it, too, has the formula C_4H_{10}. This substance is called 2-methylpropane. The longest straight chain of carbon atoms is three. So we say it is based on a propane chain. There is a CH_3 group, called a methyl group, on the second carbon atom along the chain. It is therefore called 2-methylpropane. It is impossible to change 2-methylpropane into butane without breaking bonds. They are **structural isomers** of each other.

b Explain why it is not possible to have structural isomers of propane, C_3H_8.

As carbon chains get longer so the number of possible structural isomers increases. There are three structural isomers with the formula C_5H_{12} (see fig 8).

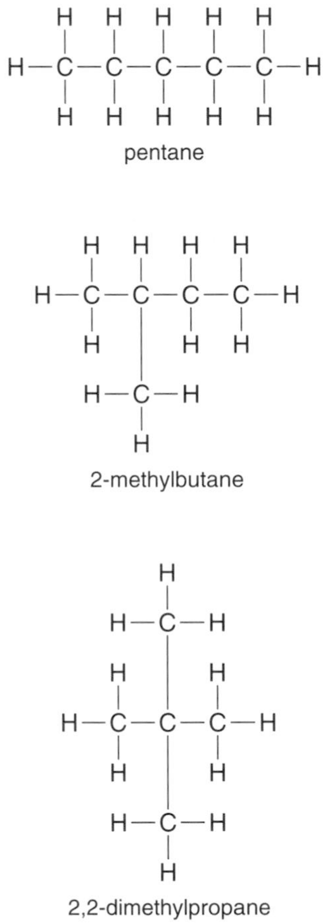

Notice that there are only three isomers for C_5H_{12}. This is because carbon-carbon bonds can rotate and so the structure shown in fig 9 is the same as the straight chain of atoms in pentane.

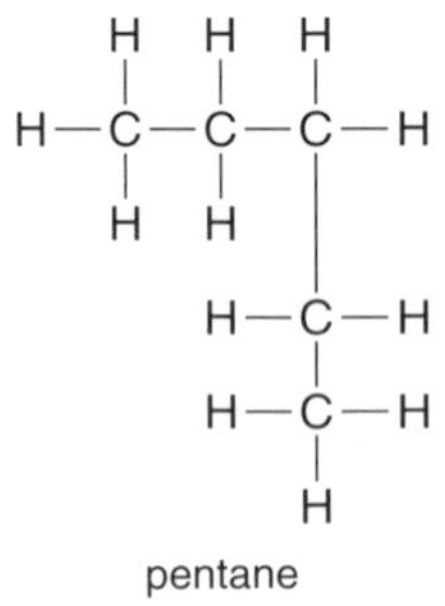

fig 8 | The three isomers of C_5H_{12}

fig 9 | Structure with a 'bent' straight chain

Alkenes

The position of the carbon to carbon double bond in alkenes with more than four carbon atoms can differ. In C_4H_8 the double bond can either be on one of the end carbon atoms or between the middle two carbon atoms (see fig 10).

We always use the lowest numbered carbon atom of which the double bond is part to identify where it is in the formula.

c Explain why we never refer to but-3-ene.

d There are two isomers of C_5H_{10}. What are their names and structures?

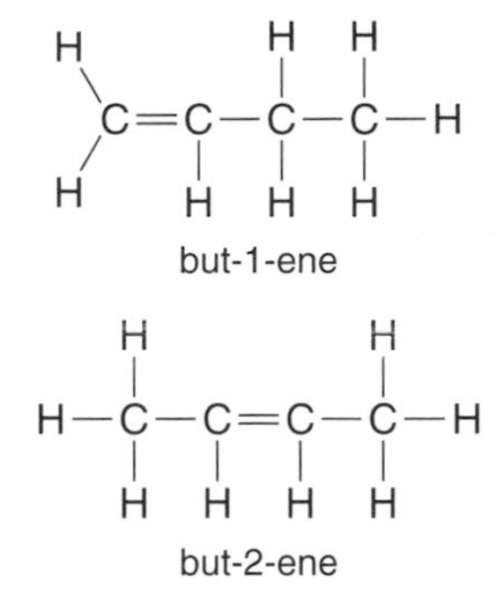

fig 10 | But-1-ene and but-2-ene

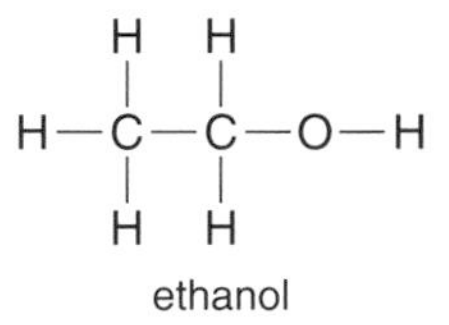

but-1-ene

but-2-ene

fig 11 | Displayed structure of ethanol

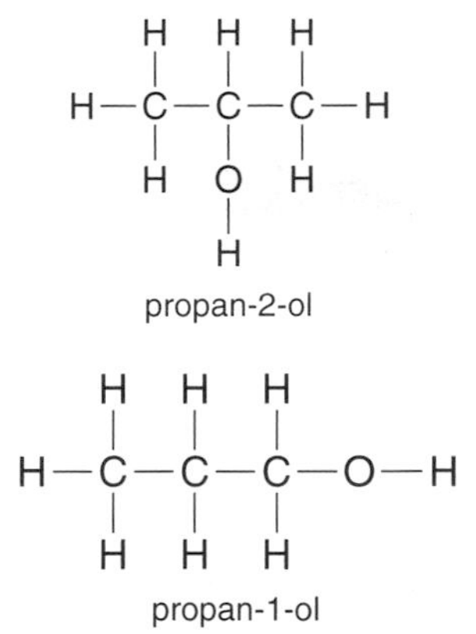

ethanol

fig 12 | Displayed structures of propan-1-ol and propan-2-ol

propan-2-ol

propan-1-ol

Alcohols

Alcohols that have the formula CH_3OH and C_2H_5OH only have one possible structure. They do not have isomers. The –OH group in ethanol, C_2H_5OH, is always on the end carbon atom.

With the formula C_3H_7OH, however, the –OH group can either go on one of the end carbon atoms or on the middle carbon atom. This produces two different structures.

Notice how we refer to the position of the alcohol group by a number followed by '-ol'.

e Draw the structures of butan-1-ol and butan-2-ol.

f What is the molecular formula for butan-1-ol and butan-2-ol?

There are two more isomers with the molecular formula $C_4H_{10}O$. These isomers have the structures shown in fig 13. Notice how the carbon chain has a branch and then the alcohol group is attached in two different places.

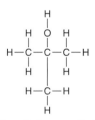

2-methylpropan-1-ol

2-methylpropan-2-ol

fig 13 | Displayed structures of 2-methylpropan-1-ol and 2-methylpropan-2-ol

Thinking further

■ **1** Explain why ethene, C_2H_4, does not have structural isomers but there are three structural isomers that have the formula C_4H_8.

◆ **2** Eight isomers have the formula $C_5H_{12}O$. The names of six of these isomers are pentan-1-ol, pentan-2-ol, pentan-3-ol, 2-methylbutan-1-ol, 2-methylbutan-2-ol and 2,2-dimethylpropanol.

a Draw the structures of these six isomers.

b Draw the structure of one of the two isomers not in the list.

KEY WORDS
structural isomers

A4.3 Ethanol

- Ethanol has many uses, including as a solvent, as a fuel and as an alcoholic beverage.
- It is made on a large scale by fermentation or from ethene.

- The use that the ethanol is to be put to largely determines its method of manufacture.
- Ethanol can be dehydrated to ethene.

Fermentation

Ethanol has been manufactured by **fermentation** for many centuries. Fermentation is still used to make dough rise in bread making, and to produce ethanol in brewing beer and in wine making. There are many starting materials that can be used; however, all must contain a sugar or starch (which enzymes can change to sugars).

Ethanol can be made in the laboratory by using the apparatus shown in fig 14. The mixture of glucose and yeast is left in a warm place. It is essential that air does not get into the apparatus because it will **oxidise** the ethanol to ethanoic acid (vinegar).

The equation for the reaction taking place is:

$$C_6H_{12}O_6 \rightarrow 2C_2H_5OH + 2CO_2$$
glucose $\rightarrow$ ethanol + carbon dioxide

a What will happen to the lime water in fig 14?

The fermentation eventually stops when the concentration of ethanol stops the enzymes working. The clear liquid at the top of the flask is decanted and distilled to obtain the ethanol.

b Why does the alcohol concentration in 'home-brew' never go above about 6%?

Manufacture of ethanol from ethene

Much of the ethanol used for solvents is made from ethene. Ethene gas, made from cracking fractions from crude oil, undergoes an addition reaction with steam.

$$C_2H_4 + H_2O \rightarrow C_2H_5OH$$
ethene + water $\rightarrow$ ethanol

The conditions used are a temperature of 300 °C, a high pressure and a catalyst of phosphoric acid.

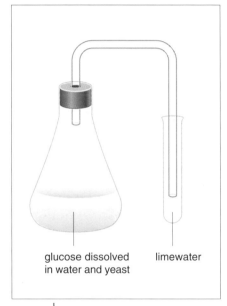

glucose dissolved   limewater
in water and yeast

fig 14 | Laboratory preparation of ethanol

IDEAS AND EVIDENCE

c A manufacturer wishes to use ethanol in some after-shave lotion. Suggest with reasons whether the manufacturer should purchase ethanol manufactured by fermentation or from ethene.

Uses of ethanol

1 As a solvent

Ethanol is an excellent solvent and dissolves many substances. It also has the advantage that it evaporates quickly and so finds use in products such as paints, varnishes and perfumes.

d Explain why ethanol is better than water for use in a varnish.

2 As a fuel

Ethanol burns with a clean, non-smoky flame releasing energy to the surroundings. It is used in small spirit burners. In countries where ethanol can be produced cheaply, cars have been adapted to use a mixture of petrol and ethanol as fuel.

e Brazil produces a lot of sugar cane. Explain why it has cars that run on 'gasohol', a mixture of ethanol and petrol.

3 As an alcoholic beverage

Different 'alcoholic' drinks have different amounts of ethanol in them. The flavour of a drink will depend on what has been used as the source of the sugar in the fermenting mixture.

fig 15 An 'alcool gasolina' fuel pump in Brazil

Evaluating the methods of making ethanol

The manufacture of ethanol from ethene is a relatively inexpensive process. The raw materials are ethene, from the cracking of crude oil, and water. The ethanol produced is pure because the addition reaction produces just a single product. This makes it ideal for use where large quantities of pure ethanol are required. This method would not be suitable for making ethanol for alcoholic beverages, however.

The fermentation method leaves traces of impurities in the ethanol; these are what give an alcoholic drink its particular taste. However, these impurities would not make the ethanol produced in this way suitable where a high degree of purity is required. Fermentation is also a comparatively cheap process, again the raw materials are cheap, but time is needed for the process as the sugars ferment. Only a dilute solution of ethanol is made.

Dehydration of ethanol

When ethanol vapour is passed over heated aluminium oxide, it is **dehydrated**. The products are water vapour and ethene.

$$C_2H_5OH \rightarrow C_2H_4 + H_2O$$

f Describe a test that you could do in the laboratory to show that ethene is formed in this reaction.

Thinking further

■ **1** A small amount of methanol is often added to ethanol when it is sold for use as a fuel or solvent. The product is called 'methylated spirits' and is cheap. Methanol is very toxic. Suggest why the methanol is added before it is sold to the public.

■ **2** What would happen to the mixture in the flask shown in fig 14 if the temperature was kept at 15 °C? What would happen if the mixture was boiled?

◆ **3** Write a balanced symbol equation for the combustion of ethanol in plentiful supply of air.

KEY WORDS
dehydrated • fermentation

Questions on carbon chemistry

● **1** The structures in fig 16 show some carbon compounds.

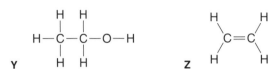

fig 16

Choose from W, X, Y or Z to answer these questions. Each letter may be used once, more than once or not at all.

a Which is NOT a hydrocarbon? *(1)*

b Which is methane? *(1)*

c Which has the formula C_2H_6? *(1)*

d Which two are in the same homologous series? *(1)*

2 ● **a** Draw the structure of the substance which has the formula C_3H_8. *(1)*

■ **b** This substance is part of an homologous series. What is the name of this series? *(1)*

c There are two substances that have the formula C_4H_{10}.

■ **i** Draw their structures. *(2)*

◆ **ii** Name them. *(2)*

◆ **iii** What name is given to compounds that have the same molecular formula but have different structures? *(1)*

● **3** Ethanol can be made by the fermentation of sugars. The apparatus shown in fig 17 is sometimes used.

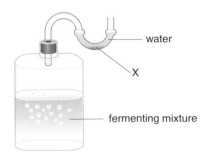

fig 17

a Name the gas produced in the fermentation process. *(1)*

b Describe how you can test for this gas and the result of the test. *(2)*

c What is the purpose of the piece of apparatus labelled X? *(1)*

d Why is the apparatus labelled X important in making ethanol? *(1)*

e What must be added to the sugar solution **to make it ferment**? *(1)*

f Why is it important that the apparatus is put in a warm place at about 40 °C, rather than being left at normal room temperature? *(1)*

■ **4** The apparatus shown in fig 18 is set up.

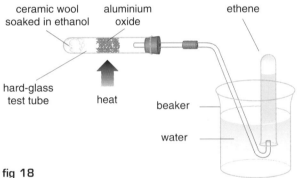

fig 18

The aluminium oxide is heated strongly and then the ethanol is gently warmed.

a Write a word equation for the reaction that takes place. *(1)*

b Write a symbol equation for the reaction. *(2)*

c What is the purpose of the aluminium oxide? *(1)*

d 5 g of aluminium oxide is used in the experiment. What mass of aluminium oxide will be left at the end. Explain your answer. *(2)*

e Why is it important that the aluminium oxide is heated before the ethanol? *(1)*

f Explain why the apparatus must not be allowed to 'suck back'. *(1)*

g Describe a test, and the result of the test, that you could do to show that the ethene gas produced is unsaturated. *(2)*

5 The table in fig 19 gives some information on five alcohols. Use the table to help answer the questions that follow.

name	formula	boiling point in °C	solubility of water
methanol	CH_3OH	64	very soluble
ethanol	C_2H_5OH	78	very soluble
propan-1-ol	C_3H_7OH	97	
butan-1-ol	C_4H_9OH		soluble
pentan-1-ol	$C_5H_{11}OH$	138	slightly soluble

fig 19

● **a** Suggest the solubility of propan-1-ol in water. *(1)*

■ **b** **i** Draw a graph showing the number of carbon atoms (horizontal axis) against boiling point (vertical axis) for these alcohols. *(2)*

ii Suggest the boiling point of butan-1-ol. *(1)*

iii Describe the connection between the number of carbon atoms in a straight chain alcohol and its boiling point. *(1)*

◆ **c** **i** Draw the structure of propan-2-ol. *(1)*

ii The boiling point of propan-2-ol is 82 °C. Suggest why it is different to that of propan-1-ol. *(2)*

◆ **d** **i** What is the general formula for an alcohol? *(1)*

ii Predict the formula for an alcohol with 15 carbon atoms. *(1)*

◆ **6** This question is about alkenes.

a Explain why the boiling point of propene, C_3H_6, is higher than that of ethene, C_2H_4. *(3)*

b Explain why propene has only one possible structure. *(1)*

c Draw and name the two structural isomers that have the formula C_4H_8. *(3)*

d State one reaction that alkanes and alkenes have in common and one in which they differ. *(2)*

◆ **7** Ethanol can be produced from ethene and water.

a Write a symbol equation for the reaction. *(1)*

b State the conditions that are necessary for this reaction. *(3)*

c Explain why producers of medicines may prefer ethanol manufactured from ethene rather than ethanol produced by fermentation. *(1)*

IDEAS AND EVIDENCE

8 Brazil grows lots of sugar cane. In the 1970s the high price of oil encouraged Brazil to grow more sugar cane to produce 'gasohol'. 'Gasohol' is a mixture of petrol and ethanol. By 1985 90% of new cars in Brazil had specially designed engines that could run on 'gasohol'. However, the price of oil dropped in the 1980s and it cost 15 times as much to produce 'gasohol' as petrol. Also the price of sugar had risen on the world market. Since 1990 Brazil has discovered large deposits of oil offshore. Also very few imported cars could run on 'gasohol'. By 1995 only 4% of Brazil's cars were using 'gasohol'.

a Write a word equation for the formation of ethanol from sugar (assume that the sugar is glucose, $C_6H_{12}O_6$). *(1)*

b Write a balanced symbol equation for the reaction. *(1)*

c Write a symbol equation for the combustion of ethanol in a plentiful supply of air. *(2)*

d Suggest two reasons why fewer cars in Brazil now use 'gasohol'. *(2)*

e Suggest reasons why, in the long term, the use of 'gasohol' may well become important both in Brazil and around the world. *(6)*

f One of the problems in using 'gasohol' is that the combustion takes place at a higher temperature than ordinary petrol. Suggest what effect this may have on the lifetime of an engine, which is mostly made from iron. Explain your answer. *(2)*

A5.1 Formulae and the mole

Key points

- The simplest formula of a compound can be calculated from the percentage composition of that compound.
- The simplest formula shows the simplest ratio of atoms in the compound.
- The molecular formula of a compound shows the actual number of each type of atom present in the compound.

- The formula mass of a substance, in grams, is called one mole of that substance.
- One mole of any substance contains the same number of particles; this is called the Avogadro number.

Calculating the simplest formula of a compound

Chemists can find the percentage by mass of each element in a compound by experiment. Using this information it is then possible to find the simplest formula of that compound. To do this we also need the relative atomic mass of each element present in the compound.

a Where is there a list of relative atomic masses of elements?

Here is an example.

An oxide of carbon contains 27.3% carbon.

b What other element is present in the oxide of carbon?

c How do we know that the percentage of this other element must be 72.7%?

In order to find the simplest formula, we divide each percentage by the relative atomic mass of each element. This allows a comparison of the different numbers of atoms of each element that are present. We get a ratio of each element with respect to each other, as shown in fig 2.

To get a whole number ratio, we now divide each of these ratios by the smallest. This is shown in fig 3.

The result shows us the simplest ratio of atoms, in this case one carbon to two oxygen atoms. The simplest formula is CO_2.
The simplest formula of a compound is called its **empirical formula**.

carbon	$\dfrac{27.3}{12} = 2.27$
oxygen	$\dfrac{72.7}{16} = 4.54$

fig 2

carbon	$\dfrac{2.27}{2.27} = 1$
oxygen	$\dfrac{4.54}{2.27} = 2$

fig 3

Molecular formula

The **molecular formula** of a compound shows the actual number of atoms present in the compound. Sometimes, as in the example of CO_2, it is the same as the empirical formula. This is not always the case, however. Here is an example. A compound contains 85.7% carbon and 14.3% hydrogen.

d Show that its empirical formula is CH_2.

In order to find the molecular formula we have to know the relative formula mass of the compound. For this compound it is 28. This means that a certain number of empirical formula units, in this case CH_2, must have a mass of 28.

As the mass of one CH_2 unit is 14, there must be two CH_2 units in the molecule. This means that the molecular formula must be C_2H_4, i.e. two lots of CH_2 units.

$$n(CH_2) = 28$$

fig 4

The mole

The idea of the **mole** is used by chemists to carry out calculations concerning quantities of substances. It is a way of comparing similar numbers of particles. For atoms, one mole is the relative atomic mass in grams. For molecules, one mole is the relative formula mass in grams.

e What is the mass of one mole of carbon atoms?

f What is the mass of one mole of carbon dioxide molecules?

One mole of any sort of particle always contains the same number of that particle. This number is called the **Avogadro Constant**. It is 6×10^{23}, an enormous number! This means that 12 g of carbon contains 6×10^{23} atoms of carbon and 44 g of carbon dioxide contains 6×10^{23} molecules of carbon dioxide. In the equation $C + O_2 \rightarrow CO_2$, 6×10^{23} atoms of carbon make 6×10^{23} molecules of carbon dioxide. We say one mole of carbon atoms makes one mole of carbon dioxide molecules. This is what the balanced equation tells us and it is very important in helping chemists with calculations.

Thinking further

(See page 214 for relative atomic masses.)

■ **1** The table in fig 5 gives some data about two oxides of copper, A and B.

	percentage copper	percentage oxygen
oxide A	80	20
oxide B	88.9	11.1

fig 5

Calculate the simplest formula of each oxide.

■ **2** An oxide of hydrogen contains 94.1% oxygen.

   a What is the percentage of hydrogen?

   b Calculate the empirical formula of the oxide.

   c The relative formula mass of the oxide is 34. Calculate the molecular formula of the oxide. Show your working.

◆ **3** Calculate the mass of one mole of each of the following.

   a H_2O **d** KCl

   b NH_3 **e** Na_2CO_3

   c O_2

KEY WORDS

Avogadro Constant • empirical formula • mole • molecular formula

A5.2 Using the mole

The number of moles of a substance

When we compare quantities of substance it is impossible to use the masses of individual atoms or molecules.

a Why is it so difficult?

Chemists use a quantity called the mole as a sort of 'counting unit' to compare quantities of substance that we can easily measure. The number of moles of any substance can be found by knowing the mass of that substance actually present and the relative formula mass of that substance.

$$\text{number of moles} = \frac{\text{mass of substance actually present in grams}}{\text{relative formula mass of that substance}}$$

For atoms, the relative atomic mass is used instead of the relative formula mass.

b The relative formula mass of water is 18. You have 36 g of water. How many moles of water is this?

Gases and the mole

Many chemical reactions involve liquids and solids only. It is quite straightforward to find the mass of these by weighing them. However, when a gas is involved, either as a reactant or a product, finding its mass is difficult. It is much easier to measure the volume of a gas.

Scientists found that equal volumes of any gas, at the same temperature and pressure, always contain the same number of particles. At room temperature and pressure (r.t.p.) one mole of any gas has a volume of 24 dm^3. This is very useful in predicting quantities of gases involved in chemical reactions.

The number of moles of gas at r.t.p. can be calculated by using the following equation:

number of moles of gas = $\dfrac{\text{volume of gas actually present in } dm^3}{24}$

c What volume is occupied by 3 moles of any gas at r.t.p?

d What volume is occupied by 88 g of carbon dioxide at r.t.p.?

Note that $1\,dm^3 = 1000\,cm^3$.

Calculations using the mole

Look at this balanced equation.

$$CaCO_3 + 2HCl \rightarrow CaCl_2 + H_2O + CO_2$$

The equation tells us that 1 mole of calcium carbonate reacts with 2 moles of hydrochloric acid.

e How many moles each of calcium chloride, water and carbon dioxide are formed?

We can use the equation to carry out calculations on quantities. For example, the equation tells us that 1 mole of calcium carbonate produces 1 mole of carbon dioxide.

f What is the mass of 1 mole of calcium carbonate and 1 mole of carbon dioxide?

This proportion is always the same. For example, $\frac{1}{2}$ mole of calcium carbonate would make $\frac{1}{2}$ mole of carbon dioxide. So 50 g of calcium carbonate ($\frac{1}{2}$ mole) would produce 22 g of carbon dioxide ($\frac{1}{2}$ mole). We could also say that we would get 12 dm³ of carbon dioxide at r.t.p.

g What mass of calcium chloride is made by reacting 200 g of calcium carbonate completely with hydrochloric acid?

Solutions

One way to measure the concentration of solutions is in grams per cubic decimetre (g/dm³) (see Teaching block A1). However, this does not give us information on the number of particles present in the solution because each solute will have a different relative formula mass. If we measure concentrations in moles per cubic decimetre (mol/dm³) then we can make direct predictions about the numbers of particles present.

concentration in moles per dm³ = $\dfrac{\text{mass present in 1 } dm^3 \text{ of solution}}{\text{mass of one mole}}$

For example, if 4 g of sodium hydroxide, NaOH, relative formula mass 40, is dissolved in 1 dm³ water, its concentration in mol/dm³ is 4/40 = 0.1 moles per dm³.

h What is the concentration, in mol/dm³ of a solution containing 80 g of sodium hydroxide in 1 dm³ of water?

Thinking further

(See page 214 for relative atomic masses.)

◆ **1** Look at this equation:

$Mg + H_2SO_4 \rightarrow MgSO_4 + H_2$

a What are the relative formula masses of each of the reactants and products?

b What mass of magnesium sulphate is made by completely reacting 48 g of magnesium with sulphuric acid?

c What volume of hydrogen is made by completely reacting 12 g of magnesium with sulphuric acid at room temperature and pressure?

d What mass of magnesium is needed to make 120 cm³ (0.12 dm³) of hydrogen at room temperature and pressure?

e What mass of sulphuric acid is needed to dissolve 1.2 tonnes of magnesium?

A5.3 Volumetric analysis

Equipment

The quantity of solid used or formed in a reaction can be found by using an accurate balance. The volume of a liquid can be found approximately by using a measuring cylinder.

a Measuring cylinders come in many sizes. Why is a measuring cylinder with total volume of $10\,cm^3$ more useful than one of total volume $100\,cm^3$ for measuring out $6\,cm^3$ of a liquid?

To measure out an accurate quantity of a liquid chemists use a calibrated **pipette**. Pipettes allow us to accurately measure fixed volumes of solutions. A piece of equipment called a **burette** allows us to measure the volume of liquid added in a reaction.

Getting results

Using pipettes and burettes allows us to compare reacting quantities of solutions. A typical example is the reaction between hydrochloric acid and sodium hydroxide solution. It may be that we know the concentration of the sodium hydroxide solution but not the concentration of the acid. A pipette is used to measure out $25\,cm^3$ of the sodium hydroxide. This is put in a flask and an indicator added.

A burette is filled with the hydrochloric acid. The acid is added to the flask until the indicator shows that the solution is now neutral.

b It is useful to put a white tile underneath the flask. Why?

c Name a device that can be used instead of an indicator to find the neutral point.

The amount of acid is found by subtracting the initial reading on the burette from the final reading. This method of finding reacting quantities of solutions is called a **titration**.

d When chemists find the reacting volumes of solutions they usually repeat the titration at least three times. Suggest why.

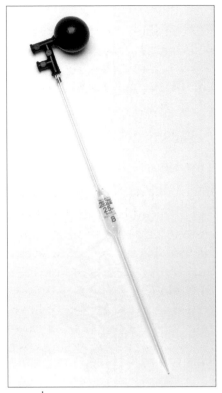

fig 6 | $25\,cm^3$ pipette and a pipette filler (used to fill and empty pipettes)

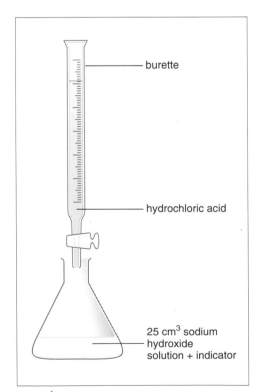

fig 7 | A titration

Using titration results

The reaction between sodium hydroxide and hydrochloric acid is:

$$NaOH + HCl \rightarrow NaCl + H_2O$$

We can find the concentration of hydrochloric acid if we have a solution of sodium hydroxide of known concentration by carrying out a titration. Say that we have a solution of sodium hydroxide containing 0.1 mole of sodium hydroxide per cubic decimetre of solution (0.1 mol/dm^3).

e What mass of sodium hydroxide should be dissolved to make 1 dm^3 of sodium hydroxide solution of concentration 0.1 mol/dm^3?

25 cm^3 of the sodium hydroxide solution are put in a flask, indicator added and then hydrochloric acid is added from a burette until the solution is neutral. Say that the amount of hydrochloric acid added was 25 cm^3. This is the same volume as that of the sodium hydroxide used. The equation shows us that one mole of sodium hydroxide reacts with one mole of hydrochloric acid. As we have the same volume of each, both must be the same concentration, i.e. the hydrochloric acid is 0.1 mol/dm^3. This example was easy because the volumes were the same.

Look at the table of results in fig 8 for another titration between 25 cm^3 samples of 0.1 mol/dm^3 sodium hydroxide and hydrochloric acid of unknown concentration.

titration number	volume of hydrochloric acid added in cm³
1	20.00
2	19.90
3	20.10

fig 8

The average volume of hydrochloric acid added is 20.0 cm^3.

The next step is to find the number of moles of sodium hydroxide used in each titration. In each 25 cm^3 of the 0.1 mol/dm^3 solution there are:

$$\frac{25}{1000} \times 0.1 \text{ moles} = 0.0025 \text{ moles}$$

As the equation shows us that one mole of sodium hydroxide reacts with one mole of hydrochloric acid, there must be 0.0025 moles of hydrochloric acid in the average titration result of 20.0 cm^3.

To find the concentration of the hydrochloric acid we have to find out how many moles are in 1000 cm^3 (1 dm^3).

$$\begin{array}{ccc} 0.0025 \text{ moles} & & 1000 \times 0.0025 \text{ moles} \\ \text{are in } 20.0 \text{ cm}^3 & \text{so} & \overline{20} \quad \text{ are in } 1000 \text{ cm}^3 \end{array} = 0.125 \text{ moles}$$

Thinking further

■ **1** Explain why a pipette is more useful than a 100 cm^3 measuring cylinder to measure out exactly 25 cm^3 of a solution.

■ **2** Explain why it is important to carefully swirl the reaction flask when carrying out a titration.

◆ **3** 50 cm^3 of sodium hydroxide of concentration 0.2 mol/dm^3 is exactly neutralised by 35.2 cm^3 of hydrochloric acid. What is the concentration of the hydrochloric acid in mol/dm^3? Show your working.

KEY WORDS
burette • pipette • titration

Questions on quantitative chemistry

(See page 214 for relative atomic masses.)

1 Your teacher tells you to measure out exactly $25.0\,cm^3$ of sodium hydroxide solution and put it into a conical flask.

● **a** Why it is better to use a $25\,cm^3$ pipette rather than a $100\,cm^3$ measuring cylinder? *(1)*

● **b** Why it is better to use a $25\,cm^3$ pipette rather than a $10\,cm^3$ measuring cylinder? *(1)*

● **c** Why is it important to use a pipette filler to fill the pipette? *(1)*

● **d** Your teacher tells you to put some hydrochloric acid into a burette. What will you use to help transfer the acid into the burette? *(1)*

● **e** How are the graduations on a burette different to those on a pipette? *(2)*

● **f** You now put a pH meter into the sodium hydroxide solution. Suggest the reading on the pH meter. *(1)*

● **g** You add the hydrochloric acid to the sodium hydroxide until the neutral point is reached. What is the reading on the pH meter at the neutral point? *(1)*

● **h** The initial reading on the burette showed $2.50\,cm^3$. The final reading on the burette showed $15.80\,cm^3$. What volume of acid has been added? *(1)*

■ **i** Why is it important to obtain several more titration results? *(1)*

■ **j** Write a symbol equation for the reaction between sodium hydroxide and hydrochloric acid. *(2)*

◆ **k** How many moles of sodium hydroxide react with one mole of hydrochloric acid? *(1)*

2 Two oxides of sulphur, A and B, are found in a sample of pollutant gases. The oxides are analysed. Oxide A contains 50% sulphur and 50% oxygen by mass. Oxide B contains 40% sulphur by mass.

● **a** What is the percentage of oxygen in oxide B? *(1)*

■ **b** Work out the simplest formula for oxide A and oxide B. Show your working. *(8)*

■ **c** Name oxide A and state the environmental problem that this oxide causes when it is present in the atmosphere. *(2)*

3 A hydrocarbon, X, contains 85.7% carbon and 14.3% hydrogen.

■ **a** What is the empirical formula of X? Show your working. *(4)*

■ **b** The relative formula mass of X is 56. What is the molecular formula of X? Show your working. *(3)*

■ **c** Explain why it is important to use a molecular formula and not an empirical formula when writing a balanced equation. *(1)*

◆ **d** Another hydrocarbon has the formula C_4H_{10}. Write a balanced symbol equation for the combustion of C_4H_{10} in a plentiful supply of air and explain how the equation shows that 4 moles of carbon dioxide are formed for every mole of hydrocarbon that burns. *(4)*

◆ **4** Copy and complete the table in fig 9 to show the number moles and number of particles present in the masses of each substance shown. The first one has been done for you. *(5)*

mass of substance	number of moles	number of particles
24 g of carbon, C	2	12×10^{23}
6 g of carbon, C	0.5	
3 g of carbon, C		
132 g of carbon dioxide, CO_2		

fig 9

b Copy and complete the table in fig 10. *(3)*

substance	mass	number of particles
water	18 g	
ammonia		12×10^{23}
	2 g	6×10^{23}

fig 10

c What name is given to the number 6×10^{23}? *(1)*

◆ **5** Sodium reacts with water as shown in this equation:

$$2Na + 2H_2O \rightarrow 2NaOH + H_2$$

Calculate the volume of hydrogen gas, at room temperature and pressure, which is produced when 0.46 g of sodium completely reacts with water. Show your working. *(3)*

◆ **6** Look at this equation. It shows two gases reacting to make another gas.

$$2NO(g) + O_2(g) \rightarrow 2NO_2(g)$$

40 cm³ of NO reacts with 20 cm³ of O_2. What volume of NO_2 forms? (All volumes are measured at room temperature and pressure.) *(1)*

◆ **7** A student carries out a titration reaction, using 1.0 mol/dm³ sodium hydroxide, to find the concentration of acid in some vinegar.

Vinegar contains ethanoic acid. It reacts with sodium hydroxide as shown in this equation.

$$CH_3COOH + NaOH \rightarrow CH_3COONa + H_2O$$

25 cm³ of the vinegar was put in a flask and some indicator added. Sodium hydroxide was added from a burette until the indicator just changed colour. The volume of sodium hydroxide added was 15 cm³.

a How many moles of sodium hydroxide are present in 15 cm³ of the 1 mol/dm³ solution? *(1)*

b How many moles of ethanoic acid react with your answer to part **a**? *(1)*

c How many moles of ethanoic acid must be present in the 25 cm³ of vinegar? *(1)*

d How many moles of ethanoic acid are present in 1 dm³ of the vinegar? *(1)*

e What is the concentration of the ethanoic acid in the vinegar? *(1)*

IDEAS AND EVIDENCE

8 A fertiliser company wishes to buy some ammonium nitrate, NH_4NO_3. It can obtain this from a manufacturer that makes ammonium nitrate from ammonia.

The manufacturer first makes ammonia by this reaction:

$$N_2 + 3H_2 \rightleftharpoons 2NH_3$$

a What is the maximum mass of ammonia, NH_3, which could be made from 28 tonnes of nitrogen? *(1)*

b Explain why this amount may not be produced by this reaction. *(1)*

c What volume of hydrogen would react with 24 dm³ of nitrogen in the reaction? *(1)*

d Ammonia reacts with nitric acid to form ammonium nitrate.

$$NH_3 + HNO_3 \rightarrow NH_4NO_3$$

i Suggest how nitric acid can be made from ammonia. *(1)*

ii What sort of reaction occurs between the ammonia and the nitric acid? *(1)*

iii What mass of nitric acid is needed to completely react with 8.5 tonnes of ammonia? Show your working. *(2)*

e Another fertiliser has the percentage composition shown in the table in fig 11.

element	percentage by mass
nitrogen	21.2
hydrogen	6.1
sulphur	24.2
oxygen	

fig 11

i Copy and complete the table to show the percentage of oxygen present. *(1)*

ii Show that the empirical formula of the substance is $N_2H_8SO_4$. *(4)*

iii One mole of the substance has a mass of 132 g. What is its molecular formula? Show your working. *(2)*

f i A developing country imports its supplies of ammonium nitrate. It has just discovered that it has reserves of crude oil off shore. Explain why the country should consider making its own fertiliser. You should refer to the process and the raw materials in your answer. *(6)*

ii Briefly suggest why the country should warn its farmers to avoid overuse of the fertiliser, especially near rivers and lakes. *(3)*

A6 Electrochemistry and its applications

Links to Double Award

1 Chemical reactions
2 Metals
3 Atomic structure and the Periodic Table
Physics 7 Using electricity

Introduction

Conduction of electricity

All metals conduct electricity, either when solid or when molten. The structure of a solid metal has positive ions surrounded by a sea of electrons.

The electrons between the positive ions are free to move. When the metal is connected to the + and − of a power supply a current flows. Electrons flow through the metal.

Nearly all non-metals do not conduct electricity. They are electrical insulators. They do not have freely moving electrons to carry the current.

An exception to this rule is the non-metal graphite. This is a form of carbon. This solid has an unusual structure. The atoms are joined in layers by covalent bonds, but between the layers there are weak bonds with electrons that can move freely, allowing electrical current to flow.

When electricity flows through a solid or liquid metal or through solid graphite no chemical reaction takes place.

Acids, alkalis and salts

These compounds are made of positive and negative ions. When + and − connections from a power supply are made to a solution of an acid, an alkali or a salt in water, the ions move towards their opposite charge. This carries the electrical current through the solution.

These compounds are called electrolytes.

The same movement of ions can take place when the compound is molten, but these compounds will not conduct electricity when solid. In the solid state the ions are firmly held in place and cannot move to the opposite charge.

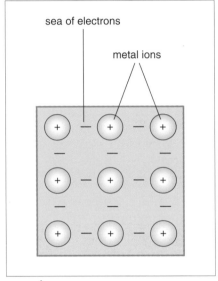

fig 1 | The structure of a solid metal

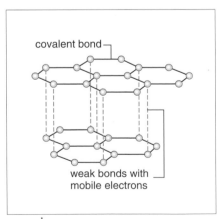

fig 2 | Structure of graphite

Electrolysis

As electrical current passes through an electrolyte a chemical decomposition takes place. Chemical reactions at the positive and negative connections, called electrodes, produce products.

All electrolytes have ionic bonds. They must contain ions to carry the electrical current. Covalent compounds do not contain ions and so do not conduct electricity, even if they are liquid or in a solution. Therefore only ionic compounds can undergo electrolysis.

Check-up

1 Which of the following elements will conduct electricity?

aluminium • chlorine • iron • phosphorus • potassium • sulphur • tungsten • zinc

2 Divide the following compounds into two lists: ionic compounds and covalent compounds.

ammonia	potassium bromide
carbon tetrachloride	phosphorus(v) oxide
iron(II) sulphate	sodium chloride
magnesium nitrate	sulphur dioxide

3 Which of the two lists in question 2 has compounds that conduct electricity? Explain your answer.

4 A solution containing iodine does not conduct electricity but a solution containing potassium iodide does. Explain this.

Contents of the Teaching block

A6.1 Electrolysis reactions

During electrolysis metals are discharged at the negative electrode and non-metals at the positive electrode.

Electrolysis of ionic compounds when molten or when dissolved in water may produce different products. The substance used for the electrodes can also change the reactions taking place.

A6.2 Acidified water

The electrolysis of dilute sulphuric acid produces hydrogen and oxygen gases. Twice as much hydrogen as oxygen is produced. The quantity of electricity used in electrolysis, measured in Coulombs, can be related to the mass or volume of substance discharged.

A6.3 Electrolysis in industry

The electrolysis of brine produces hydrogen, chlorine and sodium hydroxide. Electrolysis can also be used to coat a more reactive metal with a thin layer of a less reactive metal. This will protect or make more attractive the metal underneath.

A6.1 Electrolysis reactions

Molten zinc chloride

Zinc chloride is an ionic compound containing zinc ions, Zn^{2+}, and chloride ions, Cl^-.

When molten **anhydrous** zinc chloride is electrolysed, positive zinc ions are attracted to the negative electrode and negative chloride ions are attracted to the positive electrode.

When zinc ions reach the negative electrode they become zinc atoms. When chloride ions reach the positive electrode they become chlorine molecules. Zinc and chlorine are **discharged** during the electrolysis.

During the electrolysis of a molten ionic compound the metal is always formed at the negative electrode (cathode) and the non-metal is always formed at the positive electrode (anode).

a What substances would be discharged during the electrolysis of molten anhydrous magnesium bromide?

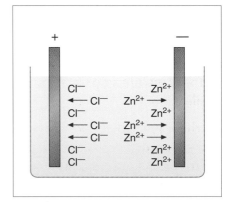

fig 3 | Ion movement in electrolysis of molten anhydrous zinc chloride

Aqueous copper(II) sulphate

An electric current will also pass through a solution of an electrolyte in water, called an **aqueous** solution.

If inert electrodes, e.g. carbon, are used, the products may be the same as during the electrolysis of the molten electrolyte.

If a more reactive material is used for the electrodes, this may be involved in reactions at the electrodes.

When a solution of copper(II) sulphate in water is electrolysed using electrodes made of copper metal, the negative electrode becomes covered in discharged copper atoms.

At the positive electrode copper atoms in the electrode become copper ions and dissolve in the solution.

b How will the mass of the two copper electrodes change as the electrolysis continues?

c The blue colour of copper(II) sulphate solution is caused by copper ions. What will be the appearance of this solution after the electrolysis has continued for some time?

During the electrolysis of molten anhydrous zinc chloride, zinc metal and chlorine gas are produced.

At the negative electrode the zinc ions gain electrons to become zinc atoms.

$$Zn^{2+} + 2e^- \rightarrow Zn$$

Zinc metal is therefore discharged at the negative electrode.

At the positive electrode the chloride ions lose electrons to become chlorine atoms. These join in pairs to form molecules of chlorine gas.

$$2Cl^- \rightarrow Cl_2 + 2e^-$$

Chlorine gas is therefore discharged at the positive electrode.

d Write ionic equations for the reactions at the electrodes during the electrolysis of aqueous copper(II) sulphate using copper electrodes.

As these reactions take place electrons leave the negative electrode and go onto the positive electrode. The electrons joining the positive electrode are not the same ones that left the negative electrode.

Despite this, the effect is the same as if the electrons had passed through the electrolyte. Electrons are traveling from the power supply to the negative electrode and from the positive electrode back to the power supply.

Electricity is passing through the electrolyte, but not in the simple way that it passes through solid or molten metal.

In electrolysis the passage of electricity causes the metal and non-metal ions to be discharged. This leads to the decomposition of the ionic compound.

Thinking further

■ **1** Describe how the passage of electricity through a piece of zinc is different to the passage of electricity through molten zinc chloride.

■ **2** What products would you expect to be discharged during the electrolysis of zinc bromide in each of the following conditions:

 a when molten

 b dissolved in water using carbon electrodes

 c dissolved in water using zinc electrodes?

◆ **3** Write an ionic equation for each of the electrode reactions in **2 a**, **b** and **c**.

┌─ **KEY WORDS** ─────────────
│ **anhydrous • aqueous • discharged**

 Electrolysis of zinc chloride.

A6.2 Acidified water

> ### Key points
>
> - The electrolysis of dilute sulphuric acid produces hydrogen and oxygen gases.
> - The quantity of electricity used in electrolysis can be related to the mass or volume of substance discharged.

Dilute sulphuric acid

Water which has been acidified by the addition of a little sulphuric acid can be electrolysed. This is generally carried out in apparatus called a Hofmann voltameter, shown in fig 4.

The electrodes are made of platinum, which is inert and takes no part in the electrode reactions.

During this electrolysis oxygen gas is produced at the positive electrode and hydrogen gas is produced at the negative electrode.

When the volumes of these two gases are compared, twice as much hydrogen as oxygen is produced.

This means that the compound decomposed in this electrolysis is water, H_2O.

a Look at the apparatus shown in fig 4. How are the gases produced at the electrodes collected separately?

b How can you test the gases released at the electrodes to show that they are hydrogen and oxygen?

c How do the results of this electrolysis show that water is being decomposed?

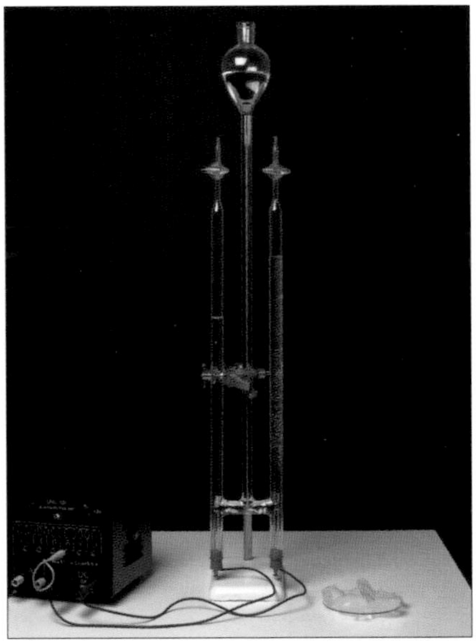

fig 4 | A Hofmann voltameter

Dilute sulphuric acid

Dilute sulphuric acid contains three ions: hydrogen, H^+; hydroxide, OH^-; and sulphate SO_4^{2-}.

Hydrogen ions are attracted to the negative electrode. They collect electrons and discharge as hydrogen gas.

d Write an ionic equation for this reaction.

Hydroxide ions discharge at the positive electrode, producing oxygen gas.

$$4OH^- \rightarrow O_2 + 2H_2O$$

Sulphate ions remain in the solution.

Quantitative electrolysis

By measuring the current, I, and the time, t, for which it flowed, it is possible to find the quantity of electricity passed through the cell using the formula:

$$Q = I \times t$$

where Q is the quantity of electricity, measured in **Coulombs**. The current is measured in amperes, and the time in seconds.

The discharge of the formula mass in grams of an ion with a single charge, e.g. 108 g silver, Ag^+, requires 96 000 C of electricity.

This quantity of electricity is called one **Faraday**.

Copper has the ion Cu^{2+}. To discharge the formula mass in grams of copper, 64 g, requires two Faradays of electricity.

e What quantity of electricity would discharge 27 g of aluminium ions?

Sample calculations

What mass of copper is deposited by the passage of 2.0 A of current for a period of 20 minutes?

$$Q = I \times t = 2.0 \times 20 \times 60 = 2400\,C$$

$$Cu^{2+} + 2e^- \rightarrow Cu$$

64 g Cu^{2+} ions is discharged by $96\,000 \times 2 = 192\,000\,C$

Mass of copper discharged $= 64 \times 2400/192\,000 = 0.8\,g$

What volume of hydrogen, measured at r.t.p., is released by the passage of 2.8 A for a period of 33 minutes?

$$Q = I \times t = 2.8 \times 33 \times 60 = 5544\,C$$

$$2H^+ + 2e^- \rightarrow H_2$$

24 dm^3 hydrogen at r.t.p. is discharged by $96\,000 \times 2 = 192\,000\,C$

Volume of hydrogen $= 24 \times 5544/192\,000 = 0.69\,dm^3$

Thinking further

■ **1** The electrodes in the Hofmann voltameter are made of platinum. Suggest another inert material that could be used for the electrodes.

■ **2** Suggest what would happen if copper electrodes were used in the Hofmann voltameter.

◆ **3** Electricity is passed through an aqueous solution of copper(II) sulphate using copper electrodes. A current of 3.5 A is passed for a period of 40 minutes.

a What mass of copper is deposited on the negative electrode?

b What mass of copper is lost from the positive electrode?

┌─ **KEY WORDS** ─────
│ Coulombs • Faraday │
└──────────────────

A6.3 Electrolysis in industry

The chlor–alkali industry

The electrolysis of concentrated **brine**, salt water, is an important industrial process. The three products, hydrogen, chlorine and sodium hydroxide, are the basis of the chlor-alkali industry.

Electrolysis of concentrated brine may be carried out in the membrane cell, shown in fig 5.

Compartments containing the positive and negative electrodes are separated by an ion-exchange membrane.

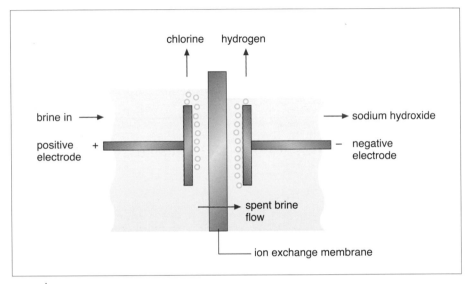

fig 5 | A membrane cell

At the negative electrode hydrogen is discharged. At the positive electrode chlorine is discharged. The two gases are kept apart and are collected separately.

a List the four ions present in brine.

b Which ions are discharged?

c Which ions remain in solution after the electrolysis?

Sodium and hydroxide ions collect in the compartment containing the negative electrode, giving the third product, sodium hydroxide.

The products of this electrolysis have a wide range of uses.

Hydrogen is used to make ammonia and in the manufacture of margarine.

Chlorine is used to kill bacteria in swimming pools and domestic water supplies. It is also used to make plastics.

Sodium hydroxide is used to make soap, paper, bleach and rayon fibres.

d Why is the chlor–alkali industry so important?

Electroplating

Electrolysis can be used to coat a thin layer of a less reactive metal onto a more reactive metal. This process is called **electroplating**.

The thin layer of less reactive metal will provide protection from corrosion for the more reactive metal underneath. It may also make the product more attractive to look at.

Steel can be electroplated with chromium. This prevents the steel from rusting and gives it a shiny, silver finish.

e Describe and explain what happens to chromium-plated steel when the chromium layer is chipped or scratched.

Nickel can be electroplated with silver. This will make, for example, a nickel candlestick look like a much more expensive solid silver one.

The nickel candlestick and a block of silver are used as electrodes and the electrolyte is a soluble silver salt.

f Suggest why a silver plated candlestick is still not as good as a solid silver one.

g Which electrode, positive or negative, should the candlestick be?

Electrolysis of brine

In the membrane cell for the electrolysis of brine the following reaction takes place at the negative electrode.

$$2H^+ + 2e^- \rightarrow H_2$$

h Write an ionic equation for the reaction that takes place at the positive electrode.

A different type of cell is used to carry out the electrolysis of molten sodium chloride. Chlorine gas is again produced at the positive electrode.

i What is produced at the negative electrode?

Electroplating

During the electroplating of a nickel article with silver, the reaction at the negative electrode deposits silver atoms.

$$Ag^+ + e^- \rightarrow Ag$$

j Write an ionic equation for the reaction at the positive electrode.

Thinking further

■ **1** During the electrolysis of brine in the membrane cell, hydrogen and chlorine are kept apart from each other. Explain why this is necessary.

■ **2** When an article is electroplated with silver, why must one of the electrodes be made of silver metal?

◆ **3** To silver plate a nickel goblet, 4.0 A of current are passed for a period of 45 minutes. What mass of silver is plated onto the goblet? (See page 214 for relative atomic mass.)

KEY WORDS
brine • electroplating

Questions on electrolysis

● **1** Which of the following solids will conduct electricity?

aluminium
boron
iodine
iron(III) oxide
lead
manganese
phosphorus
silver
sodium chloride
sugar
sulphur   *(4)*

● **2** Which of the following liquids or solutions will conduct electricity?

dilute hydrochloric acid
hexane
aqueous copper(II) nitrate
aqueous sodium hydroxide
aqueous silver nitrate
petrol
pure water
acidified water   *(5)*

■ **3** Carbon forms a chloride with the formula CCl_4. Potassium forms a chloride with the formula KCl.

a Will either of these two compounds conduct electricity at room temperature? *(1)*

b Explain your answer to **a**.   *(2)*

c Will either of these two compounds conduct electricity when heated?   *(1)*

d Explain your answer to **c**.   *(2)*

■ **4** Electrolysis can be used to cover one metal with a thin layer of another metal. For each example below suggest why the first metal is covered with a layer of the second:

a a nickel candlestick with silver   *(1)*

b a steel watch with gold   *(1)*

c a steel can with tin   *(1)*

d a nickel headphone plug with gold.   *(1)*

■ **5** Lead(II) bromide will not conduct electricity when solid. Molten lead(II) bromide will conduct electricity.

a Explain this difference.   *(2)*

b What would you expect to **see** as the molten lead(II) bromide conducts an electric current?   *(2)*

■ **6** When an electric current passes through molten zinc no chemical reaction takes place. When an electric current passes through molten zinc chloride a chemical reaction does take place.

Explain this difference.   *(4)*

■ **7** What are the products of electrolysis of the following compounds using the conditions given. State which product is formed at the positive and which at the negative electrode.

a Copper(II) chloride solution in water using copper electrodes.   *(2)*

b Copper(II) chloride solution in water using carbon electrodes.   *(2)*

c Molten potassium bromide using carbon electrodes.   *(2)*

■ **8** Diamond and graphite are different forms of carbon. Diamond does not conduct electricity but graphite does.

Explain these facts.   *(4)*

■ **9** When dilute sulphuric acid is electrolysed the products are hydrogen and oxygen. A series of experiments was carried out to find how the volume of each gas evolved varies with the electrical current used. The table in fig 6 shows the volume of hydrogen, measured under the same conditions, produced after the same length of time for each current value.

current in amps	volume of hydrogen in cm^3
1.0	12
2.0	24
3.0	35
4.0	48
5.0	58

fig 6

a Use graph paper to plot these results. *(3)*

b What conclusions can you draw about the relationship between volume of hydrogen and current in these experiments? *(1)*

c Sketch on your graph the results you would expect for the volume of oxygen measured in the same experiments. *(2)*

d What is the relationship between the volume of hydrogen and the volume of oxygen in these experiments? *(1)*

e Explain your answer to **d**. *(2)*

◆ **10** A factory uses membrane cells for the electrolysis of brine. A cell operates for 24 hours each day with a current of 4 A.

a What is the volume of hydrogen, measured at r.t.p., produced by this cell each day? *(3)*

b What volume of chlorine, measured at r.t.p., is produced per day by the same cell? *(3)*

c What is the mass of sodium hydroxide produced by this cell each day? *(3)*
(Volume occupied by the relative formula mass in grams of any gas at r.t.p. is 24 dm^3. See page 214 for relative atomic masses.)

◆ **11** During an electrolysis of copper(II) sulphate solution in water using copper electrodes, the positive electrode lost 1.7 g of mass. The current used was 2.5 A.

a What was the mass of copper gained by the negative electrode during the electrolysis? *(1)*

b For how long did the current flow? *(3)*

◆ **12** Magnesium metal is extracted by the electrolysis of molten magnesium chloride. A major source of magnesium is sea water. Each kilogram of sea water contains 5.15 g of magnesium chloride.

a What is the maximum mass of magnesium which can be extracted from each tonne of sea water? *(3)*

b Consider where a factory to produce magnesium should be sited. Suggest a suitable location and support your choice with reasons for using this location. *(4)*

◆ **13** A student tried to silver-plate a nickel medallion using electrolysis in a solution of silver nitrate. He used the medallion as the negative electrode and a carbon rod as the positive electrode. The medallion was poorly plated. In places the silver coating was very thin. A friend made the following suggestions to improve the silver-plating. For each one say whether it would give an improvement, and explain why.

a Use a more concentrated solution of silver nitrate. *(1)*

b Use silver for the positive electrode. *(1)*

c Rotate the medallion in the solution. *(1)*

d Use a small current for a long time. *(1)*

IDEAS AND EVIDENCE

14 Chlorine gas is a product of the chlor–alkali industry. Chlorine is used to sterilize the water in swimming pools and domestic water supplies, and to make plastics (such as PVC), bleach, solvents for dry cleaning and hydrochloric acid.
An important use of chlorine is the production of chlorofluorocarbons (CFCs).

In the early part of the 20th century there was little use for chlorine. This held back the development of the chlor–alkali industry. In the second half of the 20th century the use of chlorine increased dramatically, and new processes such as the membrane cell for the electrolysis of brine were developed.
More recently the use of CFCs has been banned in many countries because of the damage they cause to the ozone layer.

a Suggest why the chlor–alkali industry became more important in the second half of the 20th century. *(3)*

b Discuss what might happen to the chlor–alkali industry during the 21st century. *(3)*

Glossary (TB 1–8)

Terms set in pink are Higher tier material.

abundant (2.3) – existing in large quantities.

acid (1.5) – substance that dissolves in water to form a solution with a pH below 7. An acid contains hydrogen which can replaced by a metal to form a salt.

addition polymer (6.5) – product formed when many molecules of a monomer react to form one large molecule. No other substances are formed.

addition reaction (6.3) – reaction in which two molecules react together to form one molecule.

alchemists (1.1) – alchemy combined aspects of chemistry with mysticism. It was developed in Egypt and China over 2000 years ago. In Europe the main aim of alchemists was to turn metals such as lead into gold.

algal bloom (8.4) – excessive growth of algae, e.g. during eutrophication.

alkali (1.5) – a metal oxide (called a base) or hydroxide that dissolves in water to form a solution with a pH above 7. An alkali is neutralised by an acid to form a salt and water.

alkane (6.3) – a family of hydrocarbons containing only single carbon to carbon bonds. Alkanes have a general formula C_nH_{2n+2}.

alkene (6.3) – family of hydrocarbons containing a carbon to carbon double bond. Alkenes have a general formula C_nH_{2n}.

alloy (2.5) – mixture of two or more metals, e.g. copper and zinc in brass.

anaerobic respiration (4.4) – respiration in the absence of oxygen. In yeast glucose reacts to form ethanol and carbon dioxide; in muscle lactic acid is formed.

atmospheres (8.1) – measurement of pressure. One atmosphere is approximately 100 000 Pa (100 000 N/m²).

atomic number (3.1) – the number of protons in an atom of an element.

average bond energy (5.8) – the amount of energy required to break a typical type of covalent bond when more than one is present in a molecule, e.g. the average bond energy of a C—H bond in CH_4 is 413 kJ.

balanced equation (1.3) – a chemical equation where the number of each type of atom in the products is the same as the number of each type of atom in the reactants.

base (1.5) – a metal oxide which reacts with an acid to form a salt and water only.

bauxite (2.3) – the main ore of aluminium. It contains aluminium oxide, Al_2O_3.

biodegradable (6.6) – substances that can be broken down by such processes as decomposition by bacteria and can therefore be reused by living organisms.

bleach (3.7) – a solution containing chloride ions (Cl^-) and chlorate(I) ions (ClO^-) made by dissolving chlorine in sodium hydroxide solution. Bleach will decolourise dyes by oxidising them.

bond energy (5.8) – the amount of energy required to break a particular type of covalent bond. It is the same as the energy released when that bond forms.

brine (3.8) – a concentrated solution of sodium chloride in water.

buckminsterfullerene (5.6) – one form of the element carbon. It exists in the form of molecules, such as C_{60}, which has the same sort of a shape as a geodesic dome.

carcinogenic (6.1, 8.4) – causing cancer. Chemical carcinogens include tar and some dyes.

cast iron (2.2) – iron made by pouring the molten metal from the blast furnace into a mould and letting it cool.

catalyst (2.5, 4.3) – a substance which increases the rate of a chemical reaction but is itself unchanged in amount.

catalytic cracking (6.4) – breaking down of long-chain hydrocarbon molecules by the action of a heated catalyst to produce smaller molecules.

cement (1.4) – substance made by heating powdered limestone with clay. On mixing with water it sets to a hard mass.

chalk (1.4) – sedimentary rock consisting of very small particles of calcium carbonate.

chemical bonds (1.2) – name that is given to the forces that hold atoms together.

chemistry (1.1) – science of the elements and the ways in which they interact with each other.

collide (4.2) – make violent contact with another object.

colourless (3.9) – without colour.

combining power (1.2) – measure of the ability of an ion to combine with others. Magnesium has a combining power of two and chloride one. Two chloride ions join with one magnesium ion.

combustion (1.6, 6.2) – combination of a substance with oxygen to release energy.

concentration (4.2) – the quantity of a solute dissolved in a stated volume of solvent.

contact metamorphism (7.5) – a type of metamorphism that occurs when a rock has been altered by the effects of high temperatures. This often occurs when igneous intrusions pass near bedding planes of rock.

corrode (2.5) – suffer chemical attack.

corrosive (1.1) – a corrosive substance may damage your eyes and skin. It is represented by a tube dropping a liquid onto a hand in the Hazchem code.

covalent bond (3.6, 5.4) – type of bonding involving the sharing of one or more pairs of electrons. The electrons are provided by the atoms that are combining.

cracking (6.4) – breaking down of long-chain hydrocarbon molecules by the action of a heated catalyst or by heat alone to produce smaller molecules.

cryolite (2.3) – the mineral sodium aluminium fluoride, Na_3AlF_6. It is used as a solvent in the extraction of aluminium.

decomposers (8.4) – micro-organisms and small animals which break down the complex molecules in dead organic matter.

decomposition (4.3) – breaking a large molecule into smaller molecules.

denatured (4.4) – when the structure of a protein molecule is permanently changed, e.g. by high temperature or extreme pH.

denitrifying bacteria (7.2) – soil bacteria that break down nitrates, releasing nitrogen gas into the air.

density (3.5) – mass per unit of volume, e.g. kg/m^3 or g/cm^3.

diamond (5.6) – one form of the element carbon. The carbon atoms are held together by strong covalent bonds in a giant structure.

diatomic (3.9) – an element which exists naturally as molecules containing two atoms.

disinfectants (3.7) – substances which kill bacteria.

displacement reaction (3.6) – a reaction where one atom takes the place of another, e.g. iron taking the place of copper in copper(II) sulphate solution.

displayed formula (6.3) – chemical formula that shows every atom and bond. It is sometimes called a graphical formula or full structural formula.

dot and cross diagrams (5.2) – drawings representing the electrons in a molecule. Dots and crosses are used to indicate the atom from which the electron has originated.

double bond (5.4) – covalent bond in which there are two shared pairs of electrons between atoms, e.g. oxygen and ethene.

E

electrode (2.3) – an electrical connection from the power supply to a conductor such as an electrolyte.

electrolysis (2.1, 2.3) – the decomposition of a compound by the passage of electricity.

electrons (3.1, 3.10) – negatively charged sub-atomic particles which exist outside the nucleus.

electroplating (2.4) – covering one metal with a thin layer of another by the process of electrolysis.

electrostatic attraction (5.3) – attraction between opposite charges. Present in ionic compounds.

energy level diagram (5.8) – diagram showing the energy content at stages during a reaction.

endothermic (1.7, 2.2) – a reaction which takes in heat from the surroundings.

erosion (7.5) – process in which rocks are worn away.

eutrophication (8.4) – the process by which excessive quantities of nitrate ions pollute lakes and rivers.

exothermic (1.7) – reaction which gives out heat to the surroundings.

extrusive rocks (7.5) – igneous rocks that have cooled and solidified as crystals on the surface of the Earth, e.g. basalt.

fault (7.6) – beds of rocks that are distorted with a loss of continuity.

formula (1.2) – a chemical formula shows how many atoms of each element combine together to make a substance.

fossil (7.6) – recognisable remains of plants or animals that lived in the past.

fractional distillation (6.1) – method of separating liquids with different boiling points.

fold (7.6) – beds of rock that are distorted without loss of continuity.

G

gauze (8.2) – a mesh of fine wire.

giant structure (5.3) – a crystal structure in which all of the particles are linked together by a network of bonds extending through the crystal, e.g. diamond and sodium chloride.

glass (1.4) – supercooled liquid which forms a hard, brittle substance which is usually transparent. Common glass is made from limestone, sodium carbonate and sand.

global warming (7.4) – rise in the average temperature of the Earth's surface. It is thought to be caused by the greenhouse effect.

graphite (5.6) – one form of the element carbon. The carbon atoms are present in layers. These layers are only weakly held to each other.

greenhouse effect (7.4) – caused by the increase in concentration of atmospheric carbon dioxide and leading to global warming.

greenhouse gases (7.4) – gases such as carbon dioxide and methane that contribute to the greenhouse effect.

groups (3.2, 3.3) – vertical columns in the Periodic Table.

halide (3.8) – a compound containing the ions of a halogen (any element in Group 7).

harmful (1.1) – a harmful substance is poisonous but less so than a toxic substance. It is represented by a cross in the Hazchem code.

Hazchem code (1.1) – set of simple representations used to warn about the dangers from chemicals.

highly flammable (1.1) – substance that catches fire easily. It is represented by a flame in the Hazchem code.

hydrocarbon (6.1) – compounds made up from the elements carbon and hydrogen only.

I

igneous (7.5) – rocks that have cooled and solidified as crystals from molten rock.

inhibitor (4.3) – substance which makes a reaction take place more slowly.

intensive farming (8.3) – techniques to enable more food to be produced from less land.

intrusive rocks (7.5) – igneous rocks that have cooled and solidified as crystals inside the Earth, e.g. granite.

ion (3.1, 5.1) – positively or negatively charged particle formed when an atom or a group of atoms loses or gains electrons.

ionic bond (5.3) – type of bonding involving the complete transfer of one or more electrons from a metal atom to a non-metal atom. Ions are formed.

ionic compound (5.2) – compound formed by the electrostatic attraction between positive ions and negative ions.

ionic equation (1.3, 5.3) – concise method of writing down the important changes to ions in a chemical reaction. Ions that take no part in the reaction are not usually included.

isotopes (3.1, 3.10) – atoms of the same element but with different numbers of neutrons. They have the same atomic number but a different mass number.

K

khemeia (1.1) – the root of the word chemistry. Its origin was from ancient Egypt and described the secret processes that were used for embalming the dead.

L

laser (3.9) – an instrument used to produce an intense beam of light.

lava (7.5) – molten rock that escapes from a volcano.

lattice (5.3) – ionic bonding leads to the formation of a crystalline structure called a lattice.

leach (4.3, 8.4) – become washed out of soil or rock by the flow of water.

limekiln (1.4) – building in which limestone is roasted and turned into quicklime.

limestone (1.4) – rock made of calcium carbonate, $CaCO_3$.

liquefy (8.1) – turn from solid or gas into liquid.

M

magma (7.5) – rock between the crust and the core of the Earth.

manure (8.2, 8.3) – fertiliser made from animal faeces.

mass number (3.1) – sum of the number of protons and neutrons in an atom.

metamorphic rocks (7.5) – rocks that were originally either igneous or sedimentary and have been altered by the effects of high temperatures and/or high pressures.

micro-organism (4.4) – plant or animal which can only be seen by the use of a microscope.

minerals (2.1) – compounds contained within rocks.

molecular structure (5.5) – type of structure built up of molecules. A substance with a molecular structure has weak forces between molecules and so has a low melting point and boiling point.

molecule (1.3) – particle with two or more atoms joined together.

monatomic (3.9) – used to describe an element which exists naturally as individual atoms.

monomer (6.5) – small molecule which joins together with other molecules to produce a polymer.

N

neutralisation (1.5) – reaction in which an acid reacts with a base or alkali.

neutralising (8.2, 8.3) – cancelling out acidity or alkalinity to make the solution neutral.

neutrons (3.1, 3.10) – neutral sub-atomic particles which exist inside the nucleus.

nitrifying bacteria (7.2) – group of soil bacteria which convert ammonia to nitrates.

nitrogenous (8.4) – containing the element nitrogen.

non-metal (3.6) – an element which is not a metal.

nucleus (3.1, 3.10) – the central part of an atom. It contains protons and neutrons.

O

open-cast mining (2.3) – a technique that collects an ore from the surface of the Earth's crust.

optimum temperature (4.4) – the temperature at which maximum reaction takes place; used to describe the action of an enzyme.

optimum pH (4.4) – the pH at which maximum reaction takes place; used to describe the action of an enzyme.

ore (2.1) – a rock which contains a large percentage of a metal or metal compound.

oxidation (1.6) – reaction in which a substance gains oxygen or loses electrons. It is the opposite of reduction.

oxidise (6.2) – to bring about an oxidation process.

P

Periodic Table (1.2) – classification of the elements in order of their atomic numbers. Elements with similar properties appear in columns known as groups.

periods (3.3) – the horizontal rows of elements in the Periodic Table.

photosynthesis (7.2) – process taking place in the green parts of a plant. Water and carbon dioxide react together in sunlight and in the presence of chlorophyll to produce sugars and oxygen.

phytoplankton (7.3) – plankton consisting of plants.

pig iron (2.2) – impure iron produced by the blast furnace. It contains a high percentage of carbon.

plate tectonics (7.6) – slow movements of parts of the Earth's crust known as plates. The driving force for this movement is thought to be convection currents in the mantle.

pollutants (7.1) – contaminants of the environment that are a by-product of human activity.

polymer (6.5) – long chain molecule built up of a large number of small units, called monomers, joined together by a process called polymerisation.

precipitation (7.3) – the separation of a solid from a solution. The solid usually settles out.

pressure (4.2) – the force exerted on an object by the collision of particles of gas with the surface of the object.

products (1.3, 4.1) – the substances which remain after a chemical reaction has taken place. They appear to the right of the arrow in the equation.

properties (3.2) – what a chemical substance is like or what reactions it will undergo.

proteins (4.4, 8.3) – large molecules which are polymers of amino acids.

protons (3.1, 3.10) – positively charged sub-atomic particles which exist inside the nucleus.

quicklime (1.4) – common name for calcium oxide, CaO.

rate of reaction (4.1) – the speed with which products are formed and reactants disappear during a chemical reaction.

reactants (1.3, 4.1) – substances that are used at the start of a chemical reaction. They appear to the left of the arrow in the equation.

reactivity (3.5) – how vigorously a substance reacts with other substances.

recycled (2.1) – used again.

redox reaction (2.4) – a reaction involving both reduction and oxidation.

reduction (1.6, 2.1) – reaction in which a substance loses oxygen or gains electrons. It is the opposite of oxidation.

relative atomic mass (3.10) – the mass of an atom measured on a scale where one atom of the isotope carbon-12 is exactly 12 units.

relative formula mass (5.7) – mass obtained by adding together the relative atomic masses of all of the atoms shown in the formula of a compound.

repeat unit (6.5) – that part of the structure of a polymer that repeats itself along the polymer chain.

rock salt (3.8) – impure salt (sodium chloride) which is present as deposits in the ground.

saturated (6.3) – compound which contains only single covalent bonds, e.g. ethane C_2H_6.

sedimentary rocks (7.5) – rocks, e.g. limestone and sandstone, that are composed of compacted fragments of older rocks that have accumulated in layers on the floor of an ancient sea or lake.

shells (3.4) – locations of electrons around the nucleus of an atom.

slag (2.2) – calcium silicate produced as a by-product of the blast furnace.

slaked lime (1.4) – common name for calcium hydroxide, $Ca(OH)_2$.

specific temperature (4.4) – a precise temperature.

stable (3.5) – not likely to take part in a chemical reaction.

state symbols (2.4) – symbols used in a chemical equation to indicate whether each substance is a solid (s), liquid (l), gas (g) or in solution in water (aq).

steel (2.2) – an alloy of iron with a small percentage (under 4%) of carbon.

sterilise (3.7) – kill bacteria.

succession (7.6) – layers of rock one above the other. Older rocks are usually at the bottom of the succession.

surface area (4.2) – the area of the surface of a solid object, usually measured in cm^2.

symbol (1.2) – one or two letters used to represent a chemical element. The first letter is always a capital.

symbol equation (1.3) – summary of a chemical reaction using the chemical symbols and formulae of the reactants and products.

thermal cracking (6.4) – breaking down of long-chain hydrocarbon molecules by the action of heat alone to produce smaller molecules.

thermal decomposition (1.4) – breaking down of compounds by the action of heat.

toxic (1.1) – poisonous substance. It is represented by a skull and crossbones in the Hazchem code. It is important not to swallow such substances or to get them on your skin.

unsaturated (6.3) – compound which contains at least one double bond, e.g. ethene C_2H_4.

W

weathering (7.5) – action of wind, rain, snow etc. on rocks. The action can be physical or chemical.

word equation (1.3) – summary of a chemical reaction using the chemical names of the reactants and products.

yield (8.1) – the percentage of the maximum possible amount of a product which is actually produced in a chemical reaction.

Glossary (TB A1–A6)

Terms set in pink are Higher tier material.

A

alcohol (A4.1) – an organic compound cotaining an OH group. A common alcohol is ethanol C_2H_5OH.

anhydrous (A6.1) – without water, e.g. anhydrous copper(II) sulphate.

aqueous (A6.1) – dissolved in water.

Avogadro constant (A5.1) – the number of particles in one mole of a sustance, 6×10^{23}.

B

brass (A3.1) – an alloy containing copper and zinc.

burette (A5.2) – a glass tube with a calibrated scale and tap. It is used to measure amounts of solutions, e.g. in titration.

C

conductivity (A2.2) – in chemistry used to indicate the extent to which a solution conducts electricity.

coulomb (A6.2) – the unit of electric charge. One coulomb of charge flows when one ampere of current passes for one second.

D

dehydration (A4.3) – a reaction where water, or the elements of water (hydrogen and oxygen), are removed from a substance.

discharged (A6.1) – formed at the positive or negative electrode during electrolysis.

E

Empirical formula (A5.1) – a formula for a compound that shows the simplest ratio of atoms present.

F

Faraday (A6.2) – the electric charge which discharges one atomic mass in grams of a monovalent ion during electrolysis. It is 96000 Coulombs.

fermentation (A4.3) – the procss in which enzymes in yeast convert glucose into ethanol and carbon dioxide.

G

galvanizing (A3.2) – covering steel with alayer of zinc, to prevent rusting.

general formula (A4.1) – a formula for a particular homologous series that shows the ratio of atoms present in general terms, e.g. alkenes have the general formula C_nH_{2n}.

H

homologous series (A4.1) – a family of organic compounds that have a general formula, e.g. the alkenes.

hydrated iron oxide (A3.2) – a form of iron(III) oxide combined with water molecules. It is the substance of rust.

I

ionic half equation (A3.3) – an ionic equation which represents only one of the two changes, reduction or oxidation, which take place in aredox reaction.

L

lather (A1.3) – the bubbles formed when soap is shaken with water.

lime scale (A1.3) – a deposit of calcium carbonate which is formed when water with temporary hardness is boiled. Sometimes called 'fur' in for examples kettles.

M

mole (A5.1) – the measure of amount of substance in chemistry. One mole of a substance has a mass equal to its relative formula mass in grams. One mole of any type of particle always contains the same number of particles, 6×10^{23}.

molecular formula (A5.1) – a formula which shows the actual number of atoms present in a molecule.

O

organic chemistry (A4.1) – the chemistry of carbon containing compounds. There are many millions of organic compounds.

oxidizing agent (A3.3) – a substance which brings out the oxidation of another substance.

P

permanent hardness, of water (A1.2) – hardness of water which is not removed by boiling the water. It is caused by dissolved calcium and magnesium sulphates.

pH meter (A2.2) – a device that allows the pH of a solution to be found without the need for indicators.

pipette (A5.2) – a graduated glass tube for delivering a measured quantity of liquid or solution. Used in volumetric analysis.

redox reaction (A3.3) – a reaction involving both reduction and oxidation.

reducing agent (A3.3) – a substance which brings about the reduction of another substance.

sacrificial protection (A2) – the corrosion of a more reactive metal in contact with a less reactive metal, which stops the less reactive metal corroding, e.g. zinc in contact with iron prevents the iron from rusting.

saturated solution (A1.1) – a solution which contains the maximum mass of a solute that will dissolve in the solvent at that temperature.

scum (A1.3) – the solid formed when soap is mixed with hard water.

solder (A3.1) – an alloy containing tin and lead, used to make joins in electrical circuits.

solubility (A1.1) – the maximum mass of a solute which will dissolve in a given volume of solvent at a specified temperature.

solubility curve (A1.1) – a graph showing how the solubility of a solute in a solvent changes with change in temperature.

solute (A1.1) – the substance which dissolves in a solvent to make a solution.

solution (A1.1) – the liquid formed when a solute dissolves in a solvent, e.g. brine is a solution of salt (sodium chloride) as the solute in water as the solvent.

solvent (A1.1) – the liquid which dissolves a solute to make a solution.

spectator ions (A2.2) – ions that are present when a chemical reaction takes place but take no part in the reaction.

stainless steel (A3.2) – an alloy containing iron, chromium and nickel. It is resistant to corrosion.

strong acid (A2.1) – an acid that completely ionizes when it dissolves in water.

structural isomers (A4.2) – substances that have the same molecular formula but different structures.

temporary hardness, of water (A1.2) – hardness of water which is removed by boiling. It is caused by dissolved calcium hydrogencarbonate.

titration (A5.2) – a method of investigating the volumes of solutions that react together.

W

water hardness (A1.2) – the difficulty in forming a lather in water caused by the presence of calcium and magnesium ions.

water softener (A1.2) – a method used to remove hardness from water.

weak acid (A2.2) – an acid that only partly ionozed when it dissolves in water and produces a low concentration of hydrogen ions, H^+.

Drawing line graphs

Many GCSE Science papers have a question requiring you to draw and use a line graph. You will probably draw a line graph for your Sc1 coursework.

Before starting to draw a graph you will need a sharp pencil, a 30 cm ruler and a piece of 2 mm^2 graph paper.

On Foundation tier papers the axes and scales of the graph will be given to you. One or two of the points may have been plotted already. All of the points will fit on a straight line or curve and there will be no points in the wrong place.

On Higher tier papers, or for coursework, you will first have to choose suitable scales and axes.

For example, here is some information from a data book.

number of carbon atoms	2	3	4	5	6	7
boiling point in °C	-89	-42	0	36	69	98

In this case the boiling point depends upon the number of carbon atoms. The dependent variable (boiling point) goes on the vertical or y-axis and the independent variable on the horizontal or x-axis.

Use a ruler to draw the axes on the graph paper and label them 'Boiling point in °C' and 'Number of carbon atoms'.

Now choose suitable scales. On the x-axis 1 large square (or 10 small squares) $\equiv$ 1 carbon atom. On the y-axis the scale needs to go from about -100 °C to +100 °C. The graph does not have to start at zero. A suitable scale is 1 large square $\equiv$ 50 °C. If you choose 1 large square $\equiv$ 100 °C you will have a smaller graph. You will lose a mark for your graph if it does not more than half fill the grid.

Now plot the points carefully, marking each plot with a small cross or a dot with a circle round it.

You will lose one or two marks if you plot points wrongly so check them carefully.

Now you have to draw a best-fit line. In this example it is close to a straight line. If the points are on a straight line use a ruler to draw it. Otherwise draw the best line, but do not just join the points together in a series of 'dot-to-dot' lines. A curve should be one continuous smooth line. Do not draw multiple or double lines.

Some computer software will draw a graph for you. Take care! Usually the computer will simply join the points dot-to-dot, rather than drawing a best-fit line. It is probably best to draw your own graphs. In examinations you will have to do this anyway.

Sometimes with experimental results there are anomalous points. They do not fit the pattern shown by the rest of the points. Draw your best line to miss these points.

Here is a set of results. Use this data to draw a graph.

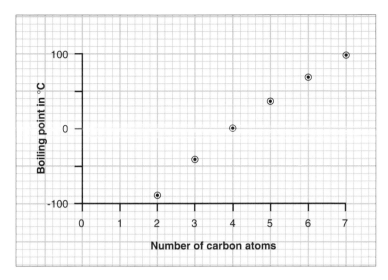

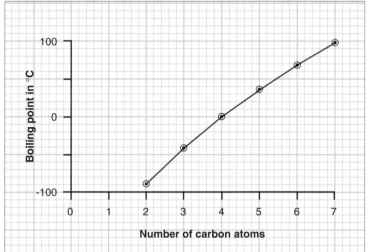

time in *s*	0	10	15	20	25	30	35	40	45
volume of gas collected in cm³	0	34	47	57	63	70	69	70	70

Improving your writing of longer answers

All GCSE Science papers have questions which you must answer with a series of linked sentences. These questions are called extended and continuous writing.

At least 25% of the marks in your examination are awarded for these questions requiring longer answers.

Most candidates do not do as well on these questions as on other types of question. It is well worth practising to get better at writing longer answers.

Here are two examples of typical long answer questions. Some help is given to show you how to answer the first one.

1 Describe how ammonia is produced in the Haber process. [6 + 1]

Before starting to answer this question, think carefully what the question is asking you to do. You are asked to *describe how ammonia is produced* in the Haber process.
The question does not ask you how the process was developed or what problems it might have. You simply have to describe the process.

There are six marks for content (shown by the 6 in brackets) so you must make a least six different points and they must be put into a correct order. The other mark (shown by the 1 in brackets) is for the quality of written communication.

Listed below are some of the points you might make. Some of the points listed here are wrong, some are correct but not relevant to this particular question and some are needed in a good answer.

Go through the statements listed and decide which statements should be included and which should not.

Now the statements have to be put in a correct order. Write out the statements you have chosen from the list below in a correct order.

- Used to produce fertilisers
- Nitrogen from air
- Ammonia removed by liquefying
- Only 10% of gases react
- Hydrogen from methane
- Mix gases together
- Recycle unreacted gases

- Pass over iron catalyst
- Compress gases to high pressure
- 3 parts hydrogen to 1 part nitrogen
- Ammonia dissolves in water
- The process was developed by Fritz Haber
- $N_2 + 3H_2 \rightleftharpoons 2NH_3$

2 **The percentage of oxygen in the atmosphere has remained constant over the last one hundred years but the percentage of carbon dioxide has increased significantly. Explain.** *[6 + 1]*

This time your answer must be an explanation and not just a description. You must explain both the constant percentage of oxygen *and* the increase in carbon dioxide.

Make a list of relevant points and then put them into an order that makes sense and write out your answer.

Although there are six marks for content you should not assume it is three marks for the oxygen percentage and three marks for the carbon dioxide percentage.

Marks are also awarded for the quality of written communication in this type of question.

In each of these questions there are six marks for content and one mark that the examiner can add for the quality of written communication.

This can be awarded for any of the following:

- the correct use of sentences with capital letter, verb and full stop
- the correct use and spelling of scientific words
- the correct use of scientific terms, e.g. photosynthesis
- putting events in the correct and logical order to ensure communication.

Your longer answers will improve if you remember and practise what you have learnt in this section.

Ideas and evidence

Mercury amalgam dental fillings

Most tooth fillings are made of an alloy called mercury amalgam. This contains 50% mercury, 35% silver, 13% tin, 2% copper and a little zinc. Mercury amalgam is cheap, easy to use and more durable than resin alternatives. It has been shown to cause less damage to tooth pulp. Composite resins also take more skill and time to place in the tooth cavity.

Unfortunately mercury is a poison more toxic than lead. Human body cells may be damaged by even the smallest concentration of the element.

Autopsy studies have shown a correlation between the number of mercury amalgam fillings and the mercury levels in the brain and kidneys.

Small amounts of mercury vapour are given off by the amalgam during brushing, chewing and eating hot or acidic foods. Most of this vapour is inhaled, allowing the element to pass through the lungs into the blood stream.

In 1993 Germany's Health Ministry recommended that no further amalgam fillings should be used for women of child-bearing age. In 1997 Sweden banned the use of mercury amalgam for tooth fillings.

Some scientists have associated the mercury in dental fillings with diseases such as multiple sclerosis, chronic fatigue syndrome and multiple chemical sensitivity.

By contrast the American Dental Association says that replacing amalgam fillings from non-allergic patients is 'improper and unethical' and that amalgams have been proved safe in studies.

The Canadian Dental Association says that there is no scientific evidence linking medical illness symptoms to mercury fillings, except relatively rare allergic sensitivity. The CDA also points out that billions of mercury amalgam fillings have been used with no apparent epidemic of ill effects.

Questions

1 Use information from the above paragraphs to write a letter to your local newspaper protesting about the use of mercury amalgam fillings by local dentists.

2 Write a reply to this letter from a local dentist who thinks that the use of these fillings is safe and necessary.

Fluoridation

In the early part of the twentieth century it was observed that people in some parts of the USA developed brown stains on their teeth. These stained teeth were highly resistant to tooth decay, called caries. The staining was caused by fluoride ions, which occurred naturally in the water in these areas.

It was later found that a low concentration of fluoride, between 0.7 and 1.2 parts per million (ppm), gave protection against dental caries, but did not stain teeth. Many long-term trials in which fluoride has been added to water supplies at this level indicate that this is a safe and effective way to reduce tooth decay. Many areas in both the USA and the United Kingdom now add fluoride to domestic water supplies.

Tooth decay occurs when organic acids are produced by the action of bacteria on food. These acids corrode away some of the tooth enamel. Without this protection, the interior of the tooth is decayed by bacteria.

During tooth development fluoride is incorporated into the tooth's mineralised structure, making the dental enamel resistant to the action of organic acids.

Fluorides are also added to many toothpastes and are present in tea and some foods.

A number of people in the USA and UK are opposed to the addition of fluoride ion to water supplies. They have formed powerful pressure groups to campaign against fluoridation.

They claim that, even at the low concentration used, fluoride causes mottling of teeth in some children.

Fluoride is incorporated into bones as well as teeth. It is claimed that this causes bones to become brittle, increasing the likelihood of fractures. It has also been claimed that fluoride is a cumulative poison, building up in the body from a number of sources.

Fluoride has also been associated with an increase in bone cancer, and even brain damage. A recent long-term study of rats fed a diet containing sodium fluoride showed damage to nerve and kidney cells.

However, the fluoridation of water at a level of 1 ppm has received approval in reports by the Surgeon General and the National Research Council in the USA, and the Department of Health in the UK. Dental associations in both countries recommend fluoridation as a safe, effective and economic measure to reduce tooth decay.

Questions

1 Write a short magazine article from an anti-fluoridation pressure group.

2 Write a leaflet to be published by a UK dental association recommending fluoridation.

Formulae and equations

Writing formulae

Elements

The formula of a substance uses symbols to show the number of atoms present in each particle.

For most elements, including all of the metals, the formula is the same as the symbol used in the Periodic Table. This indicates that the element is made of single atoms, for example: K, Mg, Al, Ne.

A small number of non-metals exist as molecules, each containing a pair of atoms joined by covalent bonding. These elements are said to be diatomic. The formulae of these elements show this by having a subscript number 2 after the symbol. These elements are: H_2, O_2, N_2, F_2, Cl_2, Br_2, I_2.

Writing the correct formula for an element is simply a matter of remembering which elements are diatomic. This is helped by the fact that all except hydrogen are close to each other in the Periodic Table.

Compounds

To work out the formula of a compound you need two pieces of information:
- the elements present in the compound
- the valency number of each element.

The valency number, also called the bonding number, tells you how many ionic or covalent bonds the element forms.
For elements in Groups 1 to 4 in the Periodic Table the valency number is the same as the Group number. For Groups 5, 6 and 7, the valency number is eight minus the Group number. Lead and tin are exceptions to the rule, as they are in Group 4, but usually have a valency of two.

Once the valency number of each element is known, the way that the elements bond to each other can be worked out.

Take as an example the compound calcium chloride. This contains the elements calcium and chlorine. Calcium is in Group 2 and has a valency of two, chlorine is in Group 7 and has a valency of one. To join these elements, two chlorine atoms have to bond to one calcium atom.

For some small groups of atoms, it is easier to work out formulae by giving them a 'group valency'. For example: hydroxide, OH, one; sulphate, SO_4, two; carbonate, CO_3, two; nitrate, NO_3, one; ammonium, NH_4, one.

For the transition metals, the valency is always quoted in brackets. For example: copper(II) sulphate has the formula $CuSO_4$. In this compound both copper and sulphate have the valency two.

Writing equations

The simplest form of equation is a word equation. It gives the reactants on the left, and an arrow leading to the products on the right. For example:

magnesium + oxygen → magnesium oxide

For each of the substances in this equation, you can write a formula, using the rules above.

Magnesium is an element, and it is not diatomic. It's formula is Mg.

Oxygen is an element, and is diatomic. It's formula is O_2.

Magnesium oxide is a compound. It contains magnesium, which is in Group 2 and has a valency of two, and oxygen, which is in Group 6, and also has a valency of two.

The atoms of magnesium and oxygen join to form MgO.

The equation now looks like this:

Mg + O_2 → MgO

Just like in a maths equation, both sides of a chemical equation have to be equal. That is, they must contain the same number of each type of atom.

The formulae cannot be changed, so you can only use numbers in front of the formulae to balance the equation.

$2Mg + O_2 → 2MgO$

Useful data

The relative atomic masses of some common elements

element	relative atomic mass
H	1
C	12
N	14
O	16
Na	23
Mg	24
Al	27
S	32
Cl	35.5
K	39
Ca	40
Fe	56
Cu	64
Zn	65
Br	80
Sn	119
I	127
Pb	207

The reactivity series of some metals

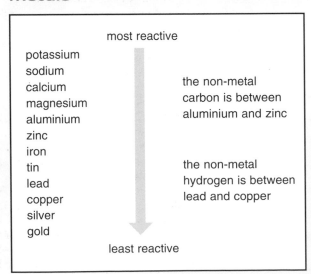

most reactive

potassium
sodium
calcium
magnesium
aluminium
zinc
iron
tin
lead
copper
silver
gold

the non-metal carbon is between aluminium and zinc

the non-metal hydrogen is between lead and copper

least reactive

Some examples of rock types

igneous	metamorphic	sedimentary
basalt	gneiss	chalk
dolerite	marble	limestone
gabbro	schist	mudstone
granite	slate	sandstone

Formulae of some common ions

Positive ions

name	formula
aluminium	Al^{3+}
ammonium	NH_4^+
barium	Ba^{2+}
calcium	Ca^{2+}
copper(II)	Cu^{2+}
hydrogen	H^+
iron(II)	Fe^{2+}
iron (III)	Fe^{3+}
lead	Pb^{2+}
lithium	Li^+
magnesium	Mg^{2+}
potassium	K^+
silver	Ag^+
sodium	Na^+
zinc	Zn^{2+}

Negative ions

name	formula
bromide	Br^-
carbonate	CO_3^{2-}
chloride	Cl^-
fluoride	F^-
hydrogencarbonate	HCO_3^-
hydroxide	OH^-
iodide	I^-
nitrate	NO_3^-
oxide	O^{2-}
sulphate	SO_4^{2-}

Index

The Periodic Table of the Elements

Group

Key

a
X
b

a = relative atomic mass
X = atomic symbol
b = proton atomic mass

1	2		3	4	5	6	7	0

1 **H** Hydrogen 1		

1	2
7 **Li** Lithium 3	9 **Be** Beryllium 4
23 **Na** Sodium 11	24 **Mg** Magnesium 12
39 **K** Potassium 19	40 **Ca** Calcium 20
85 **Rb** Rubidium 37	88 **Sr** Strontium 38
133 **Cs** Caesium 55	137 **Ba** Barium 56
223 **Fr** Francium 87	226 **Ra** Radium 88

Transition metals

45 **Sc** Scandium 21	48 **Ti** Titanium 22	51 **V** Vanadium 23	52 **Cr** Chromium 24	55 **Mn** Manganese 25	56 **Fe** Iron 26	59 **Co** Cobalt 27	59 **Ni** Nickel 28	64 **Cu** Copper 29	65 **Zn** Zinc 30
89 **Y** Yttrium 39	91 **Zr** Zirconium 40	93 **Nb** Niobium 41	96 **Mo** Molybdenum 42	99 **Tc** Technetium 43	101 **Ru** Ruthenium 44	103 **Rh** Rhodium 45	106 **Pd** Palladium 46	108 **Ag** Silver 47	112 **Cd** Cadmium 48
139 **La** Lanthanum 57 *	178 **Hf** Hafnium 72	181 **Ta** Tantalum 73	184 **W** Tungsten 74	186 **Re** Rhenium 75	190 **Os** Osmium 76	192 **Ir** Iridium 77	195 **Pt** Platinum 78	197 **Au** Gold 79	201 **Hg** Mercury 80
227 **Ac** Actinium 89 †									

3	4	5	6	7	0
					4 **He** Helium 2
11 **B** Boron 5	12 **C** Carbon 6	14 **N** Nitrogen 7	16 **O** Oxygen 8	19 **F** Fluorine 9	20 **Ne** Neon 10
27 **Al** Aluminium 13	28 **Si** Silicon 14	31 **P** Phosphorus 15	32 **S** Sulphur 16	35.5 **Cl** Chlorine 17	40 **Ar** Argon 18
70 **Ga** Gallium 31	73 **Ge** Germanium 32	75 **As** Arsenic 33	79 **Se** Selenium 34	80 **Br** Bromine 35	84 **Kr** Krypton 36
115 **In** Indium 49	119 **Sn** Tin 50	122 **Sb** Antimony 51	128 **Te** Tellurium 52	127 **I** Iodine 53	131 **Xe** Xenon 54
204 **Tl** Thallium 81	207 **Pb** Lead 82	209 **Bi** Bismuth 83	209 **Po** Polonium 84	210 **At** Astatine 85	222 **Rn** Radon 86

140 **Ce** Cerium 58	141 **Pr** Praseodymium 59	144 **Nd** Neodymium 60	147 **Pm** Promethium 61	150 **Sm** Samarium 62	152 **Eu** Europium 63	157 **Gd** Gadolinium 64	159 **Tb** Terbium 65	162 **Dy** Dysprosium 66	165 **Ho** Holmium 67	167 **Er** Erbium 68	169 **Tm** Thulium 69	173 **Yb** Ytterbium 70	175 **Lu** Lutetium 71
232 **Th** Thorium 90	231 **Pa** Protactinium 91	238 **U** Uranium 92	237 **Np** Neptunium 93	244 **Pu** Plutonium 94	243 **Am** Americium 95	247 **Cm** Curium 96	247 **Bk** Berkelium 97	251 **Cf** Californium 98	252 **Es** Einsteinium 99	257 **Fm** Fermium 100	258 **Md** Mendelevium 101	259 **No** Nobelium 102	260 **Lr** Lawrencium 103